A SAILOR'S TALE

THE STORY OF SEAMAN RAYMOND B. MOSS
BY RICHARD MOSS

Published by

MELROSE BOOKS

An Imprint of Melrose Press Limited
St Thomas Place, Ely
Cambridgeshire
CB7 4GG, UK
www.melrosebooks.com

FIRST EDITION

Cover designed by Hannah Belcher
Title page illustration by Moqing Zhu.

ISBN 978 1 907040 96 2

Printed and bound in Great Britain by:
CPI Antony Rowe. Chippenham, Wiltshire

DEDICATION

This book is dedicated to:

Lieutenant Commander H. C. Fox (1911–2000)
The Merchant Crews that delivered the goods
Old Shipmates

And to the old lady herself:
HMS *Ness*

Thanks for contributions from old Ness-Mates:
Lieutenant Commander Ted Burke, RCN
Stoker First Class Alan Gordon, RN
Professor A. J. W. Taylor
and
Steve Grubb (son of Coxswain 'Ben' Grubb)

Raymond B. Moss

AUTHOR'S NOTE

I wrote this tale while RB was recovering from the effects on his balance wrought by his four score and five – he was in hospital at the start, reading an issue of *Nuts* and entertaining the nurses.

What follows is a fusion of truth and fiction based around a set of stories that my father has told to me over fifty years or more, covering the escapades of a section of a Royal Navy crew that toiled in the bowels of one of His Majesty's warships.

I can't be sure that his memory hasn't polished a few of these stories along the way, but I do know that there has been an unerring level of consistency in the tales told from the viewpoint of Stoker First Class Raymond B. Moss. During the writing of the book, I sought help from a few of his crewmates and, from this point onward, that is the tone of the book – as if from the mouth of R. B. Moss and his messmates.

From their memories I have created the story; its foundation is steadfast – it is built on the boundless courage of the men to whom the book is dedicated – the merchant and naval sailors involved with the Atlantic and Russian supply convoys.

Richard Moss

CAST OF CHARACTERS

Raymond Boulton Moss	Me (Stoker First Class)
Freda Moss (née Hardy)	My wife
Charlie Moss	Carter – me Dad
Betsy Moss	Housewife - me Mam
Arthur Moss	My older brother
Elsie Herberts (née Moss)	My older sister
Chalky White	Leading Stoker
Haggis	Stoker First Class
Lofty Gordon	Stoker First Class
Bogie Knight	Stoker
Scouser	Stoker
Stuart Bacon – Streak	Stoker
Virge	Telegraphist (S)
Oppo	Telegraphist (S)
Mulvaney	Telegraphist (S)
Laddie	Armaments
Mr Graham	Chief Petty Officer Stoker
Anthony J. W. Taylor, RNVR	Temporary Midshipman, later Sub-Lieutenant

Robert Kerford Morton, RANVR	First Lieutenant (Australian)
C. R. C. Morrison, RN	First Lieutenant
Hubert Cornish Fox, RN	Lieutenant Commander – Captain 1945–6
Ronald Sidney Steel, RNR	Acting Temporary Lieutenant Commander – Captain 1944–5

SUPPORT ACTORS

Walter Berkley Cornock	Engineering Sub-Lieutenant + Leicestershire cricketer
C. O. Kennedy, MB, ChB	Surgeon
G. A. Lang	Lieutenant
E. G. Winterflood	Sub-Lieutenant
D. F. Webb	Sub-Lieutenant
George Wigg	Telegraphist (S)
G. W. (Ben) Grubb (1921–99)	Chief Petty Officer, Coxswain
Raymond Arthur Squires	Radar Operator
F. S. Hilby	Stoker
Jack Pine	Able Bodied Seaman
Harry Wilkinson	Able Bodied Seaman
Goodbody	Able Bodied Seaman
Blacker	Able Bodied Seaman

PREFACE

I was sailing in a sea of perfect harmony when my journey began; not a care, my world wrapped in tranquillity and complete peace. In a flash of ever-tightening pain that all changed, into chaos and pandemonium. Everything that I knew and loved was wrought asunder – I was pounded by wave after wave of shock – I could see nothing! I lost all track of time. I was in the grip of irresistible forces. Being stretched like some kind of rubber doll. Intense fear. I was dragged, pummelled, pushed, squeezed – my living area, which had been safe and strong for so long, bent and moved – the walls swelling outward, water gushing all around me. I opened my mouth to scream but nothing came out.

Instinctively I checked myself as I, sort of, floated onward. I still had two arms, I had movement in both legs, the 'old man' was still in one piece – well, a chap has to grab hold and check in situations like this. As I released my grip, I shivered. I wasn't wearing a stitch.

There was no noise, I became aware of an eerie tunnel ending in a bright, white light and as the light grew in intensity I heard voices, faraway voices, familiar and yet unknown. I was being propelled towards someone very dear, I felt an image of my mother, reaching out towards me – the pressure worsened, the fear turned to terror and I gave up all thought of fighting. I was going to a place never before known to me.

Time stopped; my head ached, I breathed in, the merest suck of air; it had a taste that was so unfamiliar. What was happening to me, now that it was happening, was beyond anything I could ever imagine!

The noise grew on, a sound of grunting and chanting – "Poosh, poosh, poosh." The light became intense; it was coming straight through my eyelids which were shut tight, and now as I slithered and slipped, I was beset by a feeling of falling into, what felt like, a pair of huge, soft-skinned hands. Suddenly I was cold to the bone. I struggled to open the sticky things that were my eyes; they were overwhelmed with light – so much light – an intensity I had never experienced.

The 'giant hands' engulfed me, it was becoming more and more surreal; a few moments ago I had felt lovely and warm – in a familiar place, dreamlike, taking comfort by sucking on a bit I haven't been able to reach for years, a bit that tasted like mother's milk, and then the shock came and I knew I could never go back to that other place again.

* * * * *

In thirty minutes' time you would be looking at a sweet baby boy, all pink and plump, a baby's chubby face and round eyes that would soon turn to a hazel brown. You would see chubby fingers on hands that were surprisingly large for an half-hour-old – I would be clean and soft and sweet-smelling, but that was in thirty minutes' time. What was going to happen in those intervening minutes would be terrifying!

Are you ready?

* * * * *

You see, I was in me Mam's bedroom, on a Saturday morning, at around 10.00 a.m. It was my birthday. I was shivering as I took my first look at this world... let me make this quite clear – it was frightening... an experience I never want to go through again... and then, in a twinkling, my fears dissolved and turned to anger.

I started to yell and immediately 'jumped' at the clarity in my hearing, which before had been so muffled. There were voices – me Mam again, asking softly if 'it' was okay, and a Scottish one just tutting and *aye*ing and rubbing and saying 'it's a wee lad' in a kind of distracted way. That my mother should be unsure of my gender panicked me and I grabbed again, just to make sure it hadn't been snapped off in all the action; he rose bravely in recognition.

Then my attention was taken by the air swirling up my nostrils, behind my eyes. I didn't like this. And the smell – phew, what was it? No, what were they?

An old clock ticked – I jumped again and made a pair of tiny fists with my hands – before an itchy woollen shawl was produced – the cord was snipped, the knot was tied and I was trussed up tighter than a Christmas turkey. I was in need of comfort, something to suck. I grabbed for my toes again, but they were out of sight.

I was less than three minutes old, it was 23rd August 1924, at number 31 Ravendale Street, in the town of Scunthorpe, which was then in the district of Lindsey, in

Lincolnshire. The fire had died in the grate and yet the heat in that room, both emotionally and physically, was building and the Scottish lady, the midwife, who had taken charge of dragging me squawking and yawping into this world, was a very worried woman.

Midwife was not worried about me; she was worried about me Mam, who wasn't doing very well.

Mam was lying on the tall metal-framed bed, where, with a little help from Charlie Moss, my troubles had first been conceived.

The bed had a panel at both ends, made from a kind of orange-coloured wood with an open grain. The panels were fixed to square metal legs and a saggy mattress rested in between them, supported by a frame full of springs, which was bolted to the bedhead and the bottom panel. Mam was covered in white linen sheets, sandy-coloured woollen blankets and a purple-patterned quilt that appeared all twisted and angry. It didn't look a very comfortable place to be; there was tension in the air alright. She was very pale and quiet.

My birth had taken all night, which seemed to have surprised them, though I don't know why – surely they didn't expect a young chap like me to be out and about before 10.00 a.m.? Not in those days – when Englishmen were Masters of the World – and especially not on a Saturday, that just wouldn't have been right. I mean, it's not even as if someone had asked me if I wanted to leave my lovely warm den for a life in pre-autumnal Scunthorpe.

'They' had just decided it was time – but they hadn't accounted for my awkward nature; I was dragging my feet – plus just about anything else that I could drag along with them.

I should explain – while we three were upstairs, my sister Elsie was downstairs, supposedly boiling water – my dad wasn't allowed in the house; he'd retreated to the Liberal Club on Cole Street the previous evening and hadn't been seen since. He'd gone, in anticipation of the actual event, to 'wet the wee un's head' with liberal quantities of any concoction that his numerous pals deemed fit to stand before him – and right at that moment Charlie Moss was snoring blissfully in his favourite corner of the snug.

We were nowhere near posh enough to have a telephone in the house; in fact neither of my parents ever used one, so my 'nearly' six-year-old brother Arthur had been despatched on the family pushbike to fetch the doctor. His legs had just grown long enough to tiptoe on the pedals without the crossbar causing permanent damage to his dangly bits – nonetheless it was slowing him down!

So, there we were in the back bedroom, me and me Mam and the midwife, the latter wanting rid of me so she could tend to me Mam, stop the leakage and clean up the mess before Doctor arrived and interfered. You see, there was no bathroom in the house – we had no running water – and no inside lavvy – it was a time of Pitcher and Ewer and the faithful old Gazunder[1]. No central heating either, just an open fire in the bedroom, with half a dozen lumps of coal struggling to flame into any kind of heat – good job it was still summer.

Midwife was a big woman with lungs like the bellows on a blast furnace. To say that she shouted to our Elsie to come up and help would be a tad over polite – she yawped so loud that horses reared up on Scunthorpe High Street, the fire briefly roared, slates moved on the roof and the rats ran out of the sewers under our house – it certainly shut me up for a bit!

I was swaddled tightly in Midwife's flopping arms. She'd been working hard and sweat was running from her every pore, she rushed – well, kind of shuffled – errrm, let's stop for a second – picture: five feet two inches tall and five feet two inches wide, imagine jelly dressed in a dark blue frock and a tabard and now imagine that vision walking as fast as it can and you will appreciate exactly what Midwife was doing.

The wooden floorboards bounced and Midwife's flab was flopping in more directions than an Atlantic storm and – believe it or not – I started to feel sick! She was looking back at the bed, with Mam on it, as she headed for the bedroom door, with me wrapped tightly in my shawl, in her arms, the nausea welling within me.

Elsie, meanwhile, was down in the parlour, moving in slow motion towards the door that opened onto the stairway; she was a dozen or more years older than me and had been playing skivvy to the midwife for the past four and a half hours. It was a job she was used to, it was her Living; our Elsie was 'In Service' to a local solicitor and his extended family. She had been fairly sure that she'd already carted up her final bowl of hot water and was grabbing at the chance to make some breakfast before she went off to face the wrath and spittle of her employer's gap-toothed housekeeper, for being late for work – the kettle was building up to a boil for her brew.

She'd just skewered a slice of bread on the toasting fork and balanced it in front of the tiny coal fire in the range's hearth when MacFanny the Foghorn screamed at her to come quick.

So, while I am wobbling and swinging around in my 'choppy' berth, heading towards mortal danger, I hear the door clatter at the bottom of the stairs as a moody Elsie (who is built like a whippet) burst through it – the next thing I see, which was

---

1   Gazunder, or Goes Under – referred to the 'potty' that was kept under the bed, to be used if the sleeper was caught short during the night and didn't fancy the trek to the outside loo.

almost the last thing I see, was a slip-on shoe, overflowing with the flesh of Fanny's fat-filled foot as it dragged open the bedroom door.

Distracted by her patient, the massive midwife missed the step down from the bedroom to the three-foot-square landing at the top of the staircase, stumbled and lurched forward, floorboards moaning under the weight.

What happens next was repeated in my nightmares for years to come – here's the scene: Elsie is halfway up the stairs. Fanny lurches and bounces off the walls at the very top of the stairs – she stumbles against the doorway of the front bedroom and her bulk tests the hinges. At the same time a low call of distress comes from Mam, capturing the attention of Midwife, whose head twists to look back through the door from which we have just emerged and as she does so her ankle twisted in her shoe and, still not looking, she thrust me towards Elsie, who was not 'quite' there yet. Luckily for me all of Fanny's bouncing and twisting energy had given me momentum. I sailed – looking something like a rugby ball – noiselessly through the void over our stairs. They said later it was only a few inches, but it seemed much further than that to me.

Elsie saw the tightly bound bundle that was me; she sprang forward a step and – bless her – caught me with a level of skill that an international wing back would be proud of.

Gad, I was scared – surely this wasn't right. I started yelling fit to wake me Dad but, as I'm the youngest of three and Sis is almost a generation older and had a number of other people's 'brats' to practise on, she was a steady hand at this childcare m'larkey. Ignoring my wails, our Elsie just carried me down into the parlour where – by now – black smoke was pouring from the carbonised slice that would have been her breakfast toast.

She snarled something that was unintelligible to a five-minute-old, whose vocabulary, so far, consisted of muted whispers, barked instructions, agonised yells, grunts, short breaths and a variety of gurgles. It hadn't encompassed swear words yet, although Elsie was doing her best to make up for that.

The air was so thick with smoke and bad language that if I'd known how to cough I would have done, but I didn't – so I didn't – and then – in the smoky atmosphere of our parlour – a very strange thing happened.

As Elsie lowered me into a Moses basket and wrapped me up even tighter, my nausea disappeared – so, I just shut up and began sucking at the woollen edges of my wrappings.

It became my first comforter – soon replaced by a scruffy old teddy bear that Elsie stuffed in with me after Fanny had eventually come banging down the stairs, washed me down and checked my belly button. Fat fingers she may have had, but she could tie a neat knot, could old Foghorn. She also discovered a set of three marks on my face, one running under my left eye, one on my left cheek and one just to the left of my lipline – it turned out to be a birthmark that I have carried ever since – "Look here, Elsie May Moss," she snapped at our Elsie, "look at these bruises you made when you took him from me!"

"Took him! Took him... more like you tossed him," Elsie might have said, but she didn't, because Fanny carried me back upstairs to me Mam and laid me at her breast. Things were looking up.

Not for Elsie though; sensing a buck being passed, she followed Fanny up and was breathing in and forming a pithy reply – "Tosser" – when, at that precise point in time, all eyes turned to the sash window and, through it, saw the gate at the bottom of the yard swing lustily open as Charlie made his entrance – all five feet and half an inch of him, dressed in his best suit and flat cap, his face twitching between concentration and an ecstatic smile.

Seeing him through the window, as he wove his first steps into the yard, our Elsie recognised the depth of his inebriation and, with only a scowl at Foghorn Fanny, bolted back downstairs and made for the front door, determined to effect an escape – she stopped just long enough to rattle the knocker of our neighbour, Mrs Judd, to alert her to my arrival. The daft old dodderer whooped happily and set off through her own house and out the back on her way to *help*.

Charlie, meanwhile, launched forward – one – two – three long steps with his short little legs, wide trousers flapping, all to his left, his right leg kind of dragging behind, trying to get in step – his face a mask of concentration – holding his breath – the third step saw him scrunch into the brick wall that divided our yard from that of Mrs Judd, and his collision with the bricks and mortar signalled that it was the turn of his right leg to take the lead, propelling him diagonally across the yard where he found a slightly more gentle welcome from the door on the outside lav. The metal latch took his weight, tensed, flexed and kind of sprung him on his next lurch, this time his right leg crossing his left and what up till now had been a very tidy zigzag turned into a wild, wide arc. His brows knit in a scowl.

Inside the parlour and thinking herself done for the day, Fanny began tidying away her baggage – what she saw through the window made her frown – Charlie was halfway across the yard and heading back towards the brick wall, completing a dainty pirouette that all but unravelled his legs as he banged once again into the brickwork, hitting it face on this time with his belly and both hands and expelling a huge outflow of boozy breath – Mrs Judd was halfway down her yard on her way to visit the new baby – me – Charlie grabbed for his hat, raised it and set off once again up and across the yard, walking backwards still facing next door – his legs completely out of control.

And, at that moment, returning on the pushbike, our Arthur stood on the pedals and yanked on the brakes, screeching to a halt by the still-open gate – Mrs Judd had reached her own gate, stepped into the ten-foot that formed the access to both houses and Arthur moved aside to let her into our yard when an authoritative banging began on our front door. Midwife Fanny went to answer it – Betsy cuddled me to her breast in her tidied bed and we watched together through the window, she with great concentration on Charlie's progress, me with a careless attitude that was being distracted by a wonderful smell coming from one of my 'pillows'.

My father managed to turn to face the direction he wanted to go and his final two steps saw him reach the door, barge it open and call out with a hearty, "Yew-hooh, I'm howwme," as, through it, he shot. Arthur and Mrs Judd were still as statues – Betsy smiled and I just opened me eyes a bit wider, stuck out me wrinkled neck and made a lunge with me pouting lips – I missed. Charlie meanwhile had got the wrong door and, accompanied by the sound of heavy objects falling, clattered to a stop somewhere in the back corner of the wash house and promptly fell deeply asleep. It was a good job really, because to call out the doctor cost two and six in those days, the same as two weeks' rent, and if he'd realised my arrival was proving so costly he would have been in the house like a whippet, doing all he could to block the doctor's entry.

As it was, Fanny let the doctor in the front door as our neighbour, Mrs Judd, came in through the back door and Arthur, picking his way through fallen washing equipment and comatose limbs, put the bike away in its usual place in the back corner of the wash house. On top of Charlie.

Charles Moss Esquire wasn't often as inebriated as he had been that morning; in fact if the landlord of the Liberal Club had cleared away all the unconsumed drinks from the previous evening he would – most likely – have made it home without incident. As it was, when he had woken up only a few minutes earlier, bloodshot eyes pounding like kettledrums, he had found two pints of flat beer and three brandies, sitting untouched on the table in front of him.

Hair of the dog or, perhaps, breakfast, either way it would have been an affront to his mates not to have shown his appreciation of their gifts.

As it was, he didn't extract himself from under the bike until about three o'clock in the afternoon, by which time a pair of energetic spiders had woven a cobweb between his fingers. He came into the room grinning like a loon, ready to inspect his third-born and trying to shake the spider's sticky construction loose of his left hand.

Anyhow, that little scene was eighteen years and nine months before this tale really begins... in the spring months of the mid-war years.

CHAPTER ONE

Eighteen years have passed. I'm a lusty young man, in a time when conquests were the stuff of explorers and mountaineers. Girls were unobtainable, life was growing easier and the rampant male energy had to be dissipated. The primeval prospect of war brought release to a young man. It came in huge rushes of righteous indignation, blinded by the silliness of youth and the almost desperate desire to mark our own personal line, on our own patch of land, beyond which our enemy must not step. It's a kind of anaesthetic of adrenalin that bubbles inside our spirit and amplifies the glories while it erases the dangers.

This initial rush to action is not courage because there is no thought attached to it – only feeling – it is just 'the way'. This is a tale of courage though, real courage of the purest kind, where men, in full knowledge of the dangers, knew they were sitting ducks and decided to risk their lives for their fellows – day after day after day. And then they'd go and do it again. Here is my tale.

It began with me getting very excited about stopping the 'Nartzy' – hoping the war wouldn't end before I got there. My brother Arthur and I had spent many nights, in the bedroom we shared, talking about what we would do when the time came to join up – we'd both come to the same conclusion. It had to be the Navy.

We reasoned that only in the Navy could we take our beds with us into the battle zones; neither of us fancied all the tramping about and sleeping in tents under grey skies that the soldier boys did. On board ship you got shelter, transport and three square meals a day, sitting at a table in the company of your messmates.

In the end Arthur missed national service because his job was a reserved occupation, he was part of the crew of the main-line steam trains, a fireman – it was his job to fuel the boilers. He found out about this when he went to the recruiting offices in Grimsby with two of his pals, Ron Judd and Les Harrison; the other two joined the Navy and they both survived the war, Arthur was left to return home disappointed! He

1

tried again at Doncaster and then a final time at Hull, where he was sent home with a flea in his ear and a severe warning not to try again – no meant no and he had to spend his war sweating mightily on the engine of one of Lincolnshire's steam locomotives. Then they transferred him to work on the Great Northern Railway in the main-line train depots in Barnsley, which, at least, made him feel as though he was a bit more involved.

When my call-up papers came, I went off to Grimsby and told them of my decision to be a sailor. Showing, perhaps, a little more of Arthur's influence I had chosen the job of Stoker – they took me in! I was 18 years and 9 months old when I signed in 1943. There had been some delays for me, because I was working on the steelworks by this time and steelworkers were also a reserved occupation – but they figured the steel makers could manage without my efforts as a trainee sample delivery boy for a while.

Two weeks later and I had passed my medical and received my letter and railway warrant and I was on a train heading for HMS *Duke*, which was the Navy's induction camp at Malvern.

Eighteen was still young back then – we didn't become an adult until we were 21 – but this wasn't my first time on a train; the family were regular passengers on the *Cleethorpes Flier* – the steam train that carried us to the nearest seaside resort and back – for a shilling! The trip to Malvern was my first train journey on my own though and I should have been quite excited, but the feeling I remember most was one of simple acceptance.

GROWING UP QUICK

Young I may have been, when I joined up, but I wasn't 'behind the door' as they say; I knew a thing or two – my time at Gurnell Street School had ended when I was 14, and for two years before that, I had a job of sorts at the Palace Theatre[1], on Cole Street.

The Palace was a grand old theatre in the classical style and ran every type of show from variety to pantomime to musicals and burlesque – and it was just around the corner from our house. My first enterprise there was taking in sausage rolls that me Mam had cooked and selling them to the 'theatricalists' as they were known – until they began to call themselves 'artists'.

Mam had been the Head Cook at the Blue Bell Hotel before I arrived so she was really good. I should just point out that the Blue Bell was a hostelry of ripe repute. Providing the more energetic of Scunthorpe's young men with gallons of booze and

---

1   Built in 1911, the Palace Theatre became the Savoy Theatre in 1938, then the Essoldo Cinema; it later became known as the Classic Cinema. It was then used as a shop – Pennywise – then Poundstretcher – it was finally demolished to make room for a shopping precinct.

a choice of girls-of-the-night and provided me with my Sat'd'y night entertainment as a thirteen- and fourteen-year-old when my gang of pals went to watch the antics of Scunthorpe's police force as they dealt with rowdy drunks after closing time. The two constables PC Paddy McGrath and PC Fairbrass would hang around on Market Park waiting for any 'scrappers' to tire themselves out before marching in and fetching one or two drunks out for a night in the cells; their sergeant, though, had an altogether different method. This was the famed Sergeant 'Long' Joe Hutchinson – later Superintendent Hutchinson – who was so big he had to ride a reinforced pushbike. There was nothing Long Joe loved more than what he referred to as a 'Recreational Brawl' and his method was to roll up his sleeves and wade straight in. Ejecting any miscreants, often through the pub's windows – whether they were open or not – and out onto the streets where his PCs could sweep them up and send them on their way! Reality TV doesn't come close.

But, that's yet to come; at this stage of my tale, I was twelve.

I had a little sideline at the theatre too – when the variety shows were on, they would feature high-kicking dancers – chorus girls – they were real beauties and some of the local toffs and businessmen, who fancied themselves as ladies' men, would call around at the stage door during the show. I had got the job of stage doorman, because Charlie had done a few favours for the theatre manager.

I should just mention that the manager was a tall, elegant bloke, well spoken, brilliantine on his hair, always very well dressed; his distinguishing feature was the colour of his eyes, they were pure blue – dark in the centre, very pale on the outside with, like, a grey line forming a circle that defined the two shades of blue. Anyway, my job meant that I was the one who the stage-door-johnnies spoke to when they were trying to contact a particular gal – I was a cocky little tyke and I made sure that I made it pay.

Lincolnshire and the district of Lindsey (which Scunthorpe was in) had a number of high-bred landowners like the Sheffield family, who had built Normanby Hall and had a history reaching back to the thirteenth century. I reckon that one or two of the stage-door-johnnies were landowners, or farm-owners, or industrialists from Scunthorpe and the surrounding towns – Grimsby, Doncaster, Lincoln, Hull and York. It was great experience dealing with those of a higher self-opinion and social station, especially as the situation they were in, panting after female company, kind of, stripped away their added status and put them on the level of any other bloke on the pull.

Certainly, some of the men who knocked on my door, seeing just a lad and being employers of 'lads' two or three years older than me at salaries of two bob or half a crown a week, could be quite rude when I gave them my price. Theirs was the big mistake – as I said, I was pretty switched on and *they* needed *me* to deliver their bunches of flowers and boxes of chocolates and messages of undying love and requests for a tryst. All they had to do was to pay me the half a crown I asked for and their gifts and messages got across to their favourite girl.

When it came to the snotty ones, I would still deliver their messages – and the flowers – but the chocolates never made it – and it still cost them two and six.

You may find this next bit a tad strange, but it's true; you see, many of the dancing girls were very well educated – with accents that could cut glass. One day, while I was doing me sausage-roll round one of them smiled her widest smile, waved towards the dressing table that I was standing next to and asked me if I would, "Be *tewwibly* kind and *parse* the eau de cologne."

She was sitting in front of a mirror concentrating hard at finishing off her stage make-up and, at the same time, holding her fan at arm's length. As you may imagine these large feather fans were pretty important for these girls, they were all that they had to hide their blushes from the audience. The next thing I hear is her neighbour, at the next mirror, speaking in thick Yorkshire, "Tha's bin splashin' perfume on all monin' – what does tha want wi't'cologne?" As she asked she snatched the fan and sniffed at it heartily, "By crickey, that old tomcat's pissed all over yer feathers."

Yorkie looked hard at me, "RAYMOND..." this last word she yelled, "can't you sling that filthy cat int't'cut?"[2]

I have to admit I did start working out a price for drowning the fleabag, in me head, but their stage call came, the posh one grabbed the perfume off me, there was a flurry of powdered bum-cheeks and G-strings and the moment just seemed to pass!

The tomcat lived to squirt another day.

I learned even more in that theatre when the 'dancer' Phyllis Dixey came to perform her burlesque show – to the authorities of the time she was nothing short of scandalous; she performed in the nude, you see – and she danced. Nude performers weren't allowed to move, they risked being closed down by the Lord Chamberlain, or the local Watch Committee, but Phyllis ignored the law and performed a kind of slow – tasteful – dance, exposing most of her charms to the audience.

Actually it was more a series of separate movements than a dance, but let's not get into an intellectual argument about it this early in my tale. Whatever Phyllis was about, it was more to do with feeling than thinking!

I watched in awe, even though I was too young to buy a ticket. My 'two' and 'one' were the wrong way round – I was 12 and you had to be 21. But my sausage rolls had got me in with the back-stage crews, and I caught her full show, in spite of the fact that Phyllis's husband – a comedian called Shuffy, or Duffy, or summat – cleared everyone

---

2 'Int't'cut' in English is: 'into the canal'. I was learning languages – anatomy – the Arts – what more could a lad want?

away from the side of the stage, with a hearty reminder that: "It's not a bleedin' peep show. Sod off... the lot of you."

But, he hadn't seen me; I had found a place up in the gantry just behind the main spotlight, where no one could see me because of the intense glow given off by the light-beam and I could see – *the lot* – errm, I mean, I could admire her artistic poses. Some of which moved me so much I nearly fell off me perch! Good job I didn't, Charlie and Arthur were sitting directly beneath me.

Actually, in 1978 Thames TV put on a play called *The One and Only Phyllis Dixey* in which she was played by Lesley-Anne Down and described as Britain's most famous striptease artiste.

To anyone reading, who may worship the modern cult of the Politically Correct, I can confirm that a twelve-year-old boy at a raunchy burlesque show (in the third quartile of the 1930s) learns how to smile very broadly indeed and no harm whatsoever could come to him. And, I can also honestly assure you that I didn't start wearing glasses until way after my 70th birthday had passed by.

By thirteen, I had a proper weekend job. I was on the local market selling household goods like wash leathers, polish and even lino. They reckoned I had the gift of the gab and would make a good salesman – once I'd learned my trade – at which time and not a moment before, the stallholder would begin to pay me a fair wage!

I'd already learned the dictum: Hold not thine breath, nor spread on your bread – the Jam of Tomorrow.

After leaving school – at fourteen – I moved into a more permanent occupation. I was an errand boy for Baths Farm at Old Brumby – in that job I had a company vehicle, an old, iron-framed, sit-up-and-beg bike with a big basket on the front to carry the milk bottles that I had to deliver.

It was like a heavier version of my dad's bike, and I reckoned I was learning some of the skills I may need to join the family business but, in the end, that never happened.

From the farm I moved my career onward to errand boy for Reno Valets; they were a dry cleaning company based in Grimsby but I worked in my hometown branch. I was fifteen by now and my clothes had never been so smart – you see, back then, shops would close for lunch hour (only, then it was called a dinner hour) and while the rest of the staff were out I'd drop my trousers and put them through the machine!

On top of this rich vein of experience to guide me through life, I had two superb teachers on how to get along in the world: my older brother Arthur and my dad, Charlie Moss.

Ever since I was no bigger than a hay bucket I'd helped Charlie in his loosely structured business. The family firm. I say loosely structured because he didn't do just one thing, but everything that he did was related to transport – oh yes, and he had the theatrical connections that had got me started at the Palace.

Charlie Moss described himself as a Carting Contractor in as much as he had a horse and cart. In those days there were some folk who referred to him as a rag-and-bone man. I don't think he was, but do you know, if he had been it wouldn't bother me; the old rag-and-bone men did more for recycling than all the different coloured plastic bins in existence today. They had the kids flocking out with rags and bones of all kinds in every street they passed through – and all it cost to collect was a stick of chewing gum or a scabby goldfish, which only ever lived two or three days – did you notice? No carbon emissions either – any emissions Charlie's power plant was responsible for could be shovelled up and spread around the roses.

These days your rag-and-bone man would probably be called a 'Resource Reclamation Expert' or an 'Environmental Management Director' and have a university qualification that proved he was clever – although not necessarily the bearer of any common sense.

As for Charlie, he did all sorts with his horse and cart. He helped people to move house, in fact he emptied a few houses too, clearing out the contents after people had died, or simply moved on quickly – all above board and we were always careful to take great care of any furniture that fell off the back of his cart. We looked after such contraband for years afterwards.

So, the business could have been called haulage – or it could have been removals. We weren't motorised, not in those days. All of the transport was powered by muscle and sinew. We had a horse and cart and a bike – just the one – between all of us. We lived in Scunthorpe, you see, everybody had a bike in Scunthorpe, it was the 'bike' capital of England.

So that you know, Scunthorpe is actually made up of five villages – from north to south they are Frodingham, Crosby, Scunthorpe, Brumby and Ashby – we lived right in the middle of Scunthorpe.

Our house was a few minutes' walk from the High Street, the Theatre (which changed its name to The Savoy when I was 14), the Liberal Club, the Market, the Bus Station, Woolworths and the Grammar School.

Here's a little-known factoid – Scunthorpe got a mention in the Domesday Book. At that time it carried its old Norse name Escumetorp, which means Skuma's village. Probably named after some marauding Viking that liked the access it had to the River Trent and the Humber Estuary and the North Sea – plus the fact that it sits on a hill so he could see any other pillaging ne'er-do-well approaching.

By the mid 1940s the villages had fused together into a town – one that had enjoyed an eighty-odd-year renaissance since iron ore mining had started again and now it had huge steelworks on two sides – Appleby-Frodingham (still there) to the east and Lysaghts (long gone) to the north – and sat second only to Sheffield as a steel producer.

THE PEOPLE WHO SHAPED MY LIFE

Anyway, back to Charlie. I mentioned that as well as being a carter, he was something in the Theatre too (you better have pronounced that the posh way – 'th-ee-ate-er'). He was the stockman, taking charge of the performing horses or the Shetland ponies that featured in shows, like *Cinderella*. He even helped the theatre manager out when they had an elephant appearing in one of the shows!

He had another little sideline too – he ran a bus service for the artists, where, for the fare of a tanner (2½p) he would run them between the theatre and their digs. I never did know where he got the bus from, or how he learned to drive it!

Despite how the Palace Theatre may have appeared in my first introduction, it was a proper theatre in those days; burlesque was just a part of the rich menu of superb shows that it put on and it was an important social centre for the town. After the war it became a fleapit cinema called the Essoldo.

Someone once told me that Essoldo was the name of Skuma's mother-in-law... but I never did believe them.

Charlie had a stable, where he kept his horse. Once – it must have been in the thirties – he looked after the horse belonging to Tom Mix, when the cowboy film star appeared at the Palace Theatre.

My dad told us something about Tom Mix one night, as he sat in his old Windsor chair in front of the fire. "Bit of a lad that Tom Mix; he rides his horse up the steps onto the stage," he breathed in heavily, "says he's half Scottish and t'uther aif's Cherokee Indian." He looked around. "He reckons he earns $17,000 every week – that's nigh on £4,250.00,"[3] Charlie's best scowl accompanied the next few words, "he might be quick on the draw but he weren't too quick to get his hand in his pocket – me and Arthur had to buy all of us own ale."

There's also a family tale about Arthur trying to sell off the Shetland ponies that were brought in to appear in the *Cinderella* pantomime, but don't you believe that!

---

3   In those days there were four dollars to the pound – a half-crown piece was often referred to as half a dollar.

CHAPTER TWO

Here's a glimpse of the way Charlie's mind worked. One afternoon, I was helping him to tie down a load from a house clearance – the cart was piled high with large pieces of furniture, plus tea chests full of 'stuff'. He was on the kerbside; I was standing on the roadside of the cart. Charlie kept hold of the end of the rope and just tossed over a loop for me to place under one of the hooks on the bed of the cart, so that he could then pull it tight, to lash down that section of the load before repeating the process. I could hear him grunting as he secured his end of the rope and was waiting for him to toss the next loop over to me so that I could secure my side. Okay. Okay. Maybe I wasn't paying full attention when the loop of rope came snaking over, but then, neither was one of Scunthorpe's cyclists, whose neck the loop of rope settled around before dragging him heartily off his bike.

The cyclist's pushbike continued down the road, until it hit a pothole and crashed towards the pavement. Cyclist didn't follow; instead, with arms rotating, he fell flat on his back into the road, his cap muffling the crack of skull against concrete, before it revolved upwards in a graceless arc, with a momentum that saw it spin along the road surface after his runaway bike. I thought we were in big trouble – there was cyclist, flat on his back, one hand groping for his flat cap, the other stuck to his throat; I was like a stone statue, daren't move. Cyclist was just beginning to sit up, rubbing the back of his head, where it had met the road surface with a bang; he was looking to see if there was any blood.

From the other side of the cart came Charlie, his tiny eyes round, his brows low, his big nose softly glowing while his thin, flat mouth was moving rapidly. "What the devil are you doing with my rope?" he bawls at the cyclist. "Don't you realise a good rope like this cost a lot of money? Why weren't you looking where you're going? Pulling a stunt like that you might have damaged it. And you've frittened the lad!"

He then set about examining the rope in great detail, completely ignoring the cyclist, who got to his feet and apologised in a very croaky voice. He rubbed his head one more time before he stuck his cap on it and picked up his bike, riding off, wobbling like an old drunk. I was still frozen in my original position, Charlie just handed me the rope and went back to his side. Not a smile, not a wink, just a few words from the side of his mouth: "Always have an answer ready – and never give them the chance to talk first, son."

The lad (me) heard him well – and stored his words of wisdom away for future use – as for the cyclist, I don't think that particular bloke could have uttered any more words if he'd had all the time in the world – the weal on his throat was vicious!

You know what – these days Charlie might have called himself an entrepreneur, only he couldn't speak French – he wasn't much good with English once the pubs had shut – he invested a great proportion of his earnings in British ales, did my father. He was a great wheeler-dealer and could never buy anything without bartering – one day, when the wind whipped his cap from his head and did it irreparable damage under the wheels of his cart he walked into the nearest hat shop and chose his replacement. The shopkeeper wrapped it carefully, handed it to Charlie and told him the price, which ensured that everything should go quiet and a distinct tension fill the air – I went invisible. After a long and steady stare Charlie simply handed the parcel back – and when asked why, he explained that the same hat was half the price in Millets, a competitor's shop. Charlie didn't move, just stood his ground and steadily the shopkeeper's resolve evaporated – having demonstrated the material and been told the other hat was made of the same stuff – having explained the quality of manufacture and been told the other hat was just as good – the price came down until it matched what Charlie had in mind. As we left the shop I looked up at him and asked him if there really was the same hat at a much lower price in Millets; his eyes just twinkled. "Can't say I know," he told me, "but I guess there must be – or he wouldn't have sold me this one for the price he did."

He was cheeky, strong willed and quick-witted and these became traits of his that I copied; they served me well over the coming years. He also taught me that drinking beer was a waste of money so, luckily, I never got into the habit. Still, Charlie was the breadwinner and he won the bread with the help of his horse – much like Tom Mix did, except the film star earned as much in a week as my dad did in a lifetime – no complaints though, it was enough to get us by.

Charlie's horse wasn't famous either. He was on his second one when I started to help him. The first one had a lovely disposition, but he'd got the current one cheap, bought it from the council because their draymen couldn't cope with it – it was a good worker and very strong – but it was evil.

It would sink its teeth into you soon as look at you and if you were ever unwise enough to get between it and the wall, it would do all it could to crush you. Being a young lad, I was small and lively and I could dip under its body to get away, but not without its rear leg coming forward to try to kick me, or its huge head turning around to try and take a lump out of one of me arms with its long yellow teeth. Eventually I grew quick enough of wit to recognise its moods and stay out the way. It got Charlie a few times – in fact their relationship was one never-ending battle and, in the end, Charlie was the loser – but that was a dozen years after the war had ended – when the horse stamped hard on Charlie's foot; he ignored the wound, gangrene set in and he passed away in the hospital in Brigg – he was 70.

Life at home for me, my brother and sister and mam and dad was a two-up, two-down terraced house, as I said; number thirty-one Ravendale Street in Scunthorpe. In my eyes that terrace looked to be a quarter of a mile long, every house the same, all with the same colour front door and the same stone step, assiduously cleaned as a sign of honour to the lady who lived there and was proud to be known as the housewife.

Our matriarch was Betsy – she was a keen Salvationist, made a mean sausage roll, did a lot of baking and some washing, but she didn't have a job. Her work as housewife was a full-time occupation.

There's someone else who had an influence on my life; she was also the strongest motivation I had for wanting to sort out the Nazis and get back to Scunthorpe – she stood five feet four inches with a smile that still has me captivated sixty-seven years later.

I was 17 when I met Freda Hardy[4]. At the time I was doing a favour for a cousin on my mother's side called Leslie Wright. His lineage held one of the family's more macabre tales – his grandmother had hung herself, from a rope tied over the kitchen door, because she thought she had cancer... but she didn't. Anyhow, one week Leslie said he wanted to learn how to dance – to help him to gain introductions to members of the fairer sex. Translated into the language of t'day that would be 'to pull the birds'.

In those days, a chap met a nice girl during an evening out by asking her for a dance – waltz, quickstep, slow foxtrot – that kind of thing. Actually I've always thought the slow foxtrot – that's slow, fox and trot – sounded very sexy. It is quite a sexy dance – today's break-dancers who swirl around by themselves don't know what they're missing. Sigh.

---

4   Raymond and Freda Moss received a telegram from the Queen congratulating them on their 60th wedding anniversary in 2004 – the Palace had sent the telegram to SS *Sunbird* where the couple were cruising in the Caribbean. Raymond was 79 and it was his first time back on ship since he left the Navy – but not the last.

Anyhow, Leslie said he wanted to learn to dance, so I said, "C'mon then," and we set off to Pop Campbell's dance school. It was situated over the Conservative Club, up near the Old Show Ground, which was Scunthorpe United's football pitch and straight across the road from the Public Baths. It's still there today – not so the baths.

Freda Hardy was at the dance school with one of her sisters, learning how to jitterbug, and when I saw her every bug in my stomach started to jitter. I was an avid attendee for the next few months, and amongst other things, Freda and I eventually became keen amateur ballroom dancers, winning a number of competitions in the 1970s. As for Leslie, he never went back after that first time and instead married a girl from the Co-op where he worked – she was a shorthand typist and was the type to keep him short-handed until he proposed, which didn't take long.

THE PLACE I COME FROM

I started to tell you about our house. The front door opened directly onto the pavement and faced another identical row at the other side of the street – smooth red brick, not very attractive, they've all gone now; in fact our bit of Ravendale Street has all but gone – where we lived has become a modern council mews called Argyll Court. The bottom half of the street still exists; now called Ravendale Street South, it leads on to Station Road, while the first bit, between Mary Street and the High Street, still exists as Ravendale Street North – and some of Argyll Court carries the old street's name.

In those days, the main entry to our house was from the ten-foot at the back – nobody used their front room or front door much – they were kept for special occasions – nowadays, I don't remember why we did that.

Any road, at the back was the ten-foot and the best way to envision what this ten-foot looked like is to imagine you are walking towards it. Along Mary Street, which also has an unbroken row of houses with front doors that open on to the pavement and windows, with net curtains so you can't easily see into the unused front rooms. Imagine these house fronts to your left, very close to you, so the immediate feeling is one of tall walls closing in on you. A narrow footpath. The houses shade the sun, so there's a shadow over everything. When you reach a gap in the houses – an alley with sheer blank walls of brick that are the ends of the two end-terrace houses, reaching upwards each side of you – ten feet apart – you've reached the opening into the ten-foot.

You turn left and in front of you is a gravelled concrete way, hemmed in both sides by a brick wall and brighter light, a white/grey sky perhaps. At the edges of this alleyway where the concrete meets the foundation of the wall, your eye is drawn downwards to an accumulation of dirt, a piece of green perhaps from a weed or the odd scrap of litter – not really bad, just a definition.

You walk through the canyon formed by the house sides and it eases open a little; the brick wall is each side of you, high enough to continue the appearance that they are closing you in. Everything is uniform brick. Or white/grey concrete. You walk on, the brick walls are about four feet six inches tall; they are rough built and patched with cement where the brick is failing – when I was little, they towered over me and seemed to be leaning over to a point where they were ready to fall over onto me. It is twenty paces, perhaps, since you entered the ten-foot and there is a break in the wall to your right – a green gate with faded paint – it is as tall as the wall, big enough so a child will struggle to reach the catch and open it.

You walk through the gate and you face the same colours as the ten-foot but this time it's a flat white/grey concrete yard that reaches fifteen yards until it meets the back wall of the house. It is narrow. Each side there is the same coloured brickwork, an unbroken wall to the left, in single brick and slightly lower than the wall to the ten-foot – there is a wall and then an outhouse to the right.

You walk into the yard and to your immediate right is the only bit of garden. A miniscule lawn, about eight feet by fifteen – it feels as though the grass is a few inches higher than the concrete and there's an undisciplined flower border spreading along the back of the grass. About eighteen inches forward of the brick wall – a butterfly bush with its spindly branches sprouts over the corner, from next door's yard, leaning out and overlapping the ten-foot – not very big, perhaps the size of a man with his arms raised.

Beyond this tiny 'lawn' there's a square of concrete, defined at its furthest point by the neighbouring wall and the brick end of the outhouse – the concrete has been laid much later than the main yard and there's a garden bench positioned here – it is the only place where you can sit and catch the sun.

The flat yard continues with the thin brick dividing wall to the left and on the right-hand side as you walk towards the house, the one – two – three – and finally four doors to the outhouse, along with the windows.

The outhouse was split into four rooms separated from each other with a brick wall and each with its own door opening onto the yard. Inside the outhouse the bricks had been painted white in a finish that we knew as distemper – it was a thick paint that gradually got more and more chalky as the years passed by.

The first room in this block (and the furthest from the back door to the house) was the toilet – its door had a pattern of V-shaped cut-outs at the top and a gap at the bottom, to aid ventilation. Inside was just a crazed white porcelain WC with a high-level tank, Shires I think.

It seemed huge when I was little and often took a couple of jumps before I got settled on it – not too difficult for a supple young lad with his trousers round his ankles. The real skill in the early years was not letting yer kecks slide off yer feet and onto the floor, which was a few inches below. If they did, the icy draft would get in them and you were in for a jump and a dance and sucking in air when you pulled them back on. When you got older and yer feet reached to the floor easily, it was that same bone-chilling draft that froze your feet and ankles and halfway up your shins and drove you out of the place as soon as you were done.

A wired roll holder hung on the wall. No washbasin.

There was a nail in the door – from the early days, when we used squares of the local paper – but we'd moved on since then. By now we were on proper toilet rolls – Izal – it was tough stuff, you would never find it breaking up under your fingers, but the downside was that it was slippery and you had to be careful that, once loaded, it didn't slide off in the wrong direction – it never felt that absorbent but it did claim to be 'medicated'.

The next room was the coalhole and the third one from the gate was the wash house, in which Charlie had slept off his celebrations on the day of my birth; this was where Mam kept all of her washday products and machinery plus the tin bath that we brought out every Friday – and the bike. The wash house had a window beneath which, inside, was a concrete top, about four inches thick; it was covered in plain ceramic tiles and a large sink was fashioned into it. No tap though.

The room in the outhouse that was nearest to the house formed the kitchen and the pantry – its door was a bit more substantial, it was the back door to the house; it was the only one with a lock, the rest had a flat metal latch that you lifted up to gain entry. The pantry also had a narrow opaque window and was covered, inside with a wire grill, to make life a bit harder for the flies.

During the war, our lawn was completely covered by an Anderson shelter, which was a bit of corrugated iron arched over like a modern pigpen. We'd dug it in and covered it in turf and sandbags but I wasn't that confident that it would protect us from a hundred pounds of the Luftwaffe's high explosives, but then I don't think any self-respecting enemy bomb would choose to land on our cobbled-together shelter!

Forgive the digression but I have heard tell that the Nazi High Command left Scunthorpe alone because they had decided that they would need the steelworks and its workforce for their own industry after they had won the war. There were plenty of more important towns around us which they gave a good pasting; Hull was probably the worst, due to the importance of its docks. There were a few raids on the ironstone mines, but the town and the surrounding works were relatively bomb-free. Freda told me of their terror when they heard a doodlebug flying over though – with its distinctive rattling engine sound that they prayed would not stop until it had passed by.

Rent for our house, our Arthur tells me, was half a crown a fortnight[5]. There was no bathroom – the kitchen was a Belfast sink on brick legs, and a cold tap; it had no fridge, we used the pantry with its stone shelves for cool storage and the only other storage was an Eastham unit that my mam had bought from the Co-op. Later on a hot-water geyser was hung on the wall beside the sink and luxury came modestly to number 31.

The cooker was a blacklead coal-fired range built into the chimneybreast in the end wall of the parlour. The range had the fire in the middle, an oven to the left-hand side that the fire could be drawn under to heat it up and an iron shelf to the right, which held the stew pot, the toasting fork and the kettle, when it wasn't hooked over the fire waiting to boil. Lit by gas lighting, we lived in that parlour.

It was a square room; you entered in the right-hand bottom corner through a door from the kitchen, one step up. In the middle of the room stood a table and six chairs, and along the wall to your right stood a fancy wooden sideboard with just enough space to pass between it and the chairs around the table, if you breathed in.

On the wall facing you there was a door at each end. The left-hand door opened into the room and led to the claustrophobic staircase, with its very high ceiling that I had known at such an early age. The stairwell was painted in a gloss cream finish, the doors in very dark lacquer, combed to look like graining – the right-hand door on that far wall opened out to the front room and the front door. Between the two doors sat a rather tired black leather chaise longue that Charlie had 'found' during a house clearance.

Décor was, at best, dour, with smoke effect (or effected) cream gloss on the wall – the only window to the parlour was on the same wall as the door from the kitchen and was very grudging about any light it might let in. While it didn't let light in, that window certainly let heat out – it was a sash window that fitted where it touched; a very thin pane of glass rattled loosely in its frame. The curtains were so thick that they didn't realise that heat was escaping; there was an equally thick velvet curtain hung on a pole over the door to the kitchen in the vain hope that the heat wouldn't squeeze through the gaps and use it as an exit. But, it did.

The rest of the furniture in that room was a wooden rocking chair for Mam that sat in the bottom right corner, almost under the window, and Charlie's wooden Windsor that sat to the right of the fire. On the floor was a loose carpet in browns and blacks and other dark colours that had surrendered years ago, with a hand-woven rag-rug in front of the fire to catch all of the embers that spat themselves out of an evening.

---

5   In those days there were four dollars to the pound – a half-crown piece was often referred to as half a dollar.

No telly of course – not until the late fifties – but we did have the flushing toilet, the one in the outhouse, down the yard, past the wash house and the coalhouse. It was never a warm enough place to linger in – in fact in winter it often froze over. There was the gazunder too, beneath the bed. The house was always clean, but I think it is fair to say that we lived with attitudes to hygiene that are a lot different to today.

The fact is that living in Scunthorpe in those days was a cold affair; it was something we just got used to. It seeped up through the footings of our house, usually accompanied by a nervous wave of damp that stained the very bottom of the walls behind the tall skirting boards and it seeped into our parlour on the air that peeped out from the floorboards. It seeped into the upstairs rooms from the roof, which was covered in tiles made of grey slate and in pretty good repair. We didn't have insulation – at least not unless we wore it. We didn't have global warming either, so it was freezing cold in winter, it was cool to cold in spring, summertime was the only time we didn't have a fire because autumn, which began in September, saw the cold return – it was cold in our house sometimes even when it was warm outside.

It was even cold in bed. We had none of these modern duvet things – it was all starched cotton sheets (gad, they could be nippy until you had warmed them up, by which time they had sucked most of the heat out of you) and woollen blankets and an eiderdown quilt. Wrapped up tighter than Tutankhamen so you couldn't move, it left your extremities (like toes) to find little pockets of cold that convinced you that they were going as black as the feet in Captain Scott's last sleeping bag. I had a thing about the cold and it influenced some of the decisions I made when I entered the Navy.

This was the life I left to go and chase off the enemies of my country.

CHAPTER THREE

When the day came for me to set off to war, Charlie, me Mam and Freda accompanied me to Scunthorpe station. I was really excited and not a little anxious; the three waving me off were trying not to look sad and failing miserably – well, Mam and Freda were, Charlie had wandered off to chat with the stationmaster, who he'd done a few jobs for and with whom he'd shared a few evenings down the pub. As I was leaving, Charlie was organising for two Canadian soldiers to take up lodgings in mine and Arthur's bedroom.

Several hours after I had set off, I landed at the station in Malvern; just me, a stomach full of nerves and an old battered brown suitcase with my changes of shirts, which I wouldn't need, and underwear, which I most definitely would. As the train pulled into the station, I breathed in; the air was sweet. Sweeter than I can ever remember it at Scunthorpe, where it was usually full of red dust from the iron and steelworks. No time for reverie though as I marched down to the training camp, which was named in the Navy way, HMS *Duke*, and began to go through what was termed Basic Training – I don't think it had changed at all since Nelson lost his eye.

On my first morning I learned about the need for vigilance when it came to Navy food. My porridge at breakfast was served by a young Wren and she seemed to have left a few locks of her hair in it as a memento. I got kit too, including my full uniform, which was a struggle to get into because they didn't have zip fasteners, but it fitted pretty well once I was in. I was given my hammock, blanket, bedcovers, vests, pants, two pairs of socks and all the rest of the kit that had to be marked with my name and stowed in exactly the correct manner – and I got a number, which was PKX 528429.

I learned how to sling and lash up my hammock, how to tie knots, how to splice ropes and how to run up and down the Malvern Hills, all wonderful skills to carry onto a modern metal warship without a sail or a rope in sight – oh yes – and they shouted a lot. And I learned how to shoot a rifle. We didn't do too much marching about, or drill as I believe they call it – where we were going there wasn't much call for marching, and anyhow, the Marines did enough of that to make up for the rest of us.

Did you know that the Marines sailed as a personal protection force for the officers of a ship – to protect them, in days gone by, against the – often press-ganged – sailors in their own crew and to protect them against the enemy in battle? Having already mentioned Lord Nelson, here's a bit of useless information; the majority of the fatal casualties on board the *Victory* at Trafalgar were Marines – and – here's some more, there were three sailors with the name Moss aboard *Victory* during the battle; I bet not one of them was a Stoker!

Here's yet another bit of useless info; Nelson was twelve when he joined the Navy – by the time he'd reached maturity, he'd lost an arm and an eye – he would have been in much less danger if he had spent his boyhood amongst the buxom beauties of the Palace Theatre.

By the end of my first week in the Navy I seemed to have caught the eye of the instructors. Maybe that was due to self-confidence or work ethic, or maybe I just asked too many questions and questioned too many orders from the minor officers. I was born awkward, it wasn't personal; anyhow my first responsibility came when I was put in charge of the Mess I shared with the other trainee sailors. The instructors impressed upon us that one thing that our Mess was not allowed to be was messy, so the floor needed a regular scrubbing.

Being in charge didn't excuse me from getting down on my knees and wheeling a scrubbing brush, but it laid upon me the responsibility for getting the job done quickly and effectively. One of the lads who I had detailed to work on the floor was an Aberdonian called Mac*Something*. He wasn't actually called Mac*Something* but in those days the Aberdeen accent was far broader than it is today. It has been softened by all those oil riggers from England and other foreign countries, like America – I digress – the fact was, you see, when he told me his name, he could have been speaking Caledonian, Macedonian or Venezuelan for all I knew.

And he was wearing gloves – so how could I know that he had cracked skin on his hands from the month he had spent digging around in the rubble of bricks that had been his bedroom, trying to find his call-up papers.

And I didn't know that he was in the grip of severe homesickness, brought on by a domestic situation that he didn't like to talk about. It seems that once he'd dug his documents out of the flattened remains of his bombed room he'd had to spend his last three days at home trying to find his mam, whom he eventually discovered in the close proximity of the bloke across the road, who, as rumour told the neighbourhood, was a waster that had kept one step ahead of the draft, and who had had a nibble at every lonely housewife down the street. Aberdeen's dad was a survivor of the screaming

Stukas at Dunkirk; he had been left in a state that saw him dive for cover at any sound louder than a goldfish's fart. He hadn't been seen since the bombs hit their house!

I'm not saying it would have made a difference to the way I behaved if I had known all of this, but at least I'd have known that he might just be in a bad mood and that making fun of his name by calling him Mac*Something* may not have been the height of wisdom.

Anyhow, the fact was that he was making a meal of scrubbing the floor... look... I didn't know about his hands... alright!

All I said to him was: "Come on – you lubber – get cracking," and he had those same hands around my neck trying to strangle me – I mean, I thought his hands were delicate!

I probably shouldn't have defended myself by delivering my punch where I did with such venom. I wasn't a little lad and – after a week at Malvern on top of the exercise I got cycling around Scunthorpe – I was as fit as a boxer's gloves – and I was used to looking after myself against bigger lads than him – like my brother Arthur – and against harder fighters – like my sister Elsie!

Anyhow my punch... to his throat... nerr... cooled his anger very swiftly.

Standing with one heavy boot on his chest while he lay flat on the floor trying to find a way to get some breath through his dented oesophagus may also have been a touch OTT too, but I was mad.

I did make a note in my diary that night though to 'be more sensitive'. The next day I sought my opponent out and tried some of the famous Moss charm on him; it seemed to work and eventually we became – if not firm friends – then good messmates. To sort out the thing about his name he told me – talking very carefully, like, as if I was a moron – "I'm *Nomuckfook'n'sumthin'*."

I just replied, "I see," and guessed his dad was Scandinavian or some such. Unfortunately, the Chief Petty Officer confiscated my diary soon afterwards and took away my reminder to be sensitive so that was that resolution in the bin!

During the next week or two I met quite a few jittery young lads; they were just plain homesick and it was a difficult thing for them to bear. It's not that many of them had the extreme kind of story that 'Aberdeen' had but it was hard for them nonetheless.

They also tried to teach me to swim at Malvern – I never did take to it and I blame me Mam, but I'll tell you about that later – no I won't, I'll tell you now.

You might have picked up that, at home, Monday was washday – clothes washing that is – well, Mam's washing machinery was nothing like today's – it was in fact made up of at least four separate parts. She had two 'dolly tubs', a 'dolly peg' and a 'mangle' or 'wringer' and none of this equipment used a spark of electricity. She kept all of her washing equipment in the wash house and arranged it all on the backyard on washday.

A dolly tub was a galvanised vat – something like a beer keg without a top – it stood about three feet tall and eighteen inches across the top – wider in the middle than at the top and bottom. One of these she filled with hot water and some gritty soap powder. She'd start with the delicates and stuff that wasn't too dirty and progress through the underwear, then the working shirts and finally the really mucky stuff. You must remember that we weren't in the habit of changing clothes every day so some of the laundry was pretty ripe.

Once the clothes were in the hot tub, she would whirl them around with the dolly peg – for those who've never seen one, a dolly peg is like a short three-legged stool, made out of wood that was bleached white with use. From the centre of the stool was a wooden pole (about two inches in diameter) around four feet long. At the end of the pole was a 'T-handle'. The way it worked was the three legs of the stool were dipped into the dolly tub and Mam swished it all back and forward using the T-handle.

Once she was satisfied that the clothes were clean enough she'd hook them out and put them in the second tub, which was full of clear(ish) rinse water. This rinse water came from a six-foot-tall tub in the yard that gathered rainwater, which she used because it was so much softer than the water from the tap.

After rinsing, the washing was put through the mangle. This was a green metal frame, with a pair of rollers about thirty inches long and with a gap between them almost the same thickness as a five-year-old boy's digits! I know all about that gap, because I had personal experience, when I was five.

People often ask me, how come I've got such big hands and long fingers?!

The rollers were 'driven' by a hand-operated handle and their function was to squeeze the water out of the clothes – the gap could be adjusted to wring more water out until the clothes were ready for the washing line. The water in the tubs did get changed a few times, because washing was a day-long affair for me Mam.

Anyway, what this has do with me swimming is that if Arthur, Elsie or me were unlucky enough to be within reach on Monday – washday – maybe during school holidays or when we were at home for some other reason and we'd forgotten what day it was, we often got volunteered to help with the washing. Being the youngest I seemed to get caught more often than the other two. But – it wasn't the work that I objected to, it was the fact that, only ever having a bath on Friday and then in water that had been used already, Mam thought (employing the 'waste not want not' attitude that we had lived with for years) that a dip in the hot dolly tub would clean off some of the tougher dirt and drown any creeping creature that may have escaped from a neighbour's dog or cat or from Lemon – which is what we called the horse.

Don't get me wrong, it wasn't the heat of the water that I objected to; by the time I reached it, it would have been comfortably cool; it wasn't even being lowered in by the ears if I was being obnoxious. What I objected to was all of the bits of sharp, gritty washing powder that would get in every possible crease and crevice with no chance of them being washed out until bath night on the following Friday.

It caused, in me, a deep dislike of being immersed in anything wet. Ergo, at Malvern, swimming wasn't a skill that I was proficient at and I didn't want to learn, 'cos I had also figured that if, as a serving matelot, I ever had to swim, it would be after having jumped off a sinking warship. While surrounded by hundreds of miles of ocean, probably in seas full of burning oil and bullets – or worse, sharks – and... I couldn't see that having gained my badge for swimming a length at Malvern Public Baths would be a whole lot of use in that kind of situation.

We had to do it anyway – the Navy required every sailor to be able to swim one length of the Malvern baths, unaided, whilst fully clothed, oh yes, and being shouted at, I guess to add a little reality, the noise of battle and all that. The first time we did it we were in our swimming trunks and we were told to line up – in two lines – one line here for those that couldn't swim and one line there for those who could. As we approached this exercise I was hardly happy but resigned to thrashing around in cold water – at least I was used to the cold. Anyway, there's this lad from Birmingham, he liked water much less than me because I don't think he'd ever seen any.

He'd decided to join the line for those who could swim, and when I asked him why, he gave me his reason – in broad Brummie – it was that if the instructors thought he could swim, they wouldn't need to teach him and he'd avoid going in the water. I thought for a while... but decided it was a bit of a risky conclusion.

It was.

I mean, why had they bothered to get the swimmers changed into their swimming gear, if not to swim?

While we non-swimmers were getting used to the water at the shallow end, they made the 'swimmers' jump in at the deep end. Brummie went straight down. One of the more junior instructors noticed his plight and, while Brummie was sitting on the bottom yelling silently in his awful Midlands' accent and filling his lungs with Malvern water, the instructor lowered a hoop to pull him out. Well, you know how water refracts light, it also refracted the instructor's aim and he clonked Brummie on the head with his rescue device causing him to lose the will to stay awake.

Meanwhile, back at my end of the pool I was discovering that the Navy's way of teaching we matelots how to swim was to yell one word at us – repeatedly: "Swim!" So, I was wading slowly up the swimming baths pretending to do the crawl stroke and trying to keep the water out of my Brylcreem. I had reached the point where the water was up to my armpits by the time a couple of the more adventurous swimmers had dived down to try and pull Brummie out and were failing miserably. They were just causing a lot of thrashing and bubbles, but by now the senior instructor had cottoned on to what was happening and let loose a broad stream of expletives to accompany the fact that he would have to get his kit off and jump in to get "the silly bugger" back. He wasn't happy – I stopped grinning and decided to look concerned – I didn't turn back though, just stood and watched while the instructor slowly peeled off his top, put his watch and whistle carefully on a poolside chair, took off his shoes and socks and launched himself in.

Even then he just looped the hoop under the shoulders of the – by now water-filled – Brummie, swam gracefully to the surface, hoisted himself out of the pool with the lithe strength of a sea lion and then turned to face the guy holding the rescue pole and encouraged him to: "Pull the dozy sod up then – before he drinks the whole chuffing pool."

We nicknamed the Brummie 'Unte' after that, a shortening of the German word for submarine – *Unterseeboot*. It was Unte that told me my Aberdonian pal's real name. He pointed at me, laughed and said, "He's called McRae. Ha-ha, they named him after you."

Of course I didn't believe a word of it, in fact I didn't understand most of it; that Brummie accent is 'orrible.

Eventually McRae, Unte and I managed to splash along for our 'length of Malvern Baths' and got our certificates – and, on top of my new swimming skills, I found that I no longer felt ill after I'd run up a Malvern hill – and I could tie a fair sheepshank.

* * * * *

Meanwhile, elsewhere in the world naval shipping was being ripped asunder like sardine cans, while fire and death flew from warship to warship covering the ocean in a very gory shade of glory. One month before I began my basic training at HMS *Duke*, Convoy *WS30*, consisting of twenty merchant ships, sailed out of the Clyde heading for Freetown in Sierra Leone – the U-boats were still very active and the convoy was well protected. It set off with the A-class Destroyer HMS *Active*, the armed merchant Cruiser HMS *Asturias*, B-class Destroyer HMS *Boadicea*, the Type 1 Hunt-class Escort Destroyer HMS *Cleveland*, River-class Frigates HMS *Exe* and HMS *Ness*, Coast Guard Cutter HMS *Gorleston*, the Grimsby-class Sloops HMS *Lowestoft* and HMS *Wellington*, the Destroyer HMS *Sardonyx*, the Polish Escort Destroyer ORP *Slavack*, the County-class Heavy Cruiser HMS *Suffolk*, the Aircraft-carrier HMS *Unicorn*, and the Shoreham-class Sloop HMS *Weston* as escorts – one of them was only with the convoy for a day, but the rest stayed for six days before being relieved by HMS

Antelope, HMS *Catterick*, HMS *Corfu*, HMS *Foxhound* and HMS *Totland*. That was a lot of protection for twenty ships and it turned out to be warranted.

On the fifth day of the convoy, two of the escorts sweeping the seas ahead of the convoy made contact with one of the Italian Navy's most successful submarines, lying in wait off the Portuguese coast, where the convoy routes turn in just north-east of the Azores and off Cape Finestrelle. The Royal Navy ships were the Destroyer HMS *Active* and the River-class Frigate HMS *Ness* and, between them, they put paid to one of Italy's most effective warships, pounding it ruthlessly to death and killing everyone on board.

Two of the frigate's crew members – the skipper, Acting Commander T. G. P. Crick, RN, and its Anti-Submarine Officer, a New Zealander, Temporary Lieutenant J. O. Wilson, were decorated. The experienced Crick won a Bar on the DSC he'd won in First World War action, while Wilson won the Distinguished Service Cross for great skill and daring in action with enemy submarines.

At the time I had no idea about the incident, and if I had, it wouldn't have meant anything to me – as time went on, however, that would change.

The same day of the action, the German Navy withdrew their U-boats from the Atlantic; they were getting a bloody nose – but they didn't stay away long.

* * * * *

I spent a week in Portsmouth after Malvern and they must have liked my spunky attitude at the camp because when my basic training finished six weeks after it had started, they asked me if I would like to stop on a bit and train to be a 'DEMS' gunner.

I was wise to Navy ways by now and imagined that the training would probably consist of – "There's the seat... sit on it – there's the trigger... pull it – don't shoot at our own ships – training over!"

DEMS, by the way, stands for a Defensively Equipped Merchant Ship. The Nazi war machine had declared that any ship belonging to the merchant marine, whether British or likely to belong to the friends of Britain, was to be treated as a warship. So every merchant ship had to be armed – initially with little more than pea-shooters but they did eventually get some beefy guns and they needed naval personnel to fire them.

Apparently they had a glut of stokers at the time and a shortage of DEMS gunners – I wondered why!

I thought long and hard for a few seconds – at the time I understood a merchantman to be an (often) slow ship that was full to the gunnels with goodies that would relieve the war effort. So much so that all of the enemy planes along with wolf pack upon wolf pack of enemy submarines were ordered to blow them out of the water in huge numbers.

Oh, yes, and the DEMS gun was the thing that the merchantman hit back with and thus was the target that the enemy aimed for first.

Oh, yes, and their position was often hanging over the back of the ship catching the coldest of cold breezes and the most freezing bits of sea spray slung up from the angry Atlantic waves.

I decided at the time that it took a special lack of mentality to be a DEMS gunner – a lack that I didn't have – and I hadn't run up all those hillsides just to become another red smudge on the surface of the Atlantic. Even the best option didn't light my fuse, sitting in a cold metal seat all day (some of them were heated) trying to ignore the pain from an aggressive batch of piles brought on by – and mercilessly irritated by – the constant salty spray.

As soon as I knew better I considered those DEMS gunners to be heroes – me – I remained a stoker.

At that time, my plan for my naval career had been carefully worked out to suit a man that likes his comforts, so I stuck to stoker and enquired about any other suitable courses – for a stoker – where it was warm – that I could do while they waited for a position to come free.

What I didn't know was that the Navy was expanding dramatically – from 73,000 men in 1939, the numbers had almost reached 600,000 by spring 1943 and their Lordships in the Admiralty were looking for a further 100,000 over the next twelve months in readiness for the Normandy landings. They had a few in the Admiralty pushing a new attitude to training and since I was being judged as good at it – training was about to entrap me. I have to say though, that by and large the Navy's attitude to training was, to say the least, quaint.

I was sent to another training camp at Eastleigh near Portsmouth where they taught me how to be a firefighter on board ship. Sounded warm enough and it was. I carry a birthmark, down the left-hand side of my face, deeper pink than a normal skin tone for a lad from t'north of England. After thirteen weeks at Eastleigh I had become so closely acquainted with the fire from burning oil that all of the skin on my face was the same vivid colour and my birthmark was paler than the rest!

Even so, I got my firefighter qualification and when I asked the Petty Officer, "What now?" he asked me to stay on at the training unit and teach the next batch. He said they still didn't have any openings for stokers – I told him I'd rather not stay, I wanted a posting, so he posted me to a place called Lowton St Mary, another teaching establishment and I taught the next batch of trainee firefighters there instead.

I'd been double-shuffled – there were a lot of good double-shufflers amongst the petty officers I had come across – I had ambitions to join them and resolved to study for my Petty Officer's ticket; this Navy lark was beginning to feel as though it was turning into a career – and a very dry one at that.

So, for now, I had to teach the latest batch of new 'students' all about firefighting on a naval vessel. In other words, I was tasked with doing unto them that which my instructors at Eastleigh had just done unto me.

I'd been in the Navy for a grand total of three months and had yet to see a warship. I had no idea how long it would be until I rode the Seven Seas. Right now, I was a lecturer and my first lecture at Lowton (which was my first lecture anywhere) was planned for the very first evening and saw me addressing an audience of 200.

I was finding already that typical naval practice was not so much to teach you how to do things, like how to prepare a lecture for an audience of 200, it was more a case of putting you in a situation and seeing if you had the wit to cope with it. If you did, you got a certificate and a badge to sew onto the sleeve of your uniform; if you didn't succeed you got swept to one side and gloriously ignored. This process applied even if you were doing something dangerous (which lecturing wasn't) like handling explosives.

With dangerous activities, if you didn't have the wit to cope you could get to meet some very pretty nurses. Tempting – but I was spoken for.

CHAPTER FOUR

Anyway, my first lecture began in front of an audience of 200 eager sailors and a bunch of bored officers at the rear, including the commander of the whole facility and me with not a lecture note to my name; you could say I was factually stifled... and the nerves kicked in. Or as my grandson would say, "I was bricking it!" At this point in the proceedings, a piece of Moss ingenuity surfaced and my first words to the audience were a question – "Is there anyone from the fire brigade in the audience?"

I saw six hands rise into the air. My second words were an invite to them to: "Come and tell us about the kinds of fires you would expect on board ship and how you would deal with these kinds of fire." The six ex-firemen joined me at the front of the room, where I was happy to blend into the background while they took over my lecture with the gusto of a great desire to share their knowledge wrought from the 'real experience' of dealing with house fires.

They got the bit totally wrong about dousing electrical fires on a metal warship, which is full of engine fuel and explosives. When the Commander caught up with me afterwards he laid the blame fair and square at my door and insisted that I make sure that everyone in the audience was given the correct information by the end of the next day. He had no expression on his face when he told me but I thought I saw a glint in his eye when he suggested I was something of a crafty sod.

So, I took the opportunity of asking him, for the first time, for a transfer to a seagoing ship. "After all," I added with what I believed to be a mischievous smile, "I din't join the Navy to spend my time ashore."

He smiled, said he'd see what he could do and then told me I was to be in charge of the crew in one of the Mess Huts – (not again, why did they always pick on me?) – a right motley crew my hut turned out to be. To use an old naval expression, I was beginning to feel as though this captain thought I'd been 'peeing in his pickles' and the hut was my slap on the hand.

At first I had them down as a crafty bunch, when my mess crew got a severe dose of idleitis and were the last to turn out on seven o'clock parade the next morning. But that was soon dispelled and I was given a clear indicator of the level of common sense they possessed and the old Moss spirit and intuition came into play again.

The mess was served its tea in a big urn – a tea kettle – ours was looking a bit dull and dingy, which was just the sort of thing a petty officer would notice and take great delight in as he ordered a punishment for tardiness – something like painting coal or dusting pebbles or some other such useful pastime. I'd done my fair share of those already so I detailed one of the hut to polish the urn; he asked what with, I told him to use Bluebell metal polish – a kind of Brasso – and he started.

He was playing at it so I gave him a gentle jolt to get cracking and told him I'd be back soon. Actually he made a great job – the outside of that tea kettle gleamed, so much so that it seemed a shame not to make a brew, which I asked him to do as a kind of reward! When he poured it, the stuff came out black – he'd only polished the inside of the kettle as well and left a good covering of raw Bluebell inside, which had a particularly weird effect on the taste and toxicity of the brew.

He was advised of his error and told to clean the metal polish out properly, but it didn't work. His mates didn't half squeal when I told them that the Mess would have to tally up for a new one. You see while the Navy would give you your first – of anything – if you lost or wrecked it, or wanted more, you had to buy the replacement.

Next morning and I had the perfect use for the old tea kettle. As I walked through their mess door at 0600 I was bashing the thing like a drum, with a metal ladle! It didn't half clatter – it was the beginning of my invitation to get their hands off their *you-know-whats* and on with their socks (which is the closest I can get to the real and well-known services wake-up greeting, and still allow my great-granddaughter to read this!). They were out on parade just after 0630 and I'm pleased to say they were never late again.

About the same time I was given the command of a tiny team of sailors in the inter-naval fire pump races and the officer (who must have had a bet on) told me there was half a knicker in it if we won. I practised the best of my sulks when I realised that my team was made up mainly of 'old men', one of them was 20 and the other almost 21 – ancient – we won... which made me feel better.

I was taking to this training lark and eventually stopped expressing my concern that I hadn't actually done any Stoker Training yet – so they gave me a star and made me Stoker First Class – that's the Navy. By now I was 19, the Italians had surrendered and I was taking lectures without needing any notes and beginning to study for my Petty Officer's ticket.

My career as a trainer in firefighting at Lowton St Mary's was becoming more and more established and I was becoming more and more frustrated. It seems that the Navy had decided they needed me to tell rookie sailors how to douse the best efforts of the enemy's firepower – it seems I was to fight the Hun from a base in deepest Warrington.

While all this land-based time slipped by I asked Freda if she would become Mrs Moss – now that... was very scary.

Actually, the first and most nerve-wracking part of it all was asking her father for her hand in marriage. I walked nervously into the front room, where he was sitting, while Freda, her mum and two of her four sisters were in the adjacent room. As a gaggle of girls listened – and I asked – he just looked, straight and level, and finally said, "If you are old enough to fight for your country, you are old enough to marry my daughter." So, Freda and I got married – 3rd April 1944. But before it happened I had an adventure that came close to doing me permanent damage of the most intimate kind – the daft things a young chap will do in search of romance! Here's what occurred.

I had been granted a couple of days' leave to get wed and caught the train from Lowton into Doncaster station, arriving quite late in the evening – on the eve of the big day. Trains to Scunthorpe had stopped running and I was supposed to be meeting up with Freda at our house for final arrangements. I'd met a Scottish lad on the train; he was in the Army, he was from Scunthorpe too and we shared a problem; there were no trains and no buses, so he asked me the obvious question: "Now what are we going to do?"

"Only one thing for it – we'll scrounge a lift." The first vehicle we flagged down belonged to British Oxygen; the driver looked at us – both in our uniforms – and agreed to take us straight away. "Only one problem, lads," he smiled, "there's no room in the cab – you'll have to sit in the back."

Now, when he said 'in' the back, well, it was really 'on' the back – there was no cover. We had to sit on top of a load of full oxygen cylinders and I don't know quite what they do to those oxygen cylinders but – they were freezing.

An April night – and forty-odd miles – with the wind whistling around our ears – and the cold from the cylinders seeping into our unmentionable bits – after a mile we couldn't talk to each other – so our teeth made up for it – just so as not to appear rude, they started chattering fit to crack.

But we got home and I gave the driver twenty cigarettes for his trouble – I was numb from the waist down – not so much shivering as shrivelled. Freda wasn't there, she'd gone home – Charlie told me she was a bit upset – nothing for it but to set off for her house – about a mile away.

Arthur had the bike so I had to walk. The thought did run through my mind that biking may have been somewhat dangerous, with my 'bits' as cold as they were it wasn't impossible they were frozen solid and the jolting of a bike ride might have snapped them off – the things a groom must consider on the eve of his nuptials!

In the end – or that might be 'in *my* end' – it was a good job really, my nether regions were close to frostbite and the walk brought the blood back to my cheeks. It also gave me the chance to pick the flies that had thrown themselves at us like kamikazes from the slipstream of the truck, out from between my teeth, where they had lodged in my frozen smile!

We were married the next day, in the Church of Saint John the Evangelist, then a classic church built from Frodingham ironstone and donated to the town by the Lord Oswald, Rowland Winn – it's an arts centre now – such a shame.

One of the things I remember about that beautiful old building was it had a magnificent organ, built in London in the 1890s for the immense sum of £1,000. And talk of that magnificent organ reminds me that – thankfully – my own had thawed out and was back in full working order. I tried to import the word immense from that last sentence as well, but I just couldn't think how to. (*Freda* – or why!)

Any road up, Arthur was my best man and Freda's bridesmaids were mainly her sisters. We had a posh reception for forty-two people at Crosby Hotel for the princely sum of £18.10s.6d. (which the father of the bride paid) and a whole day of honeymoon, staying with Freda's sister Nancy and brother-in-law Egrin in their newly rented council house near Ashby.

In truth my new bride was happy that my time in the Navy was shore-based and a long way from the glorious death and maiming being 'enjoyed' by other British servicemen, but for me it was becoming hard to take; teaching a course of firefighting really was not why I'd joined up.

Twelve months after I had begun my temporary posting at Lowton St Mary, I was sent to Portsmouth to sit for my Petty Officer's examination aboard an old battlecruiser anchored in the harbour. The journey down was eventful as the so-called Little Blitz was still raging in London with the V2 rockets hitting the capital – one of which decided to arrive as I was in transit from one London station to the next – scared me silly. I have to say those Londoners are made of very stern stuff to put up with the hammering they took.

At the same time, a rather war-weary River-class Frigate was in port and making significant changes in its crew – still no slot for a stoker though – not yet.

During my stay in Portsmouth I had what, for me in the Navy, was a rare occurrence. I met the first of very few real 'bully' officers, a PTO or Physical Training Officer, a short man, hairy legs, muscles on his flabby bits and the neatest full beard I've seen. It was his responsibility to keep us fit and one of the ways he was going to do this was – to take us on a route march around Portsmouth.

Fair enough. Except he didn't do that, instead he took us straight to the nearest café and as soon as the 'teas were in' he looked at me and told me to get up on the table and sing them all a song. He obviously didn't know me. I have the singing voice of a drowning tomcat, so he would have really regretted it if I had gone along with his orders. But that wasn't all he didn't know about me – when I wanted it to be, *awkward* could be my middle name and – I'd got his number – I'd sussed that he was trying to chat up one of the waitresses.

Maybe it was the gnawing feeling that I was about to leave behind a life that I had found comfortable and was staring again at times unknown that had me feeling edgy. Maybe it was the fact that I had over eighteen months of Navy life under my belt already and wasn't as raw as the PTO's usual intake which spurred my reaction. Had I been thinking rationally, I would have considered that I had come up against bullies in my life before the Navy and I knew that the only way to react is to stand up to them, but I wasn't thinking. I was churning inside, my chest full of worms and my eyes full of fire, and I was reacting to that. So I told him – in my most aggressive and least misunderstandable tone – to go forth and multiply.

He coughed, then he went grey around the face and finally he dashed towards me like a ferret on heat and he stopped so close to me that I got lashed by the hairs hanging from the end of his nostrils. He repeated his order, informing me that if I disobeyed him, he would put me on report as soon as we got back to the ship. He then reminded me that the Navy required every order to be obeyed. Further, he reminded me that in the case of a seaman complaining against an unjust order – the Navy required the order to be followed first and then the complaint to be made. When I held his glare and calmly told him that I hoped he would report me, because it would give me the chance to ask why he had neglected the route march for a dalliance in the nearest café with a young waitress, he just continued to stare for a long while. He reminded me of a softer version of Charlie's horse and I couldn't help but smile – and then he changed tack. "Right!" he said. "As punishment for disobeying an order, you'll *all* run back to the ship and the last one there will be on a charge."

He was trying to drop me in it with the rest of them and I felt my temper spiral, but I held it and replied sweetly: "I am so sorry, sir, but I don't think that I can run, seeing as how I stubbed my toe on the step coming into *the café*." The rest of the lads cottoned on and soon every one of us had a café-related injury that would slow down any attempts to run and which we may have to report to the Medical Officer when we returned.

He just yelled at us to get out but, with my temper quietly steaming, I hung back, as I knew he'd want a moment alone with the young lady he had his eye on. When everyone else had left the café and he was heading for the door, I stood across his path and turned to face him down, sharing my thoughts with him: "You are all mouth and trousers; try anything with me again and I'll have you!" Not an advisable thing for a rating to say to a non-commissioned officer, but he deserved it.

He slid away to try and find someone else to bully while we strolled back to barracks; when we got to the gate there he was standing alongside the biggest MP you can imagine; if he was trying to intimidate me I have to say it didn't work. The difference in height between the two of them was so extreme that it was all any of us could do to keep ourselves from laughing at him. We walked past him without a word being exchanged.

My exams over, I tried again, this time with a different CO – I once again expressed my keenness to get into the war before I was too old: "When I signed up," I told him, "it wasn't part of my plan that I should fall overboard and get nettled!"

* * * * *

Remember that River-class Frigate I mentioned earlier? It had left harbour and was on its way to Scotland to give the new members of its crew a crash course in U-boat warfare; it had a Stoker First Class on board, who had been part of the crew since the ship had been commissioned ten months earlier. Recently he'd been hearing more and more grumbles that he could no longer ignore – they were coming from his appendix.

The Captain I had just been speaking to sent in his request for my posting just as the captain of the frigate sent in his request for a Stoker First Class.

Within a few days I was in Stamshore Camp, Portsmouth, lined up with a group of seamen. We were all due a new posting and we were about to see where that posting would be. My name, Moss, was called out – and then I heard the word submarine. Oh no, not subma-*ruddy*-rines. I hated submarines – why did I have to be put on a sub – oh well – I guess it was better than nothing. Right! I'm going to be a submariner – that'll teach me. All of this was running through my head and I had just accepted my fate, when the selection officer called out a forename and a number that wasn't mine – it wasn't me, there was another Moss in the line-up.

It was still all submarines though – the next six names announced were all heading for submarines – I remember letting myself get thoroughly used to the idea that it would be a submariner's life for me, when the officer in charge did call my name and number and told me I was to join the River-class Frigate HMS *Ness*.

I was gone the next day on the train chasing HMS *Ness* up to Scotland.

CHAPTER FIVE

The steam train from Portsmouth took me to Oban, from whence I jumped on board the early ferry, sailed up the Sound of Mull and disembarked to HMS *Western Isles* training base on the Isle of Mull and in particular the jetty at Tobermory harbour. It was one of those rare January days where the sun was shining through any gap it could find in a lumpy cloud base that was racing along on a stiff westerly wind. I could see the motor launch from HMS *Ness* with two men aboard waiting for me and as I walked closer to it, it began to look more and more alarming, moving up and down on the swells like a demented elevator. I noticed the launch's coxswain working hard to keep his launch clear of damage as the driven waves rocked back from the jetty while they waited to pick me up from my solid, steady block of concrete at the waterside. The wheelman looked much more relaxed.

Suddenly I was wondering if leaving Lowton was such a good idea. One fairly vital bit of training that the Navy had failed to deliver was how to step into a small wooden launch when it's on the same level as you one second and six feet below you the next and rocking from side to side like a demented see-saw. It was obviously another initiative test and I didn't fancy my chances.

The sailor helping me aboard wasn't helping – he was medium height and his slight build was being exaggerated by the breeze, which filled his tunic as he swayed with the waves. His short-back-and-sides haircut was much less ruffled than he was; he had it combed with a centre parting and the 'wings' sprung over his ample forehead at each side; his hair was firmly held in place by what looked to be a handful of Brylcreem, so it heartily resisted any attempt by the breeze to disturb it. As he reached the top of the swell he tossed his cigarette end into the wind and watched it drop, sparkling, towards the grey water below, before the launch began to accelerate downwards after it. On the next upward swell he used the corner of his mouth, which was otherwise being filled with another Woodbine, and checked my identity with: "S'tha Moss?" disappearing, before I could answer, in a flash of phosphorous from the Swan Vesta cupped in his hand against the wind as he lit his next cigarette. After a moment or two of this, all I could hear was one set of expletives querying my mental abilities as he came up and another set querying my physical abilities as he went down. I meanwhile watched attentively and tried to get into the rhythm.

"Cum-m-or-rn, what's thi messin' abahtat?" came the thick Yorkshire accent, trailing cigarette smoke, on the upstroke.

"Will thee chuck tha friggin' kit bag." More flat vowels on the downstroke.

"Kit bag – now, now, now, now." Upstroke.

"Pill-oe-oe-oe-ck." Delivered with no real malice showing in his brown eyes, on the downstroke.

Then I did it – in went my kit bag just as the boat hit the top of the swell. Perfect. Then my hammock – ha heeee – easy.

Now it was time for me – neither of us breathed – I stepped off my friendly block of concrete and the waters of the Sound of Mull, with a lot of help from the rollers of the Atlantic Ocean, performed right on time. I was in. Moving with all the grace of a falling man towards my intended seat on the cross plank, I slipped backwards and found a damp patch in the floor of the launch. I was hanging on to everything but my dignity as the cox gunned the launch forward.

My helper grunted, turned towards me, thrust out a hand replete with the telltale yellow nicotine stains on the insides of his long fingers and as I scrambled into place he shook my hand, spun the wheel and told me he was Stoker Knight, adding: "T'lads call mi t'Bogie-man – d'yu want a fag?" I shook my head to say no and we set off for my new home, HMS *Ness*.

I'd sat on something resting on the bench and managed to extricate Bogie's hat from underneath me and dust it off, without him knowing, although he did seem to give it a bit of a shake and an extra look before he fitted it carefully in place ready for our embarkation from launch to ship.

As I stepped aboard, the decks of the *Ness* felt so solid compared to the bucking and tossing of the launch, which Bogie sprinted off to help winch into its position abaft the funnel on the starboard. The *Ness* got underway as soon as my feet touched the deck; she surged with confidence, seeming at peace with herself and yet, down below, in the Mess that was to be my new home, I felt a tension. It was almost physical – but, of course, I had no idea what could be up, it was just a feeling that I was amongst a crew that was very jittery; perhaps the captain was a bit of a horror, or maybe the First Lieutenant – I hadn't yet asked myself why HMS *Ness* was at Tobermory, she wasn't a new ship.

Bogie showed me where to stow my gear and then disappeared again, leaving me with another two of my messmates – Streak and Scouser. Streak was a particularly tall bloke with less meat on him than a match has timber. It looked as though he had long spindly legs, long spindly arms, a long neck and a head with rather horse-like proportions, the elongation exaggerated by his thick dark hair, which he combed straight back. It seemed as though he had no body to speak of – his uniform sort of flapped around him like a mainsail in an uncertain breeze. He came from Bournemouth and his real name was Stuart Bacon, from whence came his naval nickname. I was told later that they had tried the normal ones, like Piggy and Porky, but those two gave out a message of rotundness, which was completely inappropriate. So his mates settled on Streaky, because he had been a runner – in fact a hurdler – before he was called up; eventually they shortened it to Streak. He spoke very well and had a command of verbiage that overwhelmed his real intelligence. Streak was pseudo-posh and pretty dim. Unfortunately for me, it was his advice I followed when choosing the spot to hang my hammock, but more of that later.

Scouser came from... well, it could only be Liverpool and he became a great mate to have when we were in that particular port, because he had a talent for 'finding' things; come to think, he practised his talent in every other port we visited too. He never pinched anything from any of his shipmates, except perhaps for the odd fag if a packet was left lying around, but that kind of carelessness was seen as fair game for anyone. He was short and had a nose and face that looked too big for his head, his hair was short and his ears rather large and I never did get to see what colour his eyes were because they were always flitting around. Scouser had perhaps the thickest accent of all of us, which became even thicker when he got excited and his words kind of *elongated* a bit, like he almost had a stammer but just got hold of it in time and changed a stutter of words into just one. His other speciality was his love of a wager; he was a small-time bookie, which saw him getting excited quite a lot of the time.

It didn't take long for me to find out what was making everyone nervous, but first let me introduce you to her ladyship HMS *Ness*.

* * * * *

HMS *Ness* was launched on 22nd December 1942 – she was a River-class Frigate – which was a class of frigate named after a river – her pennant number was K-213, her R/T call sign was 'Vestry' and her motto was 'Gain Say Who Dare'.

I had missed the action that was her main claim to fame; that had taken place on 23rd May 1943, four weeks before I began my basic training. On that day, HMS *Ness*, under the captaincy of Acting Commander T. G. R. Crick, RN and in the company of the Destroyer HMS *Active*, sank the Marconi-class Italian submarine RSMG *Leonardo Da Vinci*. No survivors.

In its twenty-two-month career, the *Da Vinci* had torpedoed and sunk seventeen merchantmen, eight of which were flying the British flag. The action, which sank it, took place just north-east of the Azores and the submarine's loss was quite a blow to the Italian Navy. Commander Crick and the ship's anti-submarine control officer Sub-Lieutenant Wilson, a New Zealander, were both awarded the Distinguished Service Cross (DSC) for the part they played.

Anyway, back to the plot – HMS *Ness* was a twin prop ship designed with enough range to do 7,200 miles if we stayed at 12 knots – all handy stuff to know if you're a Stoker First Class – I never did find out what mileage she would do at full speed, which was around 19 knots.

Her main armaments were the four Mk IV depth charge throwers and the 150 or so depth charges we had on board. Our job was to detect and kill submarines – or more often kill the submarines that other ships had spotted on their Asdic[6] – later known as sonar – a kind of sound-based echo bouncing underwater radar.

It 'pinged'.

She also had some guns; initially there was something called a Hedgehog, which was a kind of multi-headed mortar, plus she had a single 4-inch gun on the foredeck; we eventually had this changed to a dual Bofors gun at South Shields and we got rid of the Hedgehog (I don't think it ever got fired).

We also had a 12-pounder gun aft and four 20mm Oerlikon guns on the deck and the aft platform. It was enough to give a U-boat a very bloody nose.

I must own up to you that I have a very bad attitude when it comes to submarines; I think of them in much the same way as I think of the rats that rustled around in the straw in me Dad's stable. Even today I detest the buggers – strong feelings deeply embedded, probably because the wolf packs were such a frightening force. Maybe because you couldn't see them, so you couldn't fight them properly – man to man, kind of thing. They would sneak up and shoot you in the back.

Anyhow, the reason I was on board HMS *Ness* was because the previous Stoker First Class had gone down with appendicitis on the way up from Portsmouth and they needed a new one. I was now a full member of the Black Squad – a Stoker – one of 141 sailors who made up HMS *Ness*'s crew.

My predecessor had sorted out what my duties were and – while it had something to do with delivering the fuel that would fire the oil-fired engines, he had a few other 'useful' duties as well.

---

6   Asdic was named after the Anti-Submarine Detection Investigation Committee that first
     initiated the system.

Primarily I would be one of the 'monkeys' that climbed around with the huge fuel hoses when it came to filling the ship's tanks. I was well qualified to take his place. I could deliver a lecture on firefighting with my eyes shut and I could swim a length of Malvern Baths while fully clothed. Oh yes, mustn't forget – I could also run up a hill and tie a sheepshank, a half-hitch and a bowline in any given piece of string – and – I knew me reef from me granny.

My inherited duties also put me in charge of the Stokers' Mess – here we go again – me – in charge of the bloody Mess – again – why me – always me. Or, was this bunch taking advantage of the new lad? Still, there were benefits, and I was a Stoker First Class after all and an expert fireman – oh yes, and I had been head of the Mess at Malvern and at Lowton – experience – that must be it.

I can't really remember how many of we stokers there were on board. I'll guess that there were around fifteen of us in total, perhaps I never knew because we worked on a watch (shift) system to keep the ship operational throughout the day and night. Let me try and remember: there was the Chief and then five, or perhaps six, Petty Officers and four Leading Stokers; seven or eight Stokers First Class and half a dozen or so with the rank of Stoker Second Class or Stoker. How many's that? Twenty-five? I was close. I do remember being a bit concerned when I learnt that most of the others had done Stoker Training at Stamshore Camp in Portsmouth, because I hadn't – when I voiced my concerns to the Chief he just winked at me and said, "Don't you worry, son, you'll soon pick it up."

I had also inherited the duties of helmsman of the ship's motor launch, which I shared with Bogie, I was also charged with looking after the ship's refrigeration and desalination plants as well as being a general banger of heavy spanners against any non-working part in the engine room until a better-qualified engineer appeared. Actually I was quite handy with me hands and quick to pick up most practical skills.

But I've drifted into talking about me, and I was talking about HMS *Ness* and why she was sailing in such a tense atmosphere.

The ship had been operational since the beginning of 1943, based most of the time at Gibraltar, and either on Ocean Escort duties for the convoys or on Patrol, seeking out enemy submarines – either Italians or U-boats. She had returned to Portsmouth recently and had a major change of officers and crew. Subsequent exercises in the English Channel had shown a need for the new crew to practise together and so she had been sent to Tobermory for three weeks under the care of Captain 'D' of the anti-sub training establishment HMS *Western Isles* – Vice Admiral Sir Gilbert Stephenson, KBE, CB, CMG.

This establishment had been set up to make sure that the growing numbers of crews of the converted trawlers, corvettes and frigates knew how to hunt and kill the U-boats and protect their own ships in the process.

The Vice Admiral had a reputation as a terror; he had a voice that could out-match Foghorn Fanny and a disposition that was Navy through and through. His teaching technique was typical Navy too, "Chuck 'em in at the deep end and if they swim, they'll do for us!"

Sir Gilbert was the reason for the tension in the crew; he was almost 70 and one of those annoyingly energetic short-arses hell-bent on making you learn through your mistakes and he seemed to love to make you feel as small as he could when you made them. The trouble was, he was the boss. Upset him and I'd be back to Lowton St Mary's cleaning out tea urns. He had everybody in a bad mood – the skipper, the First Lieutenant, the Chief Petty Officer – this was not going to be fun.

On that first day the Admiral treated the crew of the *Ness* to his tactic of unex-pectedly tossing a lifebelt over the side and observing how we would handle a 'man overboard situation' – we didn't do well – the first dozen would have drowned! Good job they were only lifebelts – I was actually quite relieved when I was detailed to lower the ship's boat and go gather them all in.

That first day ended and I slung my hammock, where Streak showed me, amongst the rest of the Stokers, in the for'ard Stokers' Mess. Down two sets of ladders to the Middle Deck, along a grey passageway and forward of the Seamans' Mess from which we were divided by a bulkhead and an attitude that would have you believing that we were the bitterest of enemies and not at all part of one big happy team. My change of routine had already woken up and tired out a few muscles I hadn't used in a while so, although I was aching steadily, my first night on the sea started very well – the gentle swell rocked me to sleep until I slumbered like a baby.

That evening HMS *Ness* left the shelter of the coast for the first of our ocean exercises.

I was blissfully sleeping as we passed the northern tip of Ireland, when, around midnight, somewhere in the very bowels of the ship, claxons, demanding a call to action, began wailing desperately, warning us that there were imaginary – or maybe real – U-boats in the vicinity.

That was the moment, with my eardrums bursting and my nerves twanging like guitar strings, I discovered that I had positioned my hammock directly underneath one of the speakers for the claxons – why hadn't anybody told me? – smirking so and so's. The noise jerked me awake so violently that my hammock almost spun right around – I am absolutely certain that I spent a few milliseconds staring at the deck before I got out of my hammock and, as I ran through the door, I looked back and it was still twirling. I didn't get very far, in fact a second or two later I was back in the Mess. Courtesy of the biggest of the petty officers, who I'd run straight into and who had propelled me back with the advice that, "The Navy didn't rush aboot in a panic – we are cool and organised and you is going nowhere until your hammock is stowed in correct Navy Fashion. Now 'urry up, you hopeless little gonad." I panicked in a calm kind of a manner and rushed with quiet Royal Navy efficiency.

* * * * *

Any road up, I was detailed to take another of my predecessor's places in one of the three-man damage-control teams and we took up our posts listening intently for the crashing explosion of a torpedo coming through the side or a glider bomb coming through the superstructure and nestling in the sector of *Ness* that was under our vigilance. Our Mess was in one of the more vulnerable parts of the ship, being immediately above the fuel tanks, which in themselves were just below sea level and at a perfect height for a torpedo attack!

HMS *Ness* manoeuvred into more open waters and began to move very erratically – the sea was rough and my initiation into the Atlantic's moods began. By dawn, the ocean had decided it was time to really let me know where I was.

If I put my foot to the left, the ocean sent the boat down on the right, if I went right it went left – if I went lower, it went higher and if I anticipated higher, well, you've got it by now.

Halfway through the morning and I was feeling queasy – wearing my boiler suit, I stepped out to the deck, thinking, 'Fresh air, that'll do me good.' I was stopped by one of my shipmates, who informed me that our new Jimmy the One (the First Lieutenant) was an obnoxious Ozzie and if he caught me on deck without my proper uniform, he'd have bits of me passed to the cook to slice and use in the place of cloves of garlic. So, I went back below.

I was kept busy during the afternoon; getting to know the location of things I had responsibility for – like the desalination plant. By suppertime, my nausea was coming back; I think the constant drum and vibration of the engines had made me worse. I knew my messmates would have been delighted at this new boy's discomfort and I was determined not to be seasick.

One or two of them taunted me with offers of the greasiest forms of food possible, "Glad you joined the Navy, mate? Food's regular. Six meals a day – three down, three up." I ignored them – and noted who they were so I could get them back, later.

I also decided that – seeing as how the sirens were likely to be serenading us loud and often while we were on sea trials – I would reposition my hammock. That night, I chose a spot beneath a light, so that I could read when I wanted to.

As I swung in my newly positioned hammock, with my light shining, reading the same paragraph time after time, my queasiness just refused to stop growing – all night, as I fretfully slept and woke, the feeling of sickness rose higher and higher. Eventually, at some ungodly hour of the morning, with the Mess in darkness and my fellows fast asleep – I knew I had to get out of my hammock – my first thought was for fresh air.

I was part way to the door in the bulkhead that led to the passageway, which took me to the ladders and onto the upper deck immediately under the bridge when an idea slowly emerged from the depths of my memory and decided me to abandon the fresh air. Deep in the recesses of my subconscious spun an image of our Elsie, she was catching a well-swaddled baby, who was also feeling motion-sick and then came an image of burnt toast – could that be the answer to my seasickness? – burnt toast!

Burnt toast – it was worth a go.

I ran along the passageway, open waterproof door number one, step over, turn (panic), close the watertight door (gulp), fasten the watertight clamps, turn, run, open waterproof door number two (bloody hell), step over, run, stop, (gulp, gulp, gulp) turn, go back, shut the door, fasten the watertight clamps, up the first ladder (panic, clamp teeth), fumbled through the hatch (oh my Gawd) into the galley, (panic) where's the bread, (hop, gulp, panic) where's the bread, where's the bread, where's the bread, (bubble – panic) found the bread (panic). Knife – I need a knife – ah, ah, ah, there's a knife – slice and again – oh no – where's the grill?

There must be a grill, there must be – somewhere – but (panic) I (panic) couldn't (panic) find it (I'm gunna hurl) – I swallowed hard and clamped my teeth together as the first ripples of liquid puke breathed onto the back of my throat (panic), Elsie drifted back (gulp) with her burnt slice (panic) on the toasting fork, (gulp) in front of the fire, (cla-a-a-ng) the fire – we had a fire – in the Mess – an electric fire – that hung over the table – that would do it – I swallowed even harder – slid back down the ladder, sprinted back along the passageway and into our Mess, I unhooked the fire, clipped off the safety-guard with shaky fingers and began to toast the bread on the electric bars. Health and Safety was a notion yet to be born and if it had been born it would have been withered rapidly in the rather more earthy attitudes of the day.

But, the toast worked, with each sniff of the blackening bread, my queasiness lessened and when I began to nibble at the black stuff my nausea retreated, until it had just about gone altogether.

And that's when the coughing and boking started.

One after another, the slumbering forms, swinging gently in the Atlantic swell, were beginning to cough. In my haste, I had put the fire down and dropped a lump of bread onto the electric elements and they were smoking now like an old steam ship. My fellow stokers were waking. I pulled the electric cable hastily from its plug, tossed the fire into a dark corner and retreated as rapidly as I could to my hammock.

The mumbling and moaning grew for a few minutes and then diminished as the smoke steadily drifted away. I, meanwhile, lay with my eyes tight shut, hoping that everyone would think I was asleep. I wasn't yet aware that I had discovered a wonder cure, but my troubles with seasickness were over. I was right chuffed. You know how, in theatrical circles, they have a saying: 'It ain't over till the fat lady sings' – well, in my dreams that night she sang up a storm and in my case the Fat Lady was a Midwife.

As the morning activity started and the winter light of the moon reflected off the water crept around the portholes I lay quiet, flat on my back, eyes tight shut, the gentle gurgling that had been spinning from my stomach to the back of my throat gone completely now – and then I opened my eyes. Right above me, defying gravity and running around my light was a family of fat purple-black cockroaches – right above me!

And into my head came the thought that I must never sleep flat on my back with my mouth open and nostrils gaping invitingly, but, that aside, I was never troubled with seasickness again.

After a day or two sailing along the edge of the Atlantic Ocean, the Admiral was satisfied that we knew our port from our starboard and our stem from our stern. We returned to the quieter waters of the Mull and a whole new set of exercises began. We did not do good – the skipper was charged with picking up survivors from a stricken ship – this required a technique called buoy-jumping – basically Bogie or I would ferry a few of our shipmates to a large flat-topped buoy anchored in the Mull, which represented the wreck. HMS *Ness* was to approach, throw a line to the 'survivors' who were standing on the buoy and then secure it and pick them up.

We approached, at some speed, threw the line – and missed – for some reason I thought of Charlie's rope trick back in Scunthorpe and how well he'd done with that! The next try was even worse; we threw the line, they caught it and secured the rope, but we carried on and knocked them all into the drink – we were back to 'man overboard' but with real men this time – we got them back safely even though one had deigned to break his wrist in the process. The skipper and the First Lieutenant didn't look good – Jimmy the One was almost pure white – it was the only time I saw him even approaching perplexed.

That alone wouldn't have been so bad except for the fact that the following day the ship failed to get its anchor to rise from the mull-bed and we missed the full day's exercises. Word around the mess table that night was that the Admiral had slipped on board unannounced at the end of the day – he marched down to the Officers' Mess and – in naval terminology – ripped a new arsehole in the First Lieutenant – a man who was not known for his placid temperament in the first place.

HMS *Ness* was in trouble and, somehow, that seemed to mean that I was in trouble!

* * * * *

The next incident – well – it wasn't my fault – it wasn't – okay – maybe there was nobody else to blame – but it was an accident – it could have happened to anyone. I'd hardly been given the time to weld my little bunch into a tight working team, like I'd taught everyone to do at Lowton, where the fires were controlled and predicted – nay, planned even. This one wasn't. I mean, where's the reality in that – having a fire visit you when you're not even at action stations.

Old 'Monkey Brand', as the Admiral was nicknamed, had just climbed on board and declared we had taken an incendiary shell from an enemy raider and we had a fire on deck.

In his eyes the whaler had been hit and was well ablaze; it was all pretend of course, but we had to react. The First Lieutenant knew that I had special knowledge of firefighting so it was me to whom he barked the order to: "*put it out now!*"

Easy – the whaler was wood, so water would do the job.

I should explain that when it comes to fire-fighting, *real men* hold the hose – in fact *real men* stand at the hot end and point the hose at the flames – we do the heroic thing – I was such a real man. I needed a suitable partner and a lad known as Lofty looked strong enough; he was a bit of a loner but tall and well muscled and I had heard a story about him climbing a towering communication mast at Freetown, which proved he had some spirit. Streak was the third man in our tight team and his first duty was to attach the hose to the water pump – then stand by.

Things could have gone wrong from the very start, when a fine mist of back-spray extinguished my spraymate's Wills Whiff, bringing on a bought of spluttering that turned to coughing. I was an old hand at this fire-dousing lark and had my whole concentration tuned to the job in hand, so for those critical first few seconds we were doing really well. I couldn't see the Admiral because he was behind we pair of hot-end holders, but I could feel his breath on the back of my neck – I was playing the hose skilfully on the imaginary fire. In an instant Lofty spat out the damp fag, recovered his composure and was holding his side of the pulsing hose, his thin mouth twitching and his eyes narrowed in real concentration; he was following my every motion and we were moulding into a magnificent team, moving as one. Our fire, had it been real, would have been just about out, with minimal collateral damage and zero casualties.

Then I heard him. Men of his age and rank should not have been using such language... the time around me almost went into slow-mo... as, shutting the hose down and handing over to my carefully arranged, replacement contingency squirter and the team's number three, Streak, I turned... *slowly*... to see what was amiss – it *slowly* became apparent that I needn't have bothered to switch off the hose, because the water would have stopped coming out of our end anyhow. It transpired that Streak, the dozy oik, had attached the hose to the pump but he hadn't secured it properly – there was water squirting – at some pressure – in all directions – and most especially in the direction of the Admiral. He looked like a drowned pensioner.

I still think that they were harsh appointing all of the blame to me, but hey, I could take it, I was a real man – nonetheless – as the three of us, me, Streak and Lofty, sat damp and dripping in anticipation of our post-exercise debrief with the Petty Officer, I couldn't escape the feeling that I had stepped smartly out of the imaginary flames and up to my neck into 'hot water' – and I'd only been aboard a week!

CHAPTER SIX

After three weeks of the Admiral's not so tender ministrations the exercises ended and, tuned to her fighting peak, HMS *Ness* slipped gracefully across the waters of the Irish Sea to Londonderry to re-provision before sailing to Gibraltar where we joined the escort for a convoy carrying troops and mail heading back to Liverpool. Upon our return we joined Escort Group 24 under Commander J. V. Waterhouse – skipper of HMS *Loch Katrine*, which had been designated Senior Officers' ship; the other ships in the group included HMS *Loch Quoich*, HMS *Loch Tarbert* and HMS *Halladale* – and we headed out the next day to take up position as escort on a 'fast' convoy heading for Gibraltar.

My first view of the convoy was amazing – there were ships everywhere – it had just left Liverpool and was splitting into the formations that would head off for their individual destinations. One to Nova Scotia, another to West Africa. The more I watched, the more rows and rows and rows of ships there appeared to be. I had seen the diagrams and been taught the theory but the reality was breathtaking.

Then a Sunderland roared low overhead and a petty officer roared loud in my ear to get below and the moment of wonderment slipped away.

We were heading deeper into the Atlantic now, tailing the convoy heading from Liverpool to Gibraltar; initially, *Ness* rode the swells beautifully – she coped easily with waves as high as five feet, but soon we were beyond the shade that had been offered by Ireland and the seas began to grow massive, building up in the brisk winds to ten-footers.

The ship was pitching belligerently into these monsters, first diving her bows deep into the waves as the water crashed along the foredeck, splashing up as far as the gun placement. Then she'd seem to shake her head and rise from the waters as the power of her twin screws drove her above the swell and towards the next furrow in the ocean.

Riding these ten-footers was really quite exciting.

At first...

But, the waves began to grow higher and the ship took on a different rhythm. Pitching and rolling as if it were captured on the beam of some old monochrome film that was flashing in the dust from the back of a cinema, the beam flickering onto an expectant screen, the projectionist's settings driving the images a wee bit too fast. The Captain too was driving on and didn't seem to be slowing down! When the waves reached as high as fifteen feet, they had me gulping hard and plaiting me legs around the bit that dangled in between, its end growing cold and tingling, feeling as though it was about to shed its control.

It was growing ridiculous and still the *Ness* ploughed on – down... down... down... down... whoooooooosh... up... up... up... up... the twenty-feet waves had me shooting around like a Sat'dy night drunk; surely we should stop or something – or maybe go back to port?

We were going under – I was sure of it – the seas were all over the decks – they must be smashing superstructure and forcing hatches, twisting scuttles and deadlights and finding their way deep inside the ship. We should all be manning the pumps – they were twenty-five feet high now, nothing could survive, we'd be on the bottom – why, I wondered was no one dashing to get their lifebelt?

I looked around but nobody else seemed to have noticed – this was not right, no wave should ever be this big – in all my experience of the sea so far (on holiday at Cleethorpes) the waves had never been any higher than my calves.

THIRTY-footers – they must be thirty-footers now – they were awful; our boat seemed to plough up them like an old omnibus chugging up Mortal Ash Hill back home and then she'd just pop over the top without any warning whatsoever – there was no way the swells could get higher.

They did. I was convinced that the THIRTY-FIVE-footers would turn us end over end – our sharp bit (the bows) was bound to become the blunt bit (the stern), the seas were like Everest. Well, actually I'd never seen Everest but the slag heaps on Scunthorpe steelworks were pretty high and these waves were higher than that. What was going on?

Now, if ever you see your first thirty-five-footer be warned – you will be convinced that it's going to be your last. I would have stood there staring with my mouth wide open at the sheer spectacle of the thing if I wasn't shaking so much from the fear that my teeth were rattling like a pneumatic drill. The manual said that HMS *Ness* could pull 19 knots flat out – in these seas we were doing half a knot going up and about 50 knots going down the other side – Malcolm Campbell, eat your heart out, here comes a new world water-speed record. Surely this could not be.

Everything had turned black and white. The sky was black, the sea was white, the ship a colour in between. A black voice yelled at me and my mood crept fearfully towards a spot so dark there was nothing I could see and then the white was back, flashing in my face, someone's teeth, a dull noise grew colourfully in my ears.

"Stoker," came a clear voice, loudly. It was Saint Peter calling me to heaven. The voice was so thunderous, but no, it was just the petty officer. He was growling about pumps and airlocks and engines stalling and what trouble we'd be in if that happened – I was catching every other word, my ears full of cotton wool. I turned unfocussed eyes on his flashing teeth and then allowed my blurred gaze to crawl up his face towards his eyes. My ears snapped open and I heard his words more clearly, "We'll never keep up with the convoy..."

The trickle charge of electricity running between my temples began to seep away and the tingling diminished; I was approaching a clarity of thinking to match my hearing and thoughts grey as storm-clouds pounded around my head... what ruddy convoy, there couldn't be one in these seas, it must have sunk, or turned back or... "STOKER"... he was bawling at me now – about time too, the bottom must have been ripped out of the ship, he'd want me to get into a lifeboat... "STOKER MOSS, will you get your idle arsehole waddling down to the engine room and sort out the fuel pumps!"

A tiny spurt of bile spat into the top of my throat while I searched for the energy to get my feet moving. The brat living deep inside me whined – it wasn't fair. I had been on board twenty-five days – probably – I had mastered the skill of embarking onto a boat that was writhing up and down like a bucking bronco, I'd found a new cure for seasickness – and ways to avoid swallowing cockroaches – I was about to be sent to a watery grave in a frigate that was being swamped by monster waves. I was not yet into my 21st year and now somebody with teeth like marble gravestones wants me to repair a pump that I have never seen before and have absolutely no knowledge of – not bloody fair. I lifted my foot to stamp it and that's when the petty officer shoved me mercilessly towards the steps.

I went – as in 'fell-in-an-almost-controlled-kind-of-way' – down the ladders, and someone tossed a spanner into my hands and I'd just found a nut that it would fit when the first of the FORTY-FOOTERS struck.

I am absolutely convinced, and nobody will persuade me any different, that the men who designed the first big dippers to be built after the war – were from the Navy, in particular they were from the Atlantic convoys.

Anyway, with this gigantic wave there came an eerie calm – peaceful and placid and I just knew I was about to die. I mean, here is a relatively new ship, 315 feet long, weighing 2,260 tons, floating through the air completely upside down. How can that be?

Well, of course, it wasn't – I was – but, the action had twisted the spanner in my hand and it had done the trick and then – suddenly – I was under fierce attack. Right in my face was the angry visage of a noisy Aussie spouting about me making sure that I was at my *flaymin'* post next time, so I didn't endanger the ship.

Without engaging any part of my brain, I bawled back, "Yes, sir."

He went crazy.

"YES, sir – YES, sir – where the hell do you think you are – a bloody school-room? This is the Navy, Stoker," he was breathing his breath right into my face, "we don't say 'yes, sir' in the Navy – do we? Well? Do we?" His words exploded from him like a fart from Charlie's horse just after it had raised its tail in the moment before a salvo of dung popped purposefully out – my face was about as far away as if I had been sitting in the seat of our cart. "Aye aye, sir, you dumb stoker – Aye flaymin' aye, sir – get it right. Okay?" With the last blast, he was gone. I still stood as still as a statue.

I had just met the First Lieutenant and I decided there and then that I did not like him. Endanger the ship, didn't he realise? – I was a hero – I had survived monster seas – surely... I had saved the ship. It wasn't even my *flaymin'* watch!

And still I didn't understand why everyone else was just walking calmly around as if they were in the queue for Skegness boating lake. Some of them weren't even hanging on to anything to steady themselves – didn't they realise we were in the eye of a hurricane and surrounded by freak waves?

By the side of me appeared a lad, who introduced himself as Leading Stoker White – Chalky – he was just grinning at me and telling me, "You wait until we hit the Bay of Biscay – then you'll see waves of forty feet and more – not these tiny rollers we're in now."

"Anyhow," he says, "thanks for opening the back-up valve. I was in the heads."

'Ha,' I thought, '...weakling.'

He had been kneeling in front of a toilet while I saved the ship, being seasick, but he just continued to talk, "The fuse box is in there and the fuse for the main pump had blown – some cloth-head in the for'ard Stokers' Mess left the guard off an electric fire and dropped it onto the wiring loom while the elements were still hot, it fused to the main pump's supply – could have happened any time since we left Portsmouth," he stopped and scratched his chin and looked upwards, "good job it wasn't discovered while the Admiral was still aboard – someone's head would have rolled."

I went paler and paler as he continued to talk and then spent the next ten minutes agreeing with him that it was a stupid thing for someone to have done. What a nice bloke, he invited me to join him and his mate Laddie for a game of dominoes later on. I can't say he was much of a sailor though; he reckoned the waves we were riding were no more than ten feet.

I guess Chalky was the first pal I made on board and Laddie not far behind; they were both very similar chaps. Chalky was a Leading Stoker and therefore of higher rank than me – I was a Stoker First Class. He came from Hull, which he pronounced 'ull; he was tall, with wiry hair that he never tried to control, it always sported the naval-standard short-back-and-sides but then it seemed to explode upwards so it looked as if he was wearing an upside down fez. He had quite a chin on him too, did Chalky, pointed and jutting, set in a strong jaw. In fact, without his hat, his whole head had the air of an inverted triangle.

I was to discover that he could be a bit on the serious side, usually quite gentle and with an enormous sense of right and wrong. Chalky had been a keen rugby player and, although he was about my age, he had a full set of dentures. He said that when two of his front teeth got knocked out during a game, his dentist had suggested he remove them all and have a false set fitted, which he could remove while he played! I thought he was joking when he told us. But he wasn't.

His pal, Laddie, was something to do with munitions – he didn't say a lot and I never found out exactly what he did, but it was linked to explosives.

Standing around five feet nine inches, Laddie was a man of natural calming disposition; he was not one for unnecessary confrontation, he spent a lot of time in our Mess and was often the peacemaker when our discussions started to get rowdy.

Chalky had a very even temper most of the time – I don't think Laddie had any temper at all – not even when he'd been celebrating, which he could do in great quantity. He came from some place near Derby, and for a long while we considered changing his nickname to Techno. Not because he was technical or anything – and it wouldn't have been short for technology because that wasn't a word we had in our vocabulary in them days – it was more because his favourite saying seemed to be: "Teck n' notice," as he poured oil onto troubled waters.

I soon met up with another messmate – and, although a quiet type, he was exactly the opposite of the first two; his was the quietness of a belligerent lump of granite standing around six feet tall. He was a Glaswegian and I found our first conversation almost as difficult to understand as the first one I'd had with my old pal McRae.

"Hayfreendwosthanǽme," the word was delivered with a slightly menacing slowness and with an air of couldn't-care-less curiosity. Meanwhile I'm washing one of the bibs to my uniform and just translating the single word back into the King's English, when this enormous fist picked up the dripping garment and squinted at the letters I'd written there: "Wohhs thaaa?" Came with a slightly stronger expression of interest?

"My name." I mean, anyone that could read, could read my name... R. B. Moss. But, not this chap.

"Aye, sowahrisit?" He just stared straight at me, eyes grey and unwavering.

"Moss, the name's Moss – initials R. B. – they stand fo..." Glasgow wasn't endowed with a surfeit of patience and the first of many interruptions came. I found out later that he was one of six brothers – all tough as a Tor top. He was used to forcing his opinions into some pretty strong-minded conversations – it was why his words came out so fast too. He had to get his words in before one of the others had the chance to interrupt him – although he managed to do that while speaking slowly – he rarely bothered with spaces between his words – and if he did, it usually spelt trouble. He didn't move his mouth much either.

Glasgow, I discovered as the weeks passed by, wasn't great with the written word; he hadn't spent much time at school, being caught most afternoons by the school's truant agent down at the local scrapyard cutting up old machinery and cars for pocket money. When he was taken back to school, he'd slip out of class and disappear somewhere amongst the other classrooms until one day he discovered something he was good at.

In some quarters, it is called a sport – boxing or wrestling – but Glasgow's version knew only one discipline – win – hard and quickly. Eventually they stopped worrying about his education and his mother taught him the basics at home. She, it seems, was a very strong woman, who believed that a thing should be written down the way it sounded. I noticed a wedding ring too.

"ErrBee – isthayernæme?" In fact he hardly moved a muscle in his whole face, when he spoke.

"No, no, no, no – R. B., they're my initials, my name's—" Here comes another interruption.

"S'worahsæd," then he mouthed the pronunciation again, trying to get a bit closer to mine, "Œrbie – ah like tha'," for some reason he chose that moment to smile and put on what he imagined was a formal accent, "Herbie – soots ya. Welcome aboard, Herbie." I understood a bit more this time – must have been getting used to his accent – but I'd hesitated – mistake – he'd gone.

"No..." said I to the broad back disappearing through the bulkhead door, "my – name – isn't – Herbie – it's... aw... just walk off, why don't you?"

I noticed something slightly unkempt about him – maybe he was used to getting dressed quickly too. Anyway, my problem was that the Glaswegian was now right about my name and I was wrong – from that moment, to the time I left the *Ness*, sixteen months later, my name was Herbie. As for the Glaswegian's name, when they could pluck up the courage to talk to him, everyone called him Jock, but I thought that was slightly disrespectful, and since he was as tough as the hide on a Highland bull – I decided to err on the cautious side and I called him Haggis instead.

Before long I was used to what the Atlantic could throw at us and confident in the *Ness*'s ability to stay afloat. She wasn't great in heavy seas, she was built for speedy manoeuvres – but she stayed on top of the water and – my part in the three-man damage-control team during action stations meant that I tended to stay below in the rougher weather, which kept my mind occupied. I always kept a couple of slices of carbonised bread in my pocket though – just in case.

above left: Taking the Scunthorpe air, well, what have I got to look happy about – when they wheel me about in this monstrosity?

above right: Enjoying our Elsie's company, it was thanks to her that I survived to be a toddler

below: Strolling with my mam, Betsy and Arthur in the early 1930s – short trousers were the order of the day even at Arthur's age

right: Me at 10 with Les Wright, smart young fellows and already an interest in rabbits

below: Me at 16 with a workmate — it seems like I've graduated to my own white coat and Simon Cowell pants

bottom right: Arthur (top right) and train crew

left: Charlie's advertising

below: Teenage fun, sitting at the seaside with mother and father (Charlie)

bottom: Taking Arthur for a ride on the family bike

above left: Charlie leaving the yard on his bike – maybe on his way to the theatre - the washing
    line tells us it was a Monday

above right: Freda

below: Me in gas mask looking out of Anderson shelter

above: The wedding (l to r): My mam and dad
– Arthur – Freda's cousin Nancy Burton -
Freda's sister, Elsie – me – Freda – Freda's
sister, Mary – my niece Sheila, daughter of my
sister Elsie – Freda's sister, Molly – Freda's
mam and dad

left: With my dad, Charlie

below: Moss family portrait – taken in ten-foot
(about 1950)

above: My youngest daughter
Carol with dog on the lawn

left: Betsy (mother) with her
grandson Richard

above: I am in the third row back – and four from the right – although you are welcome to it, this information isn't for you – it's for me – just in case I get forgetful – when I reach my old age – and I'm not telling you who any of the others are – because I have forgotten – except for McRae, fourth on my right – and Unte the dozy looking bugger with the big ears, on the back row – HMS Duke 16th June 1943

left: Moss the sailor – pictured at the start of my Naval career – 1943

*left: Navy portrait at Lowton St
Mary 20th Nov. 1943*

*below: At Lowton – I'm second
from right, we are just about
to set off on a race against
other training establishments
towing a fire tender, up a hill
and then down – we won*

CHAPTER SEVEN

O
ur duties escorting the convoys began to take on an air of routine after a while. HMS *Ness* was one of a team of warships, called an Escort Group, that sailed with the convoy and used all of the listening devices on board and all of the intelligence we could gather to repel any U-boats that were targeting our convoy. Perhaps I should try to describe how the convoy protection system worked.

In fact it begins before any of the merchantmen's masters cast off from the docks and involves a whole cast of characters following a well-practised routine that had evolved from the early convoy days of the Great War.

It begins with the ship's Master being asked to deliver a particular cargo to a particular port by his shipping line – like the Baron Line, or the Empire Line or BP – or by his Shipping Agent.

To join a convoy he would need to visit the Duty Officer of the Naval Control Service. In fact that gentleman or his department had probably already been tipped off about the voyage by the shipping agent.

The duty officer and the master will discuss the speed of the merchant ship and, adding a degree of safety, match it to a convoy that would suit its pace. Another item on the agenda for this meeting would be the route and alternative ports of call, should any problem arise.

The next person to become involved would be the Convoy Equipment Officer, who would be taken around the ship to inspect every aspect of convoy equipment from signal flags and lamps, navigation lights, special convoy lights, blackout, fog buoys. Anything that should be on board and working efficiently to keep the individual ship and the convoy as safe as possible – we'll see in a minute what can go wrong!

The Convoy Signals Officer will go on board to check the transmitters and receivers used for navigation and communication, along with any other radio that will be carried aboard – he will want to be sure that there is no chance of a signal being picked up by the enemy that will give away the position of the convoy.

They still haven't set sail and the preparations are not yet complete. The next department involved is the Naval Control Service office, which organises the convoy conference. Each convoy has a naval Commander and Second in Command, usually RNVR, often Admiral or Commodore in rank; they sail with the convoy although they don't take command of any individual ship; their job is to command the convoy and it starts on the morning of departure, with a Convoy Conference, where the commander gives the masters their final briefing. This is a group of very seasoned seamen and they will discuss and thrash out every detail they can think of. Once the conference is over the masters are met by officials from the Ministry of War Transport, who want to make extra sure that everything that the individual ships will need for the voyage is complete and in place.

Only when this routine has been completed will each ship's master take a launch to his ship and weigh anchor – even at this point there will be a Boarding Officer patrolling the departing merchant ships in his own launch, hailing each ship and making sure that no last-minute hitch has cropped up.

At this point, the Commodore takes the lead and signals his convoy to line up to pass through the gate in the boom that holds the anti-submarine nets and down the shallow channel, where the minesweepers spend their days, out into deep water. On shore, watchers inform the signal station that every ship that should have left has passed them by.

The convoy could be heading for any number of destinations but primarily it would sail west to the Americas, or south towards the Mediterranean. The southern convoy would often split up again when it reached the entrance to the Mediterranean, around eleven days later, when some of the ships would spend another day sailing to Gibraltar and the remainder sailed on until they reached Freetown in Sierra Leone, ten or eleven days further on.

From these ports the ships may join other convoys.

Once the local pilots have left the ships, the convoy reaches its mustering area out in the ocean and is arranged into the ultimate convoy pattern. At that point it would be picked up by its Ocean Escort, which would take up position around the convoy – that's where we came in.

UMBRELLA OF PROTECTION

The actual convoy system, where armed merchant ships could group together in an organised pattern, with the most valuable cargos in the centre and the perimeter protected by aggressive warships, was the primary means of protection and became a pretty powerful body of trouble for any attackers to take on.

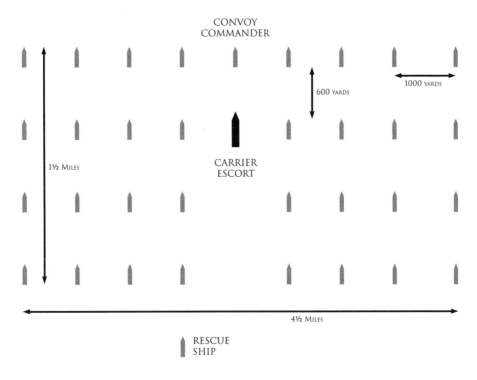

Just in case you are thinking that the merchantmen in these convoys were all strung out in a neat line – what we used to call Indian file – they weren't, they were spread over the ocean in columns and rows, something like a huge football team's 4-4-3 formation but, sometimes, with upward of sixty to eighty ships in all.

Take a convoy of thirty-three ships – this would probably travel in nine columns, with 1,000 yards between each column and four rows with 600 yards between rows. A nine-column convoy would span an area over four nautical miles wide and one and a half miles long.

It all had a military precision and every ship had its own 'flag position' or position in the row, starting top left at position 1-1, or 11, and progressing right to 21 – 31 – 41 – 51 etc.

The Commander took up position on the leading merchantman, and the Vice Commodore was positioned on one of the convoy's other ships.

The Convoy Commander was in complete charge of the convoy; he had a demanding task directing the convoy when it was forming up or when it needed to change direction, which it did regularly if the enemy was about – most of the communication was relayed by flag signals or semaphore with flashing lights.

The routes taken were another means of protecting the convoys; the Gibraltar convoys would sail out beyond 15° west, which would take them beyond the range of attack aircraft. They would also sail a zig-zag course to confuse any enemy spotter-aircraft trying to track the convoy's progress and call in the air or sea-born predators. As the trans-Atlantic convoys passed the midway sector, the US Navy and the Royal Canadian Navy took over escort duties, using the same systems and intelligence. Routes were often changed through the issue of secret orders to the Convoy Commander.

The next layer of defence would be the escorting Royal Navy warships. Very basically, they were charged with one of two functions – they were either part of an escort group that was intended to defend the convoy or they were in a support group – which was tasked with hunting out and attacking the U-boats.

The Support Groups were usually formed of, or led by, destroyers and would spend their time patrolling both flanks as well as sending individual ships to investigate or attack the enemy. The escorts were more likely to be frigates or corvettes, positioned at the front and rear of the convoy, looking for any U-boats that were sneaking up on it or driving it into an ambush. In reality, it was never quite as neat as I might be making it sound; there was often a lot of coming and going of escort and support ships as well as ships dropping out of convoys at the last minute or straggling due to mechanical problems, and bad weather could spread a convoy all over the ocean.

HMS *Ness* normally worked as one of a trio – HMS *Loch Katrine* was the senior ship under command of Commander Waterhouse, DSO, RN; HMS *Ness* under Lieutenant Commander Steel, RNR; and HMS *Halladale* under the command of Lieutenant Commander J. E. Woolfenden, DSC, RNR. We were part of the 24th Escort Group along with HMS *Loch Insh* and HMS *Dart* and we would be positioned around the convoy, sweeping the seas, watching for prowling U-boats.

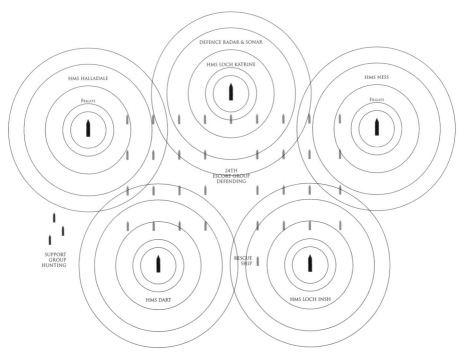

THE ESCORT SYSTEM - THE SHIPS AT THE FRONT AND REAR OF THE CONVOY ARE THE ESCORT GROUP WITH THEIR
ELECTRONIC DETECTION AND DEFENCE SYSTEMS. THIS CONVOY ALSO SHOWS A HUNTER-KILLER SUPPORT GROUP.

Much of our protection was provided by electronic means and it was shore-based as
well as being based on board. The shore-based (or air-based) protection came from
the Admiralty's Wireless Telegraphy (W/T) tracking systems allowing them to pick
up shipping movements and relay information to the Convoy Commander, which then
filtered through to us. I always felt this kind of information was an hour or two, sometimes an afternoon or a day, behind the game.

On board ship we had High Frequency Direction Finders that could pinpoint
any high frequency radio messages that passed from U-boat to U-boat – or to their
command – commonly known as HF/DF or Huffduff – manning this we had a team
of telegraphists positioned in a tiny cabin alongside and just below the bridge. In this
respect the Royal Navy enjoyed a real advantage over the Nazis, because earlier in the
war, the Navy had captured an Enigma machine from one of their ships, which allowed
our secret service to crack their codes. It meant that when we did catch them talking
to each other, even though it was in code, we knew what they were saying and it could
tell us where they were and the support groups and air squadrons could go a-hunting.

Other shipboard surveillance was provided by radar – to locate the enemy on the
surface of the water or in the air – and sonar (or Asdic), to locate the U-boats under water.
Once we had located the submerged U-boats we would use depth charges to destroy them
or drive them to the surface, and once up, we would pound them with the guns.

The depth charge stage was always worse for us below decks; adding to the 'not-knowing' what was happening, it was unsettling. 'Down below' when our depth charges exploded, the whole ship rang with a horrible vibration that made our hull hammer like an out-of-tune bell. The hull of the *Ness* had taken quite a few such shocks over its lifetime and was patched in places with loads of concrete, usually where our own explosives had caused damage.

And in all this violence and explosions we could have no idea whether our target was sinking – or loading its acoustic Gnat torpedoes to come after us. Was a tin fish just about to pierce the side and blow us into pieces before we had chance to know we were dead? – or had we been successful and every sailor on board the *Unterseeboot* had perished, brutally battered to death by the pounding we had given it?

Our safety at such times was in the ear of our sonar operators, who seemed to live their lives in high concentration and concentrated *pings* bleeping in their earphones. In fact, the sonar man was our eyes as well as our ears; with the right conditions he could tell whether a target was moving towards us, or away from us, or was still in the seas below us but not moving. We had a superb Asdic officer, chubby cheeks, nicknamed Hamster, who had served with the legendary U-boat hunter Captain Frederick 'Johnny' Walker, CB, DSO.

Walker had persuaded the Admiralty that escorting convoys wasn't enough – he wanted to take out his flotilla and go hunting – he was incredibly successful at doing so and, while there is no way to know exactly how many U-boat kills he accounted for, it was a figure beyond twenty. He died at the age of 48; most pundits say it was from overwork – he was an eccentric, terribly focussed and remarkable man.

I have to say, I often wondered whether our own commanding officer hadn't served with Captain Walker too, because the skipper of HMS *Ness* seemed to empathise entirely with the changes that Walker made to naval standing orders on convoy work.

The Admiralty's orders referred to: **'the safe and timely arrival of the convoy'**.

Walker issued orders to: **'destroy U-boats, particularly those which menace our convoys'**.

Another abstract from Walker's Operating Instructions reads: **'Our object is to kill – and all officers must fully develop the spirit of vicious offensive. No matter how many convoys we may shepherd through in safety, we shall have failed unless we slaughter U-boats. All energies must be bent to this end.'**

Having served with Walker meant that we in the Stokers' Mess were really impressed with our own Asdic officer's credentials and our mess table discourse often centred around why he had left Walker's group and joined little-old-us. Until one evening, around the stokers' table, we had a visitor, a rather serious young telegraphist who had made a friend of we stokers so that he could get access to a warm place to dry his dhobeying more easily – we did a lot of backscratching in the Navy.

The telegraphist had more trouble with washing his kit than most of us because he wore glasses. He was clever, you see, read a lot, squinted in dark places over instructions and codes and stuff... watching dials that danced up and down between radio frequencies – at least that's what we all assumed. Anyhow when he was toiling over a steamy pile of washing his specs would mist up, so he sought out the driest places to undertake the task – clever, you see. He wasn't much more than five feet seven inches and had thin hair combed in what we would now call a quiff; he was very neat and soft spoken, with a remote air of wistfulness and a certain iron in his soul.

The young telegraphist was persistent to a fault and rarely known to back down; he also had a talent for starting arguments, or 'debates' as he called them. He did this by dropping an opinion into a smooth-running conversation that was guaranteed to nudge it off the rails, after which he would argue his point all the way around until it had come full circle. Always speaking softly and with an authority bestowed upon him by the fact that we all thought him to be clever – because... of the glasses he wore and which he constantly pushed higher up the bridge of his nose.

On really important points he would take his specs off and slowly... between the pauses in his words... he would polish them on a kerchief, which he neatly unfolded and then neatly refolded again.

He told us a story of the time our Asdic officer had identified a 'contact' on the seabed and sent in a ship to attack with depth charges – unfortunately the contact turned out to be a sunken merchantman, full of munitions, which immediately blew up and took the attacking ship with it.

Ooops!

By the way, telegraphists, like our new friend, were those who operated the Huffduff. They spent all their watch twiddling their knobs to tune in their radios, listening for transmissions between U-boats and their bases or enemy aircraft. We had a nickname for this particular telegraphist – we called him 'Virgin' – or Virge – 'cos every time one of us asked him how many U-boat conversations he'd picked up he always said the same thing: "Still waiting for me first one."

He told his story about the Asdic officer very calmly and with a completely straight face – he didn't seem to notice the nervous glances that were running around the mess table like a Mexican wave. We didn't have quite the same confidence in our 'eyes and ears' after that.

There was also a growing use of Escort Carriers, which had squadrons of Swordfish or Avengers aboard, for protection from air and sea.

Aircraft like the Sunderland, the Avenger and the Swordfish gained their own fair share of U-boat 'kills' by the end of the war – they carried bombs, torpedoes and depth-charges.

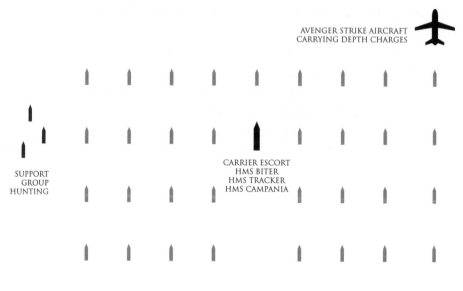

AVENGER STRIKE AIRCRAFT
CARRYING DEPTH CHARGES

CARRIER ESCORT
HMS BITER
HMS TRACKER
HMS CAMPANIA

SUPPORT
GROUP
HUNTING

RESCUE
SHIP

ALTERNATIVE PROTECTION - SOMETIMES THE CONVOYS WERE PROTECTED BY ESCORT GROUPS OFFERING AIR SUPPORT - THERE WOULD STILL BE SUPPORTING UNITS IN THE AREA IN CASE OF UNEXPECTED ATTACK.

In fact – now, keep this to yourself – HMS *Ness* almost had a nasty little friendly fire incident with a Sunderland flying boat one night. We had both picked up the same U-boat on our sonar and were keen to give it a headache. There was no moon and it was not very bright so we tossed up a star-shell to help us to see what was happening; just at that moment the pilot of the Sunderland dipped his nose towards the sea to have a go at the sub and almost caught a windshield full of our floating phosphorescent device. The language he fired at us was far from friendly as it came pouring aboard, but then the reply he got from the Captain wasn't entirely jovial either – and the sub slunk off into the darkness; so now we had a U-boat on the loose and his captain laughing at us for trying to maim each other – nuff said.

There was, of course, an airborne threat to the convoy. When we were in range there was always the possibility of a dive bomb or glider bomb attack from a Junkers JU88 dive bomber, or a torpedo attack from a Heinkel HEIIIK bomber. Even at longer range we could get an unwelcome visit by a Focke-Wulf long range bomber/spotter that fancied his chances at an attack with incendiary bombs – countermeasures included towing anti-aircraft balloons, or kites, attached by steel cables to put off any low-level strafing or bombing runs over the convoy. We could also scare them off with ack-ack from the Oerlikons we were fitted with – I heard of merchant ships fitted with a Supermarine Seafire (the sea-going version of a Spitfire), on a catapult that shot it into the air to see off an aerial attack. These weren't too popular though, because unless they could reach an airfield, they had to be landed in the drink and the pilot lifted from the water – all a bit dramatic for we naval types.

The other thing the aircraft could deliver were mines and the nasty ones were the magnetic and acoustic mines, although this was mainly in shallower water – mine sweeping around harbour entrances was a full-time job for the specialist arm of the service and at one time we were fitted with something called degaussing gear to neutralise magnetic mines. It played hell-up with the compasses though and they had to be constantly re-adjusted.

Another electronic defence that we had on the warships, but I don't think they had on merchantmen, were the Foxers, that we towed behind the ship; they were 'noise-makers', designed to confuse the homing devices on the U-boats' acoustic torpedoes.

There was also some danger from attack by surface ships, although we didn't have any experience of this on HMS *Ness*, neither did we see any of the fabled motor torpedo boats – the E-boats, which were driven by three 20-cylinder Daimler Benz diesel engines with almost 4,000 h.p. and a top speed approaching 44 knots.

The final layer of defence was the naval DEMS gun and crew that all of the merchantmen carried. There were also some 'plain-clothes' warships attached to the odd convoy that looked like merchantmen but were armed to the high-teeth. Most convoys also had a designated rescue ship – which didn't carry a cargo but was there to pick up any survivors from ships that may be hit.

Looking at the bigger picture, which we had time to do after the war, but only the heads of Government and the Services knew at the time – it was a very successful system.

While HMS *Ness* did most of her work on the Eastern Atlantic routes to Gibraltar and West Africa, most of the convoys came from the Americas, sailing out of New York and Halifax in Nova Scotia. If you take a look at the scale of our dependence on imports – the UK imported all of its oil from the USA – without it we'd have had no fuel for our ships, our Spitfires, our tanks at El Alamein, or the landing craft on D-Day.

Neither were we self-sufficient in food; before the war, the Merchant Navy had been delivering something like 55 million tons of oil, food and raw materials every year. That needed to continue – and it did – with as many as four convoys arriving in Liverpool every week.

Convoy sizes were much smaller at the start of the war and here's some actual numbers for the first two years of the war – up until the end of 1941 the number of ships reaching British ports was just over 12,000. They came in 900 convoys with a total loss of 291 ships to enemy action. In terms of vital supplies delivered to the UK that shows around 2.5 per cent of the imports was lost in transit. Only 19 of those 900 convoys lost 6 or more ships.

A less kind man than I am might suggest that after the war had ended and the status quo was re-established the dockers of Liverpool accounted for far more than 2.5 per cent of goods lost in transit. But I like the Scousers, I had one as a mate, so I would never suggest such a thing.

Later in the war, one U-boat sank seven ships in just three hours – the rat. For the whole war the U-boats in the Atlantic sunk 2,828 merchant ships, a further 820 were sunk by aircraft and 543 were lost to mines – 30,000 to 35,000 merchant sailors were killed – and yet the numbers of ships that did get through showed what a fantastic job the sailors on the convoys and their protectors did.

The sailors, of all nations, who worked on the merchant ships and the men of the Allied navies won the Battle of the Atlantic hands down – it was a more comprehensive victory than Sitting Bull's victory at Little Big Horn – and I am proud of even my tiny part in the whole thing. The U-boats were all but ineffective, so I find it a bit ironic that, these days, some people stare romantically in the air and talk of the U-boats fondly as wolf packs or as 'Grey Wolves'. Even worse was that in those days some of the U-boat commanders were given their country's highest honours and feted as 'aces' – like the fly-boys – and yet they performed so poorly.

Shame we didn't offer a much greater honour to the merchant sailors – we owe them recognition for their raw courage, their steadfastness, their stamina, their sheer hard work and no-nonsense achievement.

They kept us alive – never have so many been so royally ignored by those of us who owed them so much. But then facing the dangers of travelling the oceans in the middle of the twentieth century needed a special breed of man, more balls than brains, so perhaps it's all we normal men can do – stand and gape in wonder at their courage and call them gloriously foolhardy.

The saddest fact, perhaps, is that all of this human suffering was to such little effect; you see, the U-boat crews also suffered desperately, something like 27,500 of them lost their lives, together with 5,000 taken prisoner.

I often wondered, was that the product of the ambitions of a few evil or power-hungry men's ambitions, or was it the result of those primeval feelings in millions of young men – just like me?

KILLING U-BOATS

By and large, we did the same runs – Liverpool to Gibraltar and back. On the odd occasion we would join a support group and go off and hunt the enemy, sweeping the seas in front of the convoys to clear their way back to Liverpool, or sailing away to chase down a reported sighting.

During my time on the *Ness* we had a number of 'contacts' with the enemy and launched a lot of depth charges, winning ourselves one 'Probable', which means we think we may have sunk a U-boat but the evidence wasn't conclusive. Below decks we weren't always aware why the claxons started shrieking and HMS *Ness* suddenly started rushing about, we were too busy taking up action stations. We didn't know why we were dropping depth charges, or even why the Oerlikons had started chattering away, we just knew that the ship was at action stations and that we were at our individual damage-control positions – waiting – listening, until the word slowly began to filter down to *us*.

Killing a U-boat wasn't an easy task. They were tough. It was sometimes a case of three or four warships surrounding one submarine, or chasing after one; our attack started with the depth charges hammering away at it for hour after hour, trying to sink it outright or drive it to the surface where it could be finished off with a relentless hail of fire from the deck guns.

ESCORT GROUP 24

As I have said, from the time I joined the ship in 1944 we spent most of our time sweeping around the convoys in company with two other frigates, one River-class K417 HMS *Halladale* and one Loch-class K625 HMS *Loch Katrine*, which was the command boat for our little squadron.

Halladale was commissioned in May 1944 and *Loch Katrine*, well, the first time we met up with her in September 1944, was almost a virgin, only having been commissioned in August.

Being the most technically advanced, HMS *Loch Katrine* had a full Royal Navy officer, Commander Waterhouse, DSO, as skipper – our captain was a reservist – from the Wavy Navy – as a result HMS *Loch Katrine* had operational command of our trio.

The hull and machinery of the Loch-class frigates was essentially the same as the River-class but with design improvements to make them more seaworthy and to make them easier to build.

They used Squid mortars to fire their explosives into the sea and had far fewer depth charges than we River-class Frigates had. The latest '277 Radar' and 'Asdic 144' made them highly effective in pinpointing potential enemies. Only twenty-eight were built but mainly that was down to timing; the Battle of the Atlantic was drawing to a close when they started to be built in the Forth dockyards and the need to destroy U-boats gave way to a need to fight enemy aircraft that would be encountered in the forthcoming war in the Pacific.

Being the two new boys, with their sparkling clean hulls – compared to *Ness*'s charge-battered and concrete-filled hull of two – and then three – years' battling and our greater number of depth-charges, when either of them caught a blip on their sonar, they would send in HMS *Ness* to deliver the punches. Our companions had a nickname for *Ness* – 'Old Scrap-iron' – but what did *Loch Katrine* and *Halladale* know of a real ship, manned as they were by wet-behind-the-ears dab-toes!

In fact I don't think our skipper and Number One would have wanted it any other way.

The depth charges could do a lot of peripheral damage from a distance but were only truly lethal to a U-boat if they exploded within around thirty feet of it. We had to have the depth set correctly and the charges were slow to sink, so they gave the U-boat commanders the time to swerve and dive all over the place to avoid contact – just like a rat does under a pile of straw in a stable when you're after him with a pitchfork. The disadvantage the U-boat captains had was they couldn't see where the pitchfork was.

That's why our trio often hunted as a team, so that we could lay down a carpet of charges at different depths to a set pattern and make life hell for them. Sometimes we would see the U-boats on the surface, or see the white water stirred up by their wake; our sonar couldn't track them unless they were underneath the waves, so, in one way, that's where we preferred them. Of course, when they were on the surface they were in danger of attack from the RAF and over 260 U-boats were destroyed by attack from the air. There's an irony here, because, by and large, aircraft were as invisible to a U-boat as the subs were to surface ships.

* * * * *

One of the major dangers to merchant ships came when they were slowed by mechanical trouble and lost contact with the convoy – they were known as stragglers and were sitting ducks to attack from U-boat or air. It was just such an occurrence that showed us just what a hard and ruthless warrior our skipper was – we had been ordered to break from the convoy to attend one of the tankers that had broken down. I was called up to the bridge to stand by in case the skipper needed the launch to take him across to the stricken ship and I watched his fac,e a mask of impatience, as he spat instruction after instruction for the officer of the watch to pipe down to the coxswain to change speed and direction again and again. To keep the *Ness* moving in a never-ending and ever-changing motion around the tanker, he gave them enough time, then he gave them too much time. We had received warning from the Admiralty that there were U-boats around and the tanker was an easy target; the skipper was making us as impossible a target as he could. Then he sent out the signal to the tanker's captain: 'Ten more minutes, and then we come and take off your crew and sink you.'

The tanker's master then poured his very hot disagreement to such action through the waves of his communication device, but realised at once that only our 'warrior' was ever going to win, when he calmly replied, "Sorry, old chap," and manned our for'ard gun – luckily the tanker's engineers got her going in time.

The master of the tanker remained absolutely incensed at the thought that he'd dodged the Nazis to almost be sunk by the very people he was trying to provision – which is fair enough. So he posted a complaint, which, I think, is still somewhere low down on the Admiralty's priority list; you see, he posted it after his ship had docked... safely.

CHAPTER EIGHT

Our next trip saw us escorting one of the northern-bound convoys, *MKF 39*, I think (I never was very sure. Lofty was better with those kinds of facts than me) – it was a troop convoy, so there were a lot of escorts, nineteen ships, packed with thousands of Tommies, all heading for home after a long spell of fighting.

They were always in a strange mood on the return journey – happy to be going home, but they had been battered by the deprivation and the violence. It was as if they could dial a smile onto their face but it never reached their eyes, like their spirits were dragging along behind them, heavy with remembered fears and weakened by stoic acts of everyday bravery. Unable to talk, even to each other, of the horrors they had shared. There was something, sombre... ghostly, in the air, it affected us all; even Bogie was ready with a kind word for them.

We were three days out – about halfway home when, unknown to Admiralty intelligence – and thus unknown to us – a group of four U-boats left their base on the west coast of France, heading for a designated patrol around the Isles of Scilly and the western Channel approaches. They were being very quiet because the U-boats were very much on the back foot at that point in the war. They were following the coastline as near as they could, taking a direct route.

It wasn't unusual that we, who spent lots of our time down below, were often unaware of events unfolding in the wider world of the convoy and, just at that time, one of the troop carriers in our convoy was in some trouble. It had a heavy cargo below and the fast pace had made its engine overheat causing a small fire in the engine room, which was sucked through a ventilation shaft and blew out of one of the deck vents – it only lasted about five minutes, but the black smoke that trailed high into the sky was enough to alert a Junkers scout aircraft of our position. The pilot was young – and keen – he climbed above the cloud cover and risked a short radio message to his command post; he was ordered to shadow us and see where we were heading, but when he dropped back into clear air the convoy had already tacked west and he'd lost us.

The submarine base made a call to the *Kapitanleutnant* in charge of the quartet of U-boats and he winced – like it was a secret that we had regular convoys running between Gibraltar and Liverpool! We'd only been doing it all through the war. He wasn't happy to receive a change to his standing orders, which were to undertake the Channel patrol, not to attack Atlantic convoys; he sighed, realised he'd have to respond and ordered one of his young *Oberleutnants* to take a look – find us – and then call him so he could get ahead and spring a trap. Privately the *Kapitanleutnant* was hoping we were long gone.

As it was he led the rest of his group onwards, while the *Oberleutnant* set off to see what he could spot. The periscope on his craft cut the silver-grey surface of the seas, but he couldn't see anything, only the rolling waves, whipped into their sullen swell by the low Atlantic winds, so he surfaced and put on more speed as he cut a line across the Bay of Biscay. For the next four hours he maintained complete radio silence; the sun began to descend and the U-boats'[7] prime hunting time loomed. They loved to approach quietly and under the shadow of dusk. The classic wolf-pack tactic was for one or two U-boats to trail the convoy like a Border collie driving its charges into the jaws of the pack of steel wolves that lay ahead in ambush.

In this case, our pursuer was on his own, the young German commander was doing his best to find us and to get into position to set up an attack on our convoy, he was on the right track. We below decks on HMS *Ness*, along with everyone else onboard, were blissfully unaware that he was closing on us – in fact we'd received a message that the area was clear so our lookouts were relaxed too.

I, meanwhile, had an enlightening conversation with my Glaswegian messmate.

"Ooyerdooin', Herbie?"

That was the pleasantries over with, and he was grinning like the devil – he obviously had something to say.

"Good. You?" It was the only way to get your words in with Haggis – don't use many.

Anyway he told me that we were circumnavigating (biggest single word I ever heard him use) the Bay of Biscay and that the Bay was a favourite haunt for the U-boats; he thought they had their 'nests' there and we were crossing the routes they took to get back to base. He reckoned that the Royal Navy had sunk twenty-five U-boats in the Bay so far.

---

7   Trans-Atlantic convoys were at sea – and at the mercy of the U-boats – for around thirteen to sixteen days. Our convoys from Gibraltar lasted around ten days if they were carrying heavy cargo and if it was mainly passengers – they were designated 'Fast' and took around six days.

"Twenty-five, Herbie," he says to me, "think aboot thaaart. And... if yer idea on U-boats being like rats is right, well, ye know what they say aboot rats, Herbie," for some reason he felt that a long pause would add to the tension.

It did.

"If ye can see one rat – there's another twenty aroond somewhere close."

I was not feeling confident.

He laughed like a Glaswegian. "We're awa rodent huntin', Herbie, what d'ye think of that?"

Time for me to reply. "Haggis," I says, "while we're after them, stick by me then if we catch a torpedo and sink, the rest of us can toss you in the drink and use you as a life raft."

He looked at me hard, but I hadn't finished yet. "You're so big and so full of hot air we could use you to float all the way back to Blighty."

His reply was toneless and eloquent: "Tosser!" I liked Haggis, we were becoming friends.

The moon was high and it watched the U-boat slicing through the surface at 16 knots trying to gain more speed – the *Oberleutnant* was young and green, his confidence overwhelmed his competence – and he was itching to be on the right track to close up with us, but he wasn't certain, yet, that he was.

That was the day that the Chief Petty Officer Stoker nodded at me, "You'll be sitting next to me at dinner." It wasn't an order, but was it an invitation? The petty officers had their own separate mess, on the main deck above ours; we ordinary stokers didn't eat with them. But, the Chief had a manner about him that made you take notice. So that night I parked myself on the cushion next to his as we sat on our makeshift mess bench for the evening meal; it was a quiet affair until the main course was cleared and he said very quietly to me, "I hear Number One has had a few words with you. Take n'notice. He's a bit like the skipper; they're hard men – warriors, they don't care a stuff about anything other than killing subs. They're a pair of ruthless bastards." He looked at me, "But, if you ever get into a punch-up, you'd want them with you, not ag'inst you – and – though you haven't realised it yet – you – are in the biggest punch-up of them all."

There was a pause as he re-arranged his cushion – just as in our Mess, the 'bench' we were sitting on consisted of the fixed lockers that held our belongings; they had a leather cushion on top of them to ward off the cold and to add a bit of comfort.

He spoke again, "One day..." he stopped and quietly turned his head to stare directly into my eyes, "you'll make a good Stoker."

That was all he said, and for some reason I felt very small. He turned his head back and drew his pudding plate to him and, without looking up, he said, "Has anyone explained to you yet about this battle? The Battle of the Atlantic."

Slowly and quietly, as the table was cleared, the cigarettes lit and the drink poured, he impressed upon me the enormity that was the Battle of the Atlantic. The longest battle of the war. He explained how we (the Royal Navy) had effectively beaten the German's surface fleet when the battleship *Bismarck* and cruiser *Prinz Eugen* were dealt with in the Battle of the Straits of Denmark.

"That cost us 1,418 men when the *Hood* went down. Think about that, Stoker Moss," the alcohol was stripping away some of the formality, but when he turned that straight gaze on me again, it didn't feel too friendly. "One ship – one thousand, four hundred and eighteen of your countrymen – fathers, brothers, sons, boyfriends – most of them new to the sea – just... like... you." I wished he'd ranted and raved and got me dander up, but he didn't; he wasn't nasty, his voice was level and quiet and he spoke so slowly.

As if to emphasise his point he asked me if I knew how many men had been killed on board the flagship at one of our most glorious battles – the Battle of Trafalgar. "Lord Nelson lost just fifty-seven men, and his was the worst loss of any ship in the British fleet that day. There are almost twenty-five 57s in one thousand, four hundred and eighteen." Those level eyes and that pause again, "Does that mean the Battle of the Denmark Straits, where we lost the *Hood*, was twenty-five times more glorious?

"And if it does, how glorious is the Battle of the Atlantic?"

He had little respect for the German Navy, mentioning how the *Tirpitz* had been a bit of a nuisance but by and large, with the help of the air-boys and the Ruskies, the Royal Navy kept her in port. So the German Navy's only hope was to clear the seas of our warships and merchantmen using U-boats.

"Do you know how many of our ships the U-boats have sunk since the war began? Two thousand, seven hundred and three – think about that." His voice rose just a little.

"That's a hell of a number." From a new voice to my left, a voice that had a trace of Geordie.

"Helluva death too," this time a Middlesex accent, "burning oil, frozen waters, sharp bits of flying metal – no field dressings, no rescue, trapped in a pitch-black hulk waiting for the water to reach you. Did you see that poor sod they pulled out the drink the other week, he was ga-ga..."

Chief brought the mumblings to a stop as he continued to talk – to me – in that same even, quiet voice, "Think about how many U-boats there must be under these waters."

Then he just, kind of absentmindedly, handed me a report: "Read that."

> **At 0201 hours on 23rd September 1943, the German submarine *U-666* fired a Gnat torpedo, which hit HMS *Itchen* (Cdr. C.E. Bridgman, RNR, DSO) after 1 minute and 10 seconds. The frigate blew up after the hit in position 53.25N, 39.42W. Debris from the vessel was later found on HMCS *Morden*. 227 men, including survivors from other ships, went down with HMS *Itchen*. There were only three survivors.**

"Now read this:"

> **On 7th January 1944 HMS *Tweed* (Lt. Cdr. R.S. Miller, DSC, RNR) was torpedoed and sunk in the North Atlantic, south west of Ireland, in position 48.18N, 21.19W by the German submarine *U-305*. The survivors were rescued by HMS *Nene*.**

"And now this:"

> **On 15th June 1944 HMS *Mourne* (Lt. Cdr. R.S. Holland, RNR) from the 5th Escort Group was hit and sunk by a Gnat from *U-767* in the English Channel in position 49.35N, 05.30W. With the loss of eight officers, including Lt. Cdr. Holland, and 102 ratings.**

"HMS *Itchen*, HMS *Tweed* and HMS *Mourne* were all River-class Frigates – direct relatives of HMS *Ness*."

My stomach, which up to this point was warm and full of grub, began to chill. I looked around the faces at the table. I looked at the Chief, his face still, expressionless, except for the slightly strained look that they all shared around their eyes and in the thinness of their mouths.

I realised that as we were deep in the winter in early 1945 some of these guys had been living with these threats for almost every breath of the past five years.

"Don't we... don't we fight back?"

"Oh aye, we fight back alright – the last one, HMS *Mourne*, was just six months ago; we gave *U-767* a pasting just a few days later with depth charges from the three British destroyers HMS *Fame*, HMS *Inconstant* and HMS *Havelock*.

*   *   *   *   *

Coincidentally the young captain of the U-boat that was closing quietly on us that evening was related to Oberleutnant Dankleff, the captain of *U-767*, who had been lost in the sinking. It gave his work a personal 'edge' that night as he loaded his Gnats quietly into their torpedo tubes.

* * * * *

The Chief continued: "And – take the sinking of HMS *Asphodel* – what was that? Ten months ago, maybe more. Anyway HMS *Asphodel* was one of two corvettes escorting a convoy[8] from Gib and bound for Liverpool, just like we are now – they were three, maybe three and a half days from home – they were one of the escort ships – stationed on the starboard bow of the convoy – it was midnight and they got a contact on the radar. They set out their defences – their Foxers – and they sent up a star shell, but after two hours trying to sniff out the contact a Gnat torpedo got through and struck the ship aft – she was steaming at 15 knots.

"Poor sods went down like a brick, only five survivors – ninety-five lost. Once the other corvette, HMS *Clover*, had done what she could she called in help from the nearest hunter-killer patrol – the destroyers HMS *Whitehall* and HMS *Wrestler* and aircraft from the convoy's carrier-escort – a Lend-Lease job called HMS *Tracker* – but the U-boat was gone – the skipper had commanded his ship to drop deep and run west.

"Three days and 400 miles later on, our trans-Atlantic cousins caught up with him, the first attack coming from Canadian frigate HMCS *Prince Rupert*, which attacked with depth charges. They must have done some damage because an American destroyer USS *Hobson* and its escort USS *Haverfield* saw oil on the surface and picked him up on sonar. Their depth charges slowed him down a bit more and he stopped completely after the barrage was joined by depth charges dropped from Avenger strike-aircraft from the escort carrier USS *Bogue*.

"Eventually, all that fire-power had done enough damage to force him to surface and with eighteen killed and thirty-seven taken off – USS *Hobson*'s guns sent the U-boat to the bottom."

He paused. "A U-boat takes some killing. It is a very brutal affair."

The Geordie voice joined in again, "I have heard that there are a thousand, maybe fifteen hundred of the filthy things. Hunting alone or in their packs – and all concentrated on the convoy runs – across the Atlantic to Liverpool – in the mouth of the

---

8   Convoys spanned from 30 to 50 ships but could number as many as 80 to 90. Fast ones like this could be as few as four or five ships. It is estimated that around 30,000 Allied seamen lost their lives in the Battle of the Atlantic. If they hadn't, would we have won?

Channel and the Irish Sea – around the Bay of Biscay and the Azores, cutting off our routes to Gibraltar and Freetown."

If he had a pipe, this would have been the moment the Chief lit it, but the Chief smoked roll-ups. "The only thing putting food in your wife's stomach and bullets in our soldiers' guns and oil in our fuel tanks – is the supply convoys. If we don't stop the U-boats…" he didn't finish it.

He just looked at me. "And… y'know – we have the easy run. I have no idea how those poor sods on the Russian convoys ever get through the day – they have all the same dangers as us and on top of it – their ships get top-heavy with ice – it can be a foot or more thick. In the blink of an eye – they can get frostbite so severe they lose their fingers and hands. One breath is like an icicle filling their insides. We have the easy run. So we have no excuses. We have to get the job done."

He just stopped talking to me, picked up his cushion and went to his hammock.

I returned to my own Mess, four or five pairs of eyes watched me and I saw that same hint of strain around the edges of every one. The sheer enormity of what I was a tiny part of began to settle on me. It seemed to be extra quiet that night as I ducked under the hanging hammocks and climbed into mine. I couldn't even hear the cockroaches, scrabbling around the light. I thought for a while about everybody back home – Freda, Charlie, Arthur, Betsy and Elsie – and then, when the feeling of homesickness was at its peak, I thought about all of those submarines.

Thousands of submarines, from Germany, maybe even some of the Japanese ones snuck into the Atlantic in the south. I pulled a blanket around me but I couldn't get rid of the cold, it was inside me. I just felt useless. If the instructor from Malvern had asked me if I wanted to train to be a DEMS gunner just then, I would have jumped at the chance.

But he didn't – I was a stoker.

It was a long time before I fell asleep. When I did my dreams began to fill with an old familiar image and the unshakable thought that the Atlantic Ocean was infested with submarines in the same way as that feral tomcat in the Palace Theatre had been infested with fleas – and he was riddled with them. What I didn't know was that, at that very moment, one of those U-boats was closing on us.

* * * * *

The young *Oberleutnant* was wide awake; he ordered a shallow dive and our Asdic picked him up for the first time. While I slept a star shell went up over the starboard quarter, three pairs of binoculars scoped the surface, but it was heavy with the white tops of breaking waves. A German-built periscope slid down into its casing a few feet under the surface – the 'pop' 'ping' of the Asdic sounded in the concentrated hearing ready to inform everyone on the bridge where it was; needlessly whispering, Jimmy the One told the skipper he was sure he'd seen movement.

The Old Man didn't react, his binoculars still glued into place – staring.

Sleeping like a baby in my hammock, my dreams began to fill with an eerie wailing and beneath my swaying form crouched figures slowly accelerated into motion – one of them shoved me roughly as he passed and my dreams evaporated but the wailing did not – a call to action – my heartbeat began to sprint – mouth dry.

In every escort ship the message was piped to the team of telegraphists: 'Get everyone listening' – another star shell went up – the Huff-Duff was glowing red, searching for a direction for us to concentrate on – fingers were whirling, trying to find a radio signal. Radar waves were sweeping the empty surface and sonar was stabbing through the water, trying to find a surface to rebound from.

The German skipper came to the surface once again where he could manoeuvre more quickly while he chose his target. He already knew he wanted it to be a warship. He was invisible to us, but *Halladale* could see him on her new electronics. Every antenna on the ships of our escort group was twitching.

I joined the other two in my damage-control team and we gathered up a few bits and pieces which might help us if we were holed. We cleared up rubbish too, so that it wouldn't choke the pumps – we were piped to: 'Close red and blue' and turned our attention to shutting and securing doors and hatches, making our compartments as watertight as we could.

Sweat was pouring from us – next we turned our attention to the ventilation system, closing off any that were not essential, closing down the routes that water may take if compartments below began to flood.

* * * * *

The U-boat gathered speed. The moon behind him – glimmering off the water – hiding him. He radioed his commander, suggesting a position to set an ambush in line, ahead of us, classic wolf pack tactics (except there weren't really enough of them to be called a wolf pack). In the telegraphists' 'office' Oppo heard him as he gave his commander the position. We had his codes. HMS *Loch Katrine* ordered us to attack and we peeled off to give the U-boat a hard time and at the same time a hunter-killer patrol, with destroyers and escort, went after the other three U-boats. The commander of our convoy called for a change of course, taking it further out into the Atlantic and away from any ambush.

Throughout our convoy, gunners sprinted to their positions like disturbed ants to man guns on every ship in the convoy – every merchantman and transport had its DEMS guns pointing towards the position of likely attack. The U-boat watched coolly through his binoculars for a final target for his forward tubes.

A signal was received on HMS *Loch Alsh* from the Admiralty, telling our commander that there may be a U-boat, perhaps two, in our vicinity. Semaphore lights shared the news throughout our tense fleet and now the binoculars began to swivel on necks that were rotating through 360° – we had spotted one, where was the other? The Admiralty updated their message – to four!

Our target was still on the surface; we were the closest to him; the *Oberleutnant* fired his first two torpedoes. His speed was 17 knots, and all of the movement made his aim one that was more in hope than expectation, towards the general direction that had been the rear of the convoy. But the hunter was now on our radar, and our roles were switching – we became hunter, he the hunted. *Halladale* gave his latest position. His torpedoes whirled towards the rear of the convoy and a Dutch troop carrier with over 2,000 men aboard, ploughing resolutely along; cold sweat ran down the back of the officers' necks as they prayed it was going fast enough to clear their path. On the ship itself the action stations drill was being practised by rank upon rank of bleary souls – orders barking for 'quiet' and attention to the donning of life vests. *Loch Katrine* was moving forward, between the U-boat and the troop ship.

They were acoustic – Gnat torpedoes – the pair of tin fish 'heard' the drumming engines of HMS *Loch Katrine*, and veered towards her as she was swinging round, sitting broadside on, rolling heavily in the unhelpful seas, screws ploughing for forward motion that was slow to come.

We were deep inside the *Ness*, at action stations, and somehow, in those times, the crew moulded into one and whispers swept like blood through the ship's veins telling what was going on – or what the teller believed was going on – as the action unfolded up top. The Chief's talk of HMS *Asphodel* was bouncing around my head – my heart racing – my sweat cold, the ball of freezing fear in my guts grown so that it almost blocked my breathing.

Katrine had her Foxer deployed and both Gnats 'heard' it and exploded dramatically, but harmlessly. Made me jump – I was just closing a hatch and the sudden movement made me bang my head on a low metal beam. The young *Oberleutnant* would have heard it too. He may have smiled, but my guess is his heart was beating fast and his muscles tightening as he ordered a dive, disappearing below the surface using all the momentum of his surface speed to sink steeply; we were heading to cut him off, the depth charge teams were standing ready, the gunners were itching to fire. Where were those other U-boats?

The target slowed as the water closed around it.

We reached the position that our Asdic indicated would be directly over him and began to lay a carpet of charges. We kept at it for forty minutes, and when the final explosion died away, we had no idea whether we'd done him any damage. Nor, whether he was coming back. Nor, where the others may be. All we knew was silence.

Many miles in front of our convoy – his fellow U-boaters had scattered when they heard the destroyers were after them – the message came back to our convoy and that, we hoped, was the end of that.

We were around 15° west and 46° north. We had disturbed them coming from their base in La Rochelle, it was a bad time for the U-boats. The Royal Navy was giving them a real hammering and the *Kapitanleutnant* in charge of the group swore quietly as he set course for his original destination, secure in the knowledge that every ship and shore battery and aircraft in the area would know there were four U-boats ripe for the culling – or so we hoped.

We certainly had to keep our eyes peeled for the rest of that night – there was still a lone U-boat with a keen young captain somewhere in the vicinity; he had done his worst and called off, but we didn't know that and we didn't see or hear of him again.

CHAPTER NINE

Things always feel better in the morning, and luckily, the next morning was sunny and bright and to make it better still we were heading back to Londonderry to re-provision. The cold feeling filling my stomach had receded to just the size of an orange and with time became more like a tiny freezing marble of unshakable anxiety, that would remain there until the Battle of the Atlantic ended – I wasn't alone though, I guessed every one of my shipmates carried the same tiny freezing ball too.

The need for constant vigilance against an enemy we lads never saw was of the utmost importance, although, in the main, life aboard a Royal Navy warship could be pretty monotonous. We did our best to find some fun. I became an expert player at Uckers, which in the Royal Navy referred to the game of ludo; the Yanks had an altogether different spelling and translation of the word – I heard plenty of them bragging that they'd dropped a bundle (of cash) on hookers – of course we British lads weren't at all like that!

I was pretty mean with a set of darts (that means I could hit the board), I couldn't get enthusiastic about tombola and I just about avoided losing money in any one of the hundreds of games of cards or dominoes we played.

Scouser loved Uckers and always had a book running on one or other of the colours – the stake was usually a sip of rum or a fag, only the really daring actually used coin of the realm. He fancied himself as a darts player and so his wager was just with his opponent, and he wasn't keen on tombola having lost heavily to the CPO once – some said he was still paying his debt off, but I think that was just a romantic notion.

Lofty drifted away from our group; he started to spend more time by himself and always seemed to be sharpening a pencil, which had us thinking he was a prolific letter writer, or maybe he had a secret diary on the go; he seemed to like noting things down. He kept the Mess ledger.

After a couple of weeks, I was settling into a routine. The day started, as it always did, with yours truly bounding jauntily out of my hammock before turning it over and shaking out any dead roach or other being that may have shared at least part of the night with me. Then lashing it – in proper naval fashion – and stowing it in my locker, then I was off to the ablutions for the toilet and showers.

By the by – the inside of the locker lids were the place where many of us stuck our family photos, so that we could see our loved ones when we raised the lid. One or two of the lads had pin-ups – actually so did I – it was a reclining picture of Freda on the bench in our back yard. Bogie, of course, had a whole lidful of scanty pin-ups from a calendar he'd won off a French lieutenant in Gibraltar, plus one or two just about nude drawings from the *Esquire* magazine. Bogie reckoned that the Jerries had pin-ups of completely naked ladies (all in very tasteful poses of course – this was the 1940s); he said that it was a clear sign that we'd sunk a U-boat if the crew's naughty pictures surfaced with any other detritus – no self-respecting U-crew member would let his pin-ups go if he didn't have to. There was also talk of a lot of the Yanks having pictures of their own girlfriends shedding all for the war effort but I never saw any – all I saw were cheesy photos of Betty Grable, Dorothy Lamour and the straw-bound Jane Russell, whose pen had wished us all 'blessings' while her eyes wished something much more sinful.

Before I move on, let me just mention the sleeping arrangements – I had a place where I slung my hammock, it was the same place every night, under the light – we had twenty-one inches each to sling (hang) them. I liked hammocks, preferred them to the bunks that the Royal Navy has today and the US Navy had back then. To make mine really comfortable I had a wooden stretcher at the head end, to give me space to breathe and room for a pillow. The other thing I liked about hammocks was that if ever the ship should be holed and I was on damage control, and we didn't have any of the wooden shot plugs or the stopping mats, then a hammock could be stuffed into the breach to effect a temporary repair.

We slept in our underwear and, like many others, I kept my overalls and buoyancy belt hung over the end of my hammock so I could reach them in a hurry – they had to be tied on (with a loose knot I learned in Malvern) so that they didn't block up the pumps in the event of us being holed.

After the war, I often heard old salts building drama into their stories by talking about how hard mess life was, saying that their sleep was routinely disrupted by watch changes and bad weather – and with the mess described as crowded, stuffy and often awash with water from the heavy seas. I must have been very lucky – it took a lot to wake me up, once my head hit the pillow. And the only time we nearly had water in the Mess... well, it was my fault... and I'll maybe tell you about it sometime.

It is true that my fellow stokers worked a four-hour shift system – the Navy called them a watch. Starting with the First watch, which ran from 2000 to midnight – then the Middle watch from midnight to 0400 – the Morning watch ran from 0400 to 0800. It was followed by the Forenoon watch from 0800 to mid-day – the Afternoon watch ran from mid-day to 1600 and then, just when it all seemed logical, the Navy splits the next period of time into two-hour shifts, the Dog watch from 1600 to 1800 – and finally the Last Dog watch from 1800 to 2000. These were all accompanied by eight rings of the bell anyway, so you had to be able to selectively ignore noise. And, only two of the watch changes were fully during the night – from first watch to middle watch and from middle watch to morning watch.

Plus, my fellow messmates were usually considerate of us sleepers when the changes came. You see, for me, being in charge of driving the motorboat, the desalination plant, the refrigeration plant and being in charge of the Mess meant I didn't work these watches – not that I was a nine to fiver – I was on a working day that started around 0600 and ended around 2200. (Pause for sympathetic 'Aww – bless'.)

The good thing was that my duties got me out of the Mess for a lot of the day and gave my life on board some variety. For instance, I had begun to spend quite a lot of time in the galley developing something that, I think, was inspired by the time I spent as a kid watching my mam working on her range – it was a kind of stew concoction that simmered gently on the heat all day, constantly ready for mealtime. I just kept making sure it didn't simmer dry and adding any meat or vegetables I could lay my hands on. Because it was always full of meat it went by the old naval nickname Acting Rabbit. To be purist – for my culinary creation to qualify for the 'rank' of Acting Rabbit, it should have had a pastry lid, but my pan was too big and I saved my pastry for puddings – apple pie and the like.

I also spent some of my time in the engine room as well as quite a bit of time maintaining the desalination plant, which the ship relied on heavily for fresh water, and attending the refrigeration unit, with its obvious importance to healthy food. Along with this I'd spend time maintaining the motor launch and the whaler as well as the other miscellaneous duties I drew. I was part of a three-man-below-decks-damage-control team, every time action stations sounded. We spent time too, on exercises, training to catch hold of any torpedo coming through the side and push them back out again and then make the hole waterproof by stuffing anything or anybody into the hole. When it came to any 'body' I had one at the top of my list; you guessed, our Australian Number One – any road, pretend hole-filling beats pretend firefighting!

We got time off to relax too – normally that would be in Londonderry or Gibraltar, both ports well used to dealing with a drunken sailor, although Gibraltar seemed to take a more lenient attitude to sweeping up the flotsam of an overinebriated young man. It was while we were at a club in Gibraltar that I first noticed a certain tension' between Haggis and Laddie, both of whom had been steadily quaffing the local beer as we watched a couple of Scottish lads, singers brought out from the UK to entertain we chaps in the services. They weren't that great and Laddie, in his own gentle way, expressed what most of us were feeling when he said: "Well, well, well – I'm sure I could make a better noise than that."

Haggis, who had reached a mellow stage in his drinking and was enjoying the wails of his countrymen, disagreed – he threw Laddie a look too hot for anyone to catch; the Glaswegian was not amused.

But he didn't say anything – that was left to Bogie. "Oh yeah, Lad, bet you can – you look like a music man! Manto-bleedin-vani – ey – hey?"

The challenge was down, the harmonica came out, then an accordion appeared and Laddie began to show us that he could play a tune or two and sing them as well – Haggis, still, wasn't amused!

Another time in Gibraltar I got a go at hanging from a bosun's chair (well, it was some kind of rigging) in dry dock and helping to paint the side of the ship after the local admiral had spotted we were in the wrong colours or some such. That was breathtaking. Laddie was alongside me; he was always humming some tune or other and was the first of our hanging-men to drop his paintbrush! The bottom of the dry dock was ninety feet below us and the Petty Officer threatened to make him go all the way down there and fetch it back. Laddie wasn't good with the quick answers but I was and interceded, on his behalf: "It broke, sir, when it hit the bottom."

"You saw it, Stoker Moss, did you? Shouldn't you have been watching what you were doing?"

"No, sir, I didn't see it, sir – I heard it – it snapped, sir, and then I distinctly heard three bits bouncing about, clanging between the ship and the concrete." A little voice told me there were one too many 'sirs' and he'd know I was flannelling him.

"Hmm – perhaps I should send you to bring me the bits back and glue them back together."

"I can do, sir, I don't much enjoy hanging here – but I think it would be a complete waste of time – and I wouldn't know what to say to Number One if he thought I was malingering." We were reaching the critical point, the little voice inside my head began screaming, but did I listen to it? Oh no, I was cloth-eared. "Perhaps you had better give me the order in writing... sir."

"Awkward bastard!" Now, I don't know about you, but – personally – I thought such disrespectful language was unbecoming of a petty officer.

"Charlie, sir." Leave it, leave it, leave it. I should have... left it – but not me – me and my big mouth.

"What?"

"My *father's* name, sir – it's Charlie."

"Father?"

"Yes, sir. Father, sir. That's someone a bastard doesn't know. Know your father, do you, sir?"

It was a long way down to the bottom of that dry dock – and when I got there the paint was falling off my fellow painter's brushes like rain in an African jungle. As for Laddie's brush – it was just like new. Until I smashed the sodding thing to pieces and left enough of it behind so that it would be impossible to glue back together.

When I got back, I was streaked in sweat, dust and Navy Grey paint droppings and puffing like a man in need of an iron lung – and what does Laddie say? "Teck n'notice, Raymond – it'll come back on him – he'll reap what he sows someday."

I didn't reply, just flicked a loaded brushful of paint at him.

CHAPTER TEN

Naval life often had unexpected adventures, like the time we were in dock and I had to go down into the water tank to inspect the interior for rust and any other kind of damage. Perhaps I should explain: the water tank was about thirty inches high and the width of the ship; I never did measure how long it was but it was pretty long. It was very tight for me in there and, especially, it was tight getting in – the CPO had sent along one of my smaller, more spry, messmates to help me.

For me this duty was tricky. I had to crawl around on my hands and knees, I was okay once I was inside, but getting in was a struggle, the entry point being difficult to reach and right at the end of the tank. Entry was by way of a round hatch which I had hoisted open, before helping my assistant in and passing him down a couple of brushes and a tin of sealant to cover any rust, then in went the torches and I began the process of squeezing myself in.

I should explain that my method of entry was to lower my feet in as I supported myself with both hands on the rim of the hatch and then lower myself stiff legged into the space until my bum was on the floor. Then I kind of wriggled the rest of me in and when I was completely prone, lying on my back, I would turn over onto my belly and hoist myself onto my hands and knees to start work. This meant that I was always pointing the wrong way and my first movement was to turn myself around and, although there was only a very thin layer of water in there, I managed to soak myself in the process.

I was halfway through this activity, looking like a human reef knot, when he started to squawk.

I had no idea why, it was all very tight and I was tutting and clicking, trying to turn around to see what was ailing him; it was pitch black and he had both of the torches. When I got turned around he was scrambling like a mad-cat trying to prise the top off the sealant can and was face to face with a huge water beetle the size of a tomcat, er, a ~~hamster~~, okay, okay, a fat house mouse; it was curious as to who we were, who had invaded his territory?

'Don't panic, Mr Mannering' doesn't come close.

An instant flush of sweat seemed to explode from his every pore as he asked me to: "GOBACK... GOBACK... GOBACK!"

I thought my reply was quite reasonable?

"What?"

"ARRRGH, GOBACKGOBACKGOBACK! THERE'S A MONSTROUS BUG."

I couldn't see it properly; yet, I just got this impression of his stringy flanks trying to squash themselves into an ever shorter space – which I was filling – as he splashed at something with the contents of his sealant brush.

And then I uttered those immortal words: "Keep calm, kid, it won't hurt you."

Now, I don't expect you to believe this next bit – because I don't – and I was there. The space we were in was just big enough for a man of my size to squeeze through on his hands and knees. My knees were on the floor, the shirt on my back was only just avoiding snagging on the rivets holding the lower rim of the hatch in place. I had my left shoulder touching the metal on one side and my right shoulder touching the other – and yet all I could hear was: "Arrgghhhh, it's 'orrrrriibbbble... 'ble... 'ble," echoing *above* me. Leaving me – flat on my belly, my nose pushed up against the floor, snorting water and eyeball to eyeball with the ugliest (and biggest) beetle in the world – its shiny black shell decorated with a splash of fresh red sealant. The beetle had the added aesthetic impact of a pair of antennae waggling about on each side of its upright painted head and two of the sharpest mandibles you are ever likely to see. It was lifting its feet delicately as it paddled around in a puddle of the spilled sealant. It looked angry. I righted the can.

On its face it wore an expression that said: "Get out of my way and let me at that mouse dropping that just painted me with this evil-smelling stuff!" Only one thing for me to do – I said: "Off you go now and find some juicy cockroach to eat."

I was talking to it. Talking to it! A beetle!

You know what it did – that's right – it beetled off. I called the young lad back but he was shaking so much I had to help him back through the hatchway. He was as nervous as a kitten, glancing all around him when he asked: "Should we catch it, Stoker Moss?"

"No, no need... it won't drink much."

About two hours later we had completed the inspection and he was still as nervous as a schoolgirl.

I was reversing the entry process; I had reached the point where I was lifting myself off my back and grabbing at the rim of the hatch to hoist myself out when he, eventually, asked me the obvious question: "I wonder where that beetle has gone?"

"Oh, I've got it, it's in my pocket," I lied, "it's for my Acting Rabbit – it'll be just like lobster with its crunchy shell. Hey, why don't you join us for supper tonight?"

Why he felt the need to puke all over the inside of the tank that held our drinking water I do not know, but I left him to clean it up by himself – and hoisted myself out of the tank, taking my torch with me, then I relented and slung the light back for him. Actually I think it was caught by the beetle, which had found that it really enjoyed the taste of fresh sealant and was going back for a second helping. At least the speed that the young chap came out of the hatch when he'd finished makes that scenario a 'highly probable'.

* * * * *

Not all of my dealings with shipmates were on such a light-hearted level however, as I discovered one night after I'd been aboard a couple of months. I was lying in my hammock peacefully slumbering in that hinterland between awake and fast asleep, when I imagined a hand stroking the upper reaches of my right inner thigh. I could have been lucky of course and have passed the threshold and be dreaming about, errr, about... well, that's none of your business... the thing is, I slowly began to realise that I wasn't – wasn't dreaming that is.

There was a hand caressing my thigh. It took me a millisecond to remember that there were no ladies on board, so it could only mean one thing – well, maybe two – either it was an enormous spider the size of a hand – or it was a bloke's hand. Arrrgh, yuk, errggh – I wasn't quite sure which was worse – and then I was.

At this point, in today's PC society — it would probably be correct to say that I thought naught on it, but I did – there was my revulsion (which I still hold today) at the idea of the pervert creeping about molesting young lads as they slept and, of course, this was not today – this was the forties. In public circles, gay blokes were held in as bad a light as paedophiles today – and my natural reaction was to lash out mightily with my right arm, catching something a real good clout. The sound of the 'splat' as the back of my clenched fist met up with what felt like a face came an instant before the hand on my thigh disappeared!

I guess even in those days some of my shipmates would say that man-to-man practices were less taboo in the Navy, where some chaps seemed to think that long voyages and plenty of rum meant such dalliances were okay. Not me – I didn't drink – and in this respect I was a perfect Neanderthal. Anyhow, this particular wandering deckhand had made his escape by the time I was out of my hammock.

At least the ginger sneak knew I wasn't keen on him treating me to his unwanted advances.

I found out who it was the very next day – the Officer's Steward – I was taking some air when he came out of a doorway right beside me. He had a tray of empty mugs with him and he dropped his eyes and half turned his face away from me as he tried to sidle by. When I spun him around by the collar I could see that he had a beautiful black patch that took in both eyes and a slightly distorted nose with nostrils rimmed in dried blood; it was just the size of one of my rather large hands. The clatter of mugs hitting the steel decks must have alerted the officer of the watch and he appeared just as I was issuing my promise – to stick the steward's teeth so far down the back of his throat that he'd have to push his toothbrush up a different orifice to clean them if he tried such sneaky stuff again. I had one fist up against the side of his head and the other fist full of his uniform front, so perhaps it was a bit obvious that Raymond was seeing the red mist and it was enough to prompt the officer to ask us what was amiss.

"He's dropped a clanger and I'm just straightening things out for him, sir," I replied but without taking my glare away from the offender, "straightening his tie out that is."

Slowly it began to dawn on me that this could be awkward, it could be the officer's mug in bits on the gangway.

"Well, I can see that you aren't," the officer said and then he just stared at us for a while, while I relaxed my grip, "but I'll let it go if you are both alright with that?"

I was – he had mugs to pick up – I certainly wasn't going to help him and that was the end of it.

* * * * *

Back to business – I was Head of the Mess and that meant that it was down to me to manage the Mess budget, which the Purser's Office allowed us for food and the like – if we wanted more we had to find the money ourselves.

I had learned the value of befriending the 'right' people from Charlie before I joined up, and in this instance three such people who were important in assuring that our mess was well fed and tended for – within the budget – were the Cook, the Tanky and the head of the Naafi. It didn't take me long to realise that all three were up for a bribe and all three shared a love of the Grog – and as I didn't – but was issued with it daily – I had a currency that I could use to oil their palms. Well, lubricate their throats really, but you know what I mean.

Just in case you don't know, grog was the traditional Navy rum ration. It was neat rum mixed with water and the ration was a tot, or quarter of a pint, every day! The problem with grog was that it didn't keep very well – some lads put it in bottles and added currants, which they believed would help it keep for longer but it wasn't a great success, so the best thing to do with it was drink it – or, if like me you didn't drink, trade it quickly and regularly. I had the three regular customers and traded it in the two recognised values – either a 'Gulper' or a 'Sipper', the names indicating the quantities traded.

From the cook I got hob privileges; I was becoming quite a keen cook and, having 'found' a large cook pot, was able to keep our Acting Rabbit simmering away all day – day after day – simply adding to it with any ingredients that I could lay my hands on, which is where the tanky comes in.

The name Tanky is most common when referring to officers where it describes the midshipman that assists the Navigating Officer and the only link that I have ever been able to find is that, in earlier times, the Navigating Officer was responsible for the water tanks. But, the tanky I am talking about is not an officer, he is a seaman rating, who goes by the grand title of Captain of the Hold – that means that he has responsibility for stowage and care of the provision holds. He has in his hands the key to the food cupboard. Our tanky was also a pretty good butcher, which helped enormously with the sharks that I will tell you about later.

My third 'musketeer' is the Naafi manager – on larger ships the Naafi referred to the canteen, on the *Ness* it was a kind of a shop, on board, where we could go and buy anything we wanted, and this fellow was in charge of the shop, thus he was another great source of provisions. As coincidence would have it, he also came from Ravensdale Street in Scunthorpe, which you would have thought would make us bosom buddies – we weren't really, but it did help us to understand each other. He was always open to some gentle persuasion based around a quantity of rum, cigarettes or chocolate; in fact he became a kind of business partner for me, organising the transactions of my cigarette rations to get us the best possible deal. I knew he wouldn't fiddle me, because he knew that I knew where he lived and that Charlie and Arthur could easily go and empty his house if he unduly emptied my pockets. I never threatened to do that of course, I just made sure that he knew that it could happen – we were actually pretty solid partners and remained so until the war ended – I haven't seen him since!

Every now and again we had a Captain's Inspection of the Mess, and every time he visited the Stokers' Mess, he and I would have the same conversation.

He would query the fact that we were the only mess on the ship that wasn't over-spent and he would ask me how I did it. When I told him it was down to the excellent food and generous rations that the Navy provided... well... he knew I was stretching the truth, but that's as far as he got.

After moaning about it for a couple of years, managing the Mess actually became one of my favourite routines; it had a therapeutic effect, especially managing the mess meals – breakfast, lunch and dinner.

We didn't quite eat like kings but we didn't have many complaints either. I could put that down to the generally poor quality of services food but I prefer to think it came from my growing love of cooking – which has stayed with me ever since. When I first took it up, one of my messmates was giving me some 'acid' about it being women's work and asking why I did it. I was undertaking my first experiment with bread making and was kneading furiously. I answered: "It's great for cleaning the oil and grease out from under yer fingernails." I made sure I replied without looking at him or hesitating in my work, and when I handed the bread out later on, he declined a slice. He missed a treat, it was superb, even if I do say so myself. And... it really was great at cleaning the muck out from... no... don't wince – I *might* be joking!

I became especially adapt at puddings, being world-famous for my sponge puddings; I also did a pudding consisting of a pastry top (over a variety of fillings) that was covered in custard and my pièce-de-résistance was my rice pudding, sometimes including a secret ingredient. By the way, being world-famous wasn't that difficult because our whole world consisted of HMS *Ness*.

There were the odd occasions when my messmates may not have applauded me – had they but known what some of my secret ingredients were – like the time we were laid up in dry docks at Fort William, we'd picked up a metal hawser and it had tangled around one of our propellers causing damage that required us to go into dry-dock. The galley on board ship had been closed down so we had to use the galley on the dockside; I had promised the lads a rice pudding – but I was in a hurry, because Freda had travelled up for a few days and I was rushing around so that I could join her in the log cabin we'd hired.

My puddings were always made in big flat pans and, going back to the Mess, I was rushing down this particular gangplank – which was a number of wooden planks lashed together, covered with a bit of good honest Highland mud and a sprinkling of miniature granite chippings and miscellaneous grit from the bottom of my crewmates' shoes. I missed my footing and my Base slipped gracelessly over my Apex. Surprisingly I saved most of the rice and the 'splodge' that fell on my rather oily vest was easily recovered – the oil had only been loaded that morning so it was relatively fresh and clean. Another two or three lumps had hit the gangplank but they'd kept their shape fairly well so, after a furtive glance, I scooped them all up and stirred them back into the pan.

On my way to the mess table, I nipped into my food store and added a handful of currants – 'finishing touches' I told the crew. I only got one complaint, from Lofty, who suggested my currants had gone stale, because when he started chewing on one it was rock hard and nearly broke his tooth.

Gritty lot, we stokers.

CHAPTER ELEVEN

Then – on the 4th May 1945 – we were a day or so away from our home port, when a very excited Virge came to find me in the galley – "Guess what," he whispered, "I've just picked up a Plain Language Message." His eyes were as bright and wide as a two-year-old with a four-inch lollipop.

Not knowing a plain language message from a fancy language message, I stood dumb.

His words took a while to come out and when they did they were a rush, "Hitler's dead and some bloke called Dohnits has taken over and he's told the U-boats to surrender." He stopped, I didn't react, so he started talking again. "The new Fuehrer is an Admiral... they've been scuttling U-boats since late April..." pause, "they're giving up, Raymond, giving up, it's finished, we're off home."

We're standing toe to toe, noses nearly touching, holding both hands, jumping up and down like a pair of demented Masai, grinning like bananas when the notice comes over the tannoy – the Battle of the Atlantic was finally in its death throes.

Laddie had a few gulpers at our Mess party that night and ended up standing on the table belting out a chorus or two of 'Who's Sorry Now' – then three choruses – then four – then five – he had a pretty good voice but you do get a bit fed up of a song after twenty or thirty renditions. Haggis and Chalky eventually lifted him down and took him out onto deck and tossed him in the whaler to sleep it off. Haggis wanted to pitch him overboard, but Chalky talked him out of it; if he hadn't been such a nice guy – Laddie, not Haggis – his fate may well have been a whole lot wetter – anything to stop his crooning.

"Whoooooz shorry nhhow – whoooooos sorreeee n-h-ow – whooooo – s – horry –nowhowhow – whooz shorry nehow. Whooooose..." SPLOSH! You can feel it happening, can't you?

Actually, we were always a lot quieter around Laddie; we didn't like to make any sudden moves, we could never be sure what he had in his pockets and whether it was explosive or not.

Three days later Germany surrendered and HMS *Ness* was sent to the south-west of Ireland for ten days to help the U-boats surrender. It was an area coded 'blue', I think, and U-boats were popping up like acne on the face of a fifteen-year-old. Ha haaa... you beauties... who's sorry now?

Laddie – give us a verse or two.

Maybe I was not the most gracious of victors but I was a victor nonetheless – the rats were on my pitchfork.

I have read since about the U-boat captains being requested by German High Command to surrender using a black flag instead of white to preserve the honour of the Kriegsmarine and its leader Admiral Dönitz and also to honour the submariners' bravery and yet to still show that they had surrendered. The sentiment that usually accompanies these statements goes along the lines of the U-boat crew being the crème de la crème of the German Navy and that without such concessions they may not surrender.

What a pile of *stiersheie* – in fact an insult to all other brave military men who have ever surrendered under the white flag – these Nazi sub-boys just weren't that special.

In my experience, one thing that all German forces had in common was discipline; if they were told to fight, they'd fight, if told to surrender, they would surrender, so that last 'reason' doesn't sail far.

And whilst all these years later I no longer have any reason to think badly of the individual U-boat crew members – and I regret the thousands of them who died in the doing of their duty – I don't subscribe to the romanticism of it. The Kriegsmarine hardly deserved any honour and its commander certainly didn't.

There were more heroes on one convoy of merchantmen, setting out to fulfil a duty on rough seas in a howling gale, clear in the knowledge that they were prime targets of foe they couldn't see, than in the whole of the German Navy, which in reality had spent all of the war skulking around and hiding. At the end of April a number of U-boats had been ordered by the new fuehrer, Admiral Karl Dönitz, to scuttle their craft in an operation code named 'Regenbogen' and around 230 of them complied before the Allies told Dönitz to call it off and get them to surrender.

Pity they did really because it just meant that we had to get rid of the things after the war, when the Admiralty decided that the remaining U-boats should be dumped in the Atlantic to the north-west of Ireland. Personally, I would have a problem with using the word 'honour' if after the war one of my children asked me what I did and I found myself answering, "I had the honour of sinking my own boat!" Still, it takes all sorts.

I remember three U-boats surrendering to us – and I don't recall anything but white flags; I mean, what would they be doing with black ones, were they supposed to fly them just before a kill – like a judge of the day when passing a death sentence for murder and putting a black cloth over his wig? And flags don't fly under water, so the timing doesn't work for that scenario, or had their commander ordered a black flag aboard every sub for the day he knew they would surrender?

I do recall the U-boat that surrendered to us in the Atlantic, near to the entrance of the Irish Sea at the end of our patrol, when we were heading back to Londonderry and a spot of leave. The *Oberleutnant* in charge was flying a flag that the skipper felt was too small. I remember him levelling our guns at the conning tower, and informing the U-boat captain that if he didn't fly the biggest white flag he could find, within the next five minutes – he would not be considered to be complying with the Instrument of Surrender and we would open fire on him. I remember the U-boat finding a flag that was the size of a bed sheet, which is probably what it was – they didn't issue black bed sheets, not in those days. Some of the crew believed the Old Man was a bit peed-off because it was all over and he didn't have a definite 'kill' to his name.

Let's just hold on a mo and think about the honour and the glory in all of this. When we think of glory in the UK, we probably think about actions such as the Charge of the Light Brigade – cannon to the left of them, cannon to the right of them and all that. Again very brave British servicemen – their horses were travelling somewhere around 30 mph at full gallop and they were running into solid balls of shot – that they could often see – from artillery – and in an action that was over in an afternoon.

The convoys often travelled at less than 10 knots – a knot being 1.15 mph, so that's 11½ mph in an action that would last for day after day after day, night and day, not as glamorous as the Lancers, but is it as worthy of glory? Try it – get into your car, find a quiet farm track – the bumpier the better – and drive along it at 11½ mph and imagine a soldier behind every tree with a rocket launcher at his shoulder – aiming at you – ready to blow bits off you – imagine doing that for 15, 16, 17 days.

* * * * *

If they were lucky, the victims didn't feel a thing, or they drowned quickly; thousands of others had pieces ripped off by the high explosives or were burnt and battered, left to die wrapped in the burning stink of smoke-wreathed hulks that would not easily sink.

And every merchant sailor knew that – they had all heard the horror stories.

Read that last bit again and imagine the smell so heavy it blocked your nose, the weird crying of people you know, the pain, the fire, the banging in your head where the compressed air had smashed in most of your hearing followed immediately by a vacuum that sucked your mangled eardrums from your skull. Imagine the taste of searing air in your lungs, the sight smashed from your eyes, the crackle of skin burning on your arms, the feel of the bile filling your throat. The darkness and the terror and the disbelief that these horrible moments are the last you will have before they deliver your blackened and twisted remains back to your wife or your mother.

Those merchant sailors sat on top of a cargo that could be 10,000 tons of high-grade aviation spirit or could be ammunition. Travelling in a convoy that could only go as quickly as its slowest ship, plodding along for days on end with the constant threat – every single breath they took – of a torpedo through the side and a ride down the depths through agony.

They are the real heroes, they won because of their enormous courage and, never far away, a typically light-hearted sense of humour.

Theirs is the glory – not some arrogant rodent with a fancy leather coat and a bad attitude that turned tail at the merest sign of trouble and dived into obscurity – which after all is where the Nazi Navy deserves to be in the annals of history – in obscurity.

*   *   *   *   *

Some days I really wish I'd taken that post as a DEMS gunner, although my children definitely don't. I came very close to being a sub-man too and yet the loathing I felt for submarines then, is still very real.

While jotting this tale down, I came across a piece on the website of the Italian Navy about the submarine which HMS *Ness* helped to sink. Someone writing the Italian site mentions a passenger ship that the Italian sub torpedoed on 14th March 1943 – here's what the site says:

> **On March 14th, the *Da Vinci* sunk with two torpedoes the British transatlantic *Empress of Canada* of 21.517 t. This is a sad episode since along with 3000 British soldiers there were 500 Italian prisoners of war. The submarine succeeded only in recovering S.T. physician Vittorio Del Vecchio. The position of the sinking is given at 1° 13′ S, 9° 57′ W. This elegant transatlantic was built by the shipyards Fairfield in Glasgow in 1922, and it belonged to the Canadian Pacific Railway Co.**

If he had written those words during the war, they would have been forgivable; to write them so long after the war is unforgivable – it is no longer sad that 500 Italians died, now it's sad that any one of the 3,500 he says were on board were killed.

In fact his story looks to be just so much more Italian B/S – several other sites covering the *Empress of Canada* talk of the submarine making two attacks on the ship – the attacks being thirteen hours apart and the second attack coming as the ship was being abandoned. In total, 392 people were lost – 44 of them crew, 8 being soldiers and the balance (340) being Italian prisoners of war; the Italians hadn't just shot themselves in the foot, they had blown both legs off – as it is, the *Da Vinci* itself was sunk just over two months later in the action involving HMS *Ness*.

*　*　*　*　*

My last word on this subject is to do with the 'U-boat commanders, being the crème de la crème' thing – well, it didn't take much to be the best of the best in the Nazi Navy – and the Italian Navy was a complete joke!

The U-boats were all the Nazis had to strike back with.

Of their surface ships, one was hiding away in Montevideo and they eventually sunk it themselves because they were afraid to face the Royal Navy. Another was skulking in the fiords and wouldn't come out because it was afraid to face the Royal Navy, and their biggest and best went sprinting through the Denmark Straits trying to get its big guns levelled at merchant ships before it met up with its fate at the hands of the Royal Navy.

Ducking a fight is not the Royal Navy way, the Admiralty would much rather go straight for the throat of the enemy, often at very poor odds – and slog it out with them until it won.

Just imagine every one of Horatio's captains, while sailing on the light breeze off Trafalgar, head-on into the side of a much larger force, taking shot all the time – deciding to run away instead in the hope they could maybe sneak up on one or two of the enemy later on.

Or, imagine the officers of the *Hood* running away when they made contact with *Bismarck* and *Prinz Eugen* and allowing the two ships easy access to the Atlantic – that was never going to happen.

The power that the Allied navy had over its enemies was beating in the breasts of its seamen.

But then, perhaps I am biased.

I am proud to say the Royal Navy stood up to every enemy threat with the same steadfast courage that it had shown since – well, since before Nelson's day. If you are thinking, does he have any proof of that? – I can show you the statistics.

The largest navy in the Second World War was the US Navy with 4,848 ships – followed by the Royal Navy with 3,317 – the Soviet Navy follows with 411 ships and then the Canadians with 351 and the French with 241.

The biggest losses in fighting ships, however, sees the Royal Navy highest with 605 ships lost – the USA didn't fight shy either, they lost 351 ships. The Soviets, who, I was told by many of our lads that met them, floated on vodka not seawater, lost 134 (which is almost a third of their fleet). The Canadians lost 24 ships and the French lost 92 ships. I guess we all stood firm and took the beating.

And won.

Other navies involved in the Battle of the Atlantic on the Allied side include the Royal Dutch Navy, the Royal Australian Navy, the Royal Hellenic Navy, the Brazilian Navy, the Royal Indian Navy, the Polish Navy, the Free French Navy, the Royal Norwegian Navy, the Royal New Zealand Navy and the South African Navy and eventually the Italians (who turned their coats after their surrender).

Our tour of duty in the Atlantic now over, we had a day off to celebrate and then there was a new momentum about the ship – we weren't heading home after all, we were heading east – well, north-east first – and then east.

We had a new enemy to fight and, I guess, the skipper wanted us in the thick of things, although for him, that was not to be.

CHAPTER TWELVE

We were off to Malaya – and, with a new theatre of war to attend, we needed a change to our armaments; we were off to face an enemy with great submarines, a real and aggressive surface fleet and an air force full of pilots prepared to splatter themselves all over our superstructures. So, we'd have the same emphasis on the sub hunting and more emphasis on air defence against the pilots of the Japanese air force.

It was suddenly beginning to feel like 'out of the frying pan into some sort of furnace'. There would be landings to protect too – bloody hell – the task ahead suddenly felt very, very scary.

We were in for a long voyage and it had its fair share of danger and death, but it certainly didn't turn out like I imagined and some of our gang would never be the same when they returned as they were when they set out. The uncertainty was affecting everyone in the Mess as we sailed from Londonderry – around Scotland and into Sooth Shee'lds, where we were to be fitted with a twin Bofors gun in place of the 4-inch on the foredeck.

On the second night in South Shields, Chalky decided we needed a night on the town to try to cast off the blackness that had encompassed our mood. I had been married for just over a year and I wasn't much of a drinker, so this kind of thing wasn't really for me, but I did feel it was my duty to join in when Chalky said he'd arranged for a few dances with some girls from an Allied ship that was being repaired in the town. I wondered why the lad from Hull had such a smile on his face as he led our merry gang towards the music.

Bogie was grinning like an excited spaniel until we were introduced to the girls… they were a squad of Russians with which we shared a very close interest – they were female stokers, on a ship still powered by steam; they had forearms like Bluto and were almost as bearded. I tried to palm my huge dance partner off onto Virge, but he was deep in conversation, about radio signals, with a pretty English Wren and refused my offer.

I just managed to notice the Wren's cultured accent, her short blonde hair and her habit of nervous chain smoking, before my dance partner gripped me with the strength of a demented grizzly and threw me rhythmically around the floor, my eyes watering in the vodka haze that surrounded her head like a goldfish bowl. It was half an hour before I managed to break free. When I did, I noticed Virge and his Signals Wren leaving the dance hall. I slipped out after him but lost sight of him in the melee of sailors and locals milling around the door of the hall, so I staggered back to the ship on my own.

Next morning, as Haggis and I were dockside, I saw Virge coming back to the ship, on his own – he was grinning like a concert piano and humming a distantly familiar tune – as soon as he saw me he waved and then came the strangest thing I ever saw this studious young chap do – he broke into song:

> ♫ *I'll be loving you – always*
> *With a love that's true – always*
> *When the things you've planned*
> *Need a helping hand*
> *I will understand – always*
>
> *Always ♪*

That seemed about as far as he could get with the words but...

Just a moment – we need to stop – consider this – we around the stokers' table had decided that Virge was so serious because he was a bit on the clever side – a telegraphist and all – so, I was completely gobsmacked when he stopped singing, and started running. Towards me.

He got about twelve inches away and slung himself at me, wrapping his arms around me neck and his legs around me waist.

I burst out into a cold sweat and thought for a second that he was about to kiss me.

That's when Haggis's dulcet tones came, just behind my left lughole. "What's yon wee lassie's name, then?"

I put him right, "It's not a lass, it's Virge..." again, he didn't give me time to finish what I was saying.

"Not you, Herbie, you tosser, I was tackin' tae Virge."

"Valerie," came the dreamy reply from a head alongside mine, still clamped to me like a magnet.

Virge hadn't finished, "Harford... Marguerette... Jones-Haroldson," he seemed to be reciting a name as long as an Italian battleship's wake at the sniff of a battle. "She's a Signals Wren – sighhhhh."

"She's got enough names, or, have yee been dallying with two on 'em?" Now Haggis was laughing and I tried to join in.

My humour failed and I barked at the clinging Virge, "Get off me before I lamp you!"

Virge clung tight and just chanted his girl's name again, "Valerie Harford Marguerette Jones-Haroldson."

Haggis thought me a little harsh. "Leave the young 'un alone, Herbie, can't you see he's in love?"

"In love?"

"Aye," says Haggis – "I think we better come up with a new name for him from now on – Virge was short fer Virgin and that won't do it anymore."

My jaw dropped open, bouncing painfully down the polished buttons on Virge's jacket. "What you? Got a girl? Had a girl? Cripes, Virge, you dog." Now I was smiling in a pained, carrying a lot of weight kind of way.

Virge let go of me and we watched him hop and skip all the way back to his mess deck.

The mood had overtaken Haggis and me; we linked arms and followed, slowly, behind him, finishing off Virge's song for him:

> ♪ *Days may not be fair – always*
> *That's when I'll be there – always*
> *Not for just an hour*
> *Not for just a day*
> *Not for just a year* ♪
> *But always*

As we finished our verse – Haggis gave me a gentle shove on the back of my shoulder and propelled me forward half a dozen paces, prompting me to groan and moan about the pain of a probable dislocation, until he volunteered to put it back in for me, causing an instant kind of healing.

The big daft Scot stood and grinned; "Hey Herbie," he growled in a happy Glaswegian kind of way, "this could be the Stoker's song."

"The Stoker's song?"

"Aye. We just need to make a wee change to the worrreds," and off he went:

> ♪ *I'll be lubing you – oilways*

"Ha ha, very funny, Haggis – don't give up t'day job." But he'd caught the mood and was too pleased with himself to catch my barb.

"Aye well, I'd niver have thought on changing the lyric, Herbie, if it weren't for your weird accent." Cheeky sod, nothing left for me to do but join in.

> ♪ I'll be lubing you – oilways
> With a lube that's true – oilways
> When the things you've planned
> Need an oily hand
> I will understand – oilways ♫

> Oilways ♫ ♪ ♫

I looked at Haggis in a slightly different light from then on. Actually, he had a pretty good voice, not that Guy Lombardo had anything to worry about – it seemed, however, that the jury was 'out' on my vocal talents, which prompted a comment from the ship's lookout.

"I don't care how much pain it's in – you two make sure that rabid cat doesn't make it onto my ship!"

The man had no soul!

> ♪ ♫ Oilways ♫ ♪ ♫

The lads didn't find the story of our new song such a riveting subject at breakfast next morning either; they all seemed to have other things on their mind. It seems their assignation with their original dance partners ended when the Russians stopped dancing and began brawling with some of their crewmates who had come to get them back aboard so their ship could steam for home.

They had ended the night dancing slowly with some local ladies, Streak began to expound – his talk was unusually animated and of a distinctly amorous nature: "Why aye, man, this is one of the bonniest playces us've ever tacken ooer shore leave – tha nah – all the pubs are full of wimin. There's no men, just wimin reet e nuff, I'm ganging awa oot agin twoneet – whose cumin'?"

"What are you talking like that for?"

"It's Geordie, man, Lofty's been teaching us – it's how they talk up here – aw reet?"

"But. You're from Bournemouth."

Streak: "Y-high, I ken, but the lassies don't – and I'm gangin' huntin' the sirens of Sooth Shields."

Scouser dived into the discussion with, "You cumin', Mossy?"

"Corse not – I'm married."

Chalky: "Aye, we know – so are most of them!" The laughter refused to stop.

"Well," says I, "you'd better fill your boots, we sail in two days." My next few words just seemed to make matters worse, "Do you know where we're going next?"

Bogie: "No, where we off to, Mossy?"

"My old hunting grounds, Immingham, Grimsby, Cleethorpes."

I looked up and seven pairs of smiling eyes focussed on me – Chalky, Haggis, Laddie, Bogie, Scouser, Streak and, floating in the background, Lofty – it was his voice that asked the question.

"And are the women as mad for it in Cleethorpes, RB?"

"I don't know," pause, "but the fish and chips are terrific."

Haggis splurted half of his porridge over me as the gang cracked up in uncontrollable laughter, and while I cleared a pair of eyeholes in my new face mask, Bogie finished me off with, "I see you can still get your freaking oats, Mossy."

They were still rolling around with laughter when I came back from my second shower of the morning.

I was grumbling to Virge a bit later that day – about being so close to home and not able to get there, or even tell anyone we were anchored within waving distance – I mean, my family could have jumped on the old Flier and waved from the seafront – it would have been great to see them. I must admit I was struggling to keep up the old Moss attitude of 'Oh well, when it happens I'll deal with it' – I was nervous about facing the Nips – with their *kamikazes* and submarines that made the U-boats look like toys – some of the Jap subs even had aircraft on board! Anyhow, what I'm saying is I'd have loved to see the merry crew from Scunny – Freda, Mam, Charlie and the lot.

Then Virge said something that shocked me: "You can keep your leave, I hate leave."

"What?"

"Well, no sooner are you home than everybody you meet starts asking when you're going back. It's like you're guilty for being there and not out fighting with the rest of the Navy." His eyes were sparkling a bit so I guessed something had upset him when he was home last. I just kept quiet and listened, but he didn't say much more.

"You know, the last leave we had?" Silence. "I came back early."

"Did you?"

"Yes – you know, Ray, these days, I sometimes feel more at home – in the heart of my family like – when I'm with you lot, than when I'm at home." He stopped for a while and I kept on just listening, "I seem to have more of a 'purpose' on the ship than I have at home – I'm more involved, more useful, more important."

Cripes, what do I say now? I know: "Yes," long mulling-over type pause, "I know what you mean."

"Do you?"

"Yes."

"Wow, that's such a relief; I thought there was summat up with me." Just at that moment he looked so vulnerable, his eyes so wide and childlike, his expression so innocent.

"What apart from being ugly, stupid and a telegraphist you mean?"

He thumped me, but he was laughing while he did it – bloody hurt though!

I took his mind off his woes and on to his recent conquest, well, his only conquest, and it turned out that she'd 'conquered' him... with a chorus of:

♪ ♫ *Oilways... Oilways* ♫ ♪ ♫

* * * * *

Before dawn on the Wednesday, we sailed down to the Humber to get the upgrades we needed for the radar. The next morning we anchored off Cleethorpes. It was dead calm, water like green glass, low cloud and a quiet morning mist; I was leaning over the rail, on deck, staring wistfully towards the Humber mudbanks as we waited for the tide to turn, when Virge walked up. He was obviously feeling much better this morning and had decided to share a few of his amorous secrets with me.

"Hey up, Ray, that lass I – you know – met – in South Shields, she was something else." He'd gone all glassy eyed, "Do you know what she did...?"

"Don't tell me, don't tell me, don't tell me!"

Bloody hell, I was a young man and anchored about thirty miles from my young wife and the prat's getting me thinking about that!

My expression must have been very eloquent.

He realised and said, "Sorreee."

I left him standing there listening to the gulls singing and went off to find the Chief but my suggestion that I might take a quick trip home was taken as a joke, so I decided not to turn it into a formal request.

As it happens, I could have had a day or two with the family; it took three days to get the radar done and then, just as we sailed out of the port a thick North Sea fog descended and our revamped radar sent us off towards Oslo instead of southward to the Channel.

Well, that's what the skipper and Jimmy the One told everyone – they blamed the new technology, and who am I, a lowly stoker, to query those two fine navigators.

102

Eventually we got back to Londonderry and the sight as we sailed in was enough to take your breath. The masses of surrendered U-boats alongside those piers in the River Foyle brought on a mixture of emotions. I think the little knot of fear in my guts would have grown to such a size that it would have choked me if I'd had such a clear realisation of the number of enemy boats that we were up against as we hunted them out in the Atlantic.

And, then, there was the feeling of great joy that we'd beaten the so-and-sos, and then – in the spirit of logic standard in the Navy I was granted shore leave, well, not just me, we all were – I was in Scunthorpe the next day.

I was a day late returning to Londonderry after my leave – my steam train ran out of puff – the skipper was not amused and had a little word.

Then we all had our picture taken – and what a bonny bunch we looked too – luckily they cropped me out of the version shown on the picture pages.

Our next port of call would be Liverpool where we were to meet up with some troop ships for the soldiers taking part in the Allied invasion of Malaysia – Operation Zipper.

CHAPTER THIRTEEN

They were a cocky lot those soldier-boys; the *Ness* had only just tied up to the jetty in Gladstone Dock in Liverpool when their converted liner set off for sea; they passed very close by and were towering over us when they started hurling their 'acid' – or perhaps it was the merry banter of nervous lads.

The gist of it was – why are you Navy boys lazing by the jetty when you should be coming with us? As in 'get your arses into gear and come and protect us, you wasters!'

We knew what to expect; we'd had a troopship to look after a couple of months back – Easter weekend, it was really rough then, so rough we were excused scrubbing the mess decks – we couldn't keep the water in the buckets.

Here in the harbour it was like a millpond, but we'd just come up the Irish Sea; it hadn't been as rough as at Easter, but it was rough enough.

A voice full of laughter came drifting down from the hundreds of troops leaning over the side: "Hey – where do you keep the oars for that rusty old rowing boat?" One of our lads shouted back: "We don't." Must have been a stoker because the next line was quite witty, "She's clockwork, we winds 'er up twice a day."

And then a voice from the *Ness*, with a dark edge, not unlike Bogie's, yelled at them: "Laff now, you gobshites, 'cos yer'll not be laffin' tomorrer." Such a charmer.

Of course, we would soon be following; we were just provisioning and giving them a head start – no U-boats to worry about now – in fact the only thing we had to protect them against was the sea.

We knew, much better than those raw recruits knew, just how much damage the Atlantic could wreak amongst well-loaded ships; if it decided to wrestle up a major storm, they could be surfin' some monster swells and halfway to Nova Scotia in a matter of hours. And, of course, the sea lanes were still riddled with hazards like wrecks and mines, so, we weren't so much escorting as being there if they needed helping or rescuing.

You should have seen the grins on my crewmates' faces the next day, when we picked up their trail... of half-digested breakfasts, floating on the water for miles ahead of us – the seagulls loved it. And, we couldn't resist a little cheer when we sailed by and saw those same soldier-boys leaning, grey-faced, over the railings and puking up their egg and bacon – sorry, boys, can't help it, I'm grinning again now.

* * * * *

Anyway, we were off to tackle the Japanese in the Allied invasion of Malaya. Every man in the British forces knew that this was going to be hellish – they were ruthless little so-and-sos – well trained, well fed and so well dug in the Allies might never find them, let alone shoot at them.

But we didn't get far – first day out we caught a metal hawser around one of the propellers and had to turn back – we limped all the way to Fort William where we laid up in the dry dock for repairs. We were there a few days and, to my delight, Freda came up and we rented a log cabin from one of the local mountain rescue chaps – it was absolutely fantastic. Even though, as I have mentioned previously, it did have a negative effect on my messmates' enjoyment of their rice pudding.

* * * * *

FREDA: Can I have a say? I remember that trip – the Scunthorpe train was an old steamer, puffing and popping all the way to my first stop, Doncaster. At Doncaster I changed to the Edinburgh train, old coaches with blacked-out windows and individual compartments that would sit about eight people; I was on my own for most of the journey. Edinburgh station was something else, a huge building with an enormous spanned roof and people rushing about everywhere, all in uniform, all with kit bags, most of them talking in an accent I couldn't follow at all.

I called into a booth in Edinburgh station and bought myself some toffee – the shopkeeper asked me where I was going, and when I told him, he gave me my money back, wouldn't let me pay – and they say the Scots are a mean bunch – that wasn't how they were with me.

At Edinburgh, I changed to the Glasgow train and then it was up the West Coast line. It began to get hilly then, mountainous. I had never seen anything like it. The mood changed as the rain ran down Glen Coe. I had read about the massacre and the whole atmosphere seemed to grow heavy and cold, but it didn't last long, the train was clicking along nicely and eventually I landed at the station in Fort William.

As I left the station, looking for a taxi which were very thin on the ground, I asked a young lad where the dock was and he showed me; he was only a young lad and he walked part of the way with me, carrying my case – I remember I asked his name and he told me it was Richard. He corrected me too, when I called him Dick, he wouldn't have that and asked me to call him Richard.

We named our son after him.

* * * * *

Far too soon our little holiday was over and we were hot on the tail of that original convoy – well, not 'hot' exactly – we had to go to Londonderry first. While we were there we heard that the dry dock from Fort William had been towed out and was going to the Far East to support the action out there. For me the priority was to get back in the old routine – focussing on the bellies of my messmates, the state of the motor launch and the efficiency of the desalination and refrigeration plants. And, I had to re-cement my relationships with those three important people – Tanky, the Naafi manager and the Cook – eventually, away we went.

After four days sailing at our top speed, which for the *Ness* spanned between 12 and 14 knots depending on the weather, we were approaching the Med when a joker in a cruiser, delivering our mail – hit us. Left a nice little gash in the side, just above the waterline and immediately below our Mess, which was where the fuel tanks were. The skipper shared his huge frustrations in a very terse exchange with the captain of the cruiser; he wanted to get going and this trip wasn't getting off to a good start; the chatter around the mess table vied between everybody having taken their eye off the ball, to bad luck, approaching a jinx. Superstition was a keen shipmate of many sailors.

We sailed cautiously into Gibraltar and headed for the repair yards.

On our first trip down to the town, we began to hear quite alarming tales about the law and order in the places we were heading for. One sailor who I spoke with had just returned and he had a weapon for sale; it was a short ebony stick, about a foot long and had a great lump of lead on one end. He said it was a genuine Zulu knobkerrie – you could slip it up your sleeve, out of sight and slide it out when you needed a little personal protection – I decided to buy it.

And then a different kind of danger raised its head as I was strolling back to the ship with a gaggle of the lads and we noticed one of the repair hands welding away merrily over the split in our hull.

"'Scuse me," one of our bunch said, "but do you know we've just refuelled?"

The welder was a cockney and thought himself a comedian; "No – you hum it and I'll try and join in on the chorus."

"It's just that the fuel tank is right under where you're welding" – we all ran off then – grinning. And so did he – until he'd got the tanks emptied and a hose spraying on the areas next to his work to cool it all down – it still looked very dodgy to me though, and I spent the day as far away from him as I could.

We had some work done on the hull too. This entailed a complete de-ammunition, which was an horrendous task – and then to cap it all, while we were at Gibraltar, Captain D, who might have been Rear Admiral Crutchley (but, equally, might not have been) spotted our paintwork was not right for the Mediterranean and ordered that we get over the side and re-paint it. That was the time that Laddie lost his brush. We got it all done in five days and set off.

It was one of the lads' birthday while we were in Gibraltar and we had a right good party around the mess table that night. The highlight of the show came from Laddie, who had added a new song to his repertoire. He could now serenade us with a tune that had just been released, but wouldn't become famous until Dean Martin took it up the charts in the mid-fifties. He had a slightly Mediterranean look about him, did Laddie, and he did try to weave an air of romance into the lyrics as he gave his all to 'You're Nobody till Somebody Loves You'. He tried and tried, and with every sip he got more and more... trying!

Haggis, I noticed, made himself scarce after the second verse. I wondered what it would take to get the Glaswegian on more friendly terms with the Derbyshire man.

Halfway into our stop at Gibraltar we started to hear about a new bomb that the Americans had – they said it would only take one of them to flatten London and they had plans to drop them on the Japanese mainland. Of course, we didn't believe a word of it. Yanks! Always bragging.

On the day we left Gibraltar, the people of Nagasaki felt the full power of the birth of the nuclear age and we ran into the worst weather that the Mediterranean had seen in twenty years. It was *rough* – rougher than I'd seen in the Atlantic. In the Stokers' Mess, even the seasoned sailors were feeling sick; I had my toaster going full belt, but not everyone was a believer in my clinically untested carbon cure. I didn't share it with some of them, in fact I took my opportunity to get my own back on those who had taken great delight in adding to my discomfort during my first days on board.

Moss has a long memory!

My tormentors had used words to try and make me feel worse – I said nothing. I just started to fry up some bubble and squeak and listened to them scuttling to the heads or to the nearest bucket – it was too rough to go up on deck.

In fact one stoker – a short sprout from London who reckoned he was summat special – was so convinced that the old girl was going to capsize in the waves he took his blankets and went to sleep up in the gun turret. Haggis came up with a plan to sneak up there, load him into one of the gun barrels and fire him into the swells – but Laddie talked us out of it – pointing out that the Londoner had such a big head he wouldn't fit, but Haggis didn't see that as a problem and punched one of his fists into the other with just a bit too much enthusiasm!

Then, probably to divert us from our evil thoughts, the Derbyshire man started one of his tales – he didn't do it often, but when he did he usually grabbed our attention, 'cos he was pretty funny.

"Hey, that reminds me," he said, "you know how scared the Gunnery Officer is of mines," he paused for dramatic effect, "well, he played a blinder today," we waited, but he started laughing – first, just his shoulders shaking, then real tears, streaming down his face.

"What?" Me.

"Come on, Laddie," Chalky.

"Tell us," Lofty.

"What's so fuckin' funny?" Bogie.

"He-he-he-he-he reckoned he'd seen a-a-a mi-mi-mine – he-he-he-he-he—"

"Come on, Laddie," Chalky.

"You gunna tell us this story or what?" Haggis.

"What's so funny?" Streak.

"Aw fuck off, Laddie – I'm off for a kip," Bogie.

Laddie exploded into eloquence.

"Gunny gets it into his head that he has to put a shot in it and blow the mine up while it's still at a distance, so he starts running around. He gets the crew to man the forward gun and he's watching his target bobbing away there – through his binoculars – it's drifting closer and closer... hooooo hoo ho ho ho."

"LADDIE!" The whole table.

He had a great smile, did Laddie, it almost split his face in half and it was a dead giveaway that he was losing it again, but then he cleared his throat, dried his eyes and carried on: "Gunny screams at the crew, '*Fire. Fire. Fire,*' and one of the lads on the gun stands up and shouts back, 'Sir, is it okay if we "*Load. Load. Load,*" first...'" splutter, giggle, snort, and Laddie had fallen off his seat and was writhing on the floor trying to hold his sides – his audience was still as statues, except Streak, who, eventually, smiled. As for the rest of us, we were all sure Laddie had a secret stash of good booze somewhere.

I guess there were too many feeling the effects of the unfriendly Med to appreciate Laddie's story.

Chalky was one of the worst affected by seasickness – he took to carrying a bucket around with him all the while – dirty sod – it stank – enough to make you wretch. He had a fair quantity of his own puke swilling around in it one time, when the Petty Officer cuffed him round the ear and told him to empty it. In defence, he played the old soldier – or old sailor – and pretended to start heaving again, but he did it a bit too well and, as he made his dry wretch into the bucket, his false teeth flew out. The PO played hell up – and made him fish them out with his fingers – yuk – just thinking about it is enough to make you barff.

Meanwhile, HMS *Ness* just kept ploughing forward and a little more than seven days later we were closing at full speed towards the minefields surrounding the entrance to Port Said and the northernmost point of the Suez Canal.

CHAPTER FOURTEEN

Up on the bridge the order is blown into the speaker tube for our speed to be reduced and the turn to starboard to begin – on the deck below, the hand of Petty Officer 'Ben' Grubb – the coxswain – goes to the telegraph and signals half-ahead, while he makes his change in course. In the engine room they hear the bell, see the indicator, a whistle blew, a winch hissed and creaked and the warps were eased, slowing the screws... and in the Stokers' Mess we felt the rhythm of the ship alter.

Grubb was one of the few sailors on board who had no worries about confronting our obnoxious Australian Number One, his claim to fame being a story about the First Lieutenant shouting an order down the speaker tube that the Petty Officer took some objection to, and queried. "Who is the idiot on the end of this tube?" came the Australian's peeved question, "Which end sir?" was Grubb's straight faced reply.

Almost immediately, we slowed down again as HMS *Ness* followed the path that was, still, being carefully cleared in the minefield at the entrance to the Suez Canal.

A nervous Virge popped in; he was jabbering about the size of the minefield and how long the job of clearing the remnants of magnetic and acoustic mines would take; he reckoned there were even some moored mines still left over from the beginning of the war.

He told us that our side had laid some of the mines to keep the Nazis out of the harbour and the enemy had laid others to catch us out and block the vital route. We all knew that already, it was the same at every port we visited, so I didn't pause from making a brew and Haggis continued to lamely polish his shoes; we didn't take much notice of Virge – so, he popped out again. I took my cuppa up on deck to watch proceedings.

In spite of the German surrender, all of the layers of protection that applied as Allied shipping entered harbour were still in place and I saw a small vessel heave into sight, the outer examination vessel. He was coming to see if we were friend or foe; we ran up our identification flags and were waved on; pretty soon we met up with the inner examination vessel, with a keen young officer commanding, and received orders to stop at the examination anchorage. This second ship looked like an old trawler, but she's flying the Royal Ensign to show she is Royal Navy and orders us to the inner examination area where we sat, I noticed, under the attention of the guns from the shore battery.

Apparently, the port's Chief Examining Officer had been expecting us to arrive with HMS *Loch Katrine* and in his log we were down as 'missing', so the little jobsworth was going, strictly, by the book. We were boarded by a naval contingent and a pilot. It only took a couple of seconds to establish our credentials and, as the keen young officer was apologising for our inconvenience, Bogie slipped up beside me, summing the situation up with, "Haven't these addle-brained twats heard that the war's over?" He stopped to take a breath, "Any danger now will come from the south. Look, the wanker even has the submarine nets still drawn too." Then he looked me directly in the eye, "Do we look like a freakin' sub, Mossy?" With that he sloped off and we headed for the boom holding the submarine nets, the boom vessel drew them apart and, given a final looking over by the boom vessel and the signal station on the shore, we were guided into port.

In front of us now the canal, leading us into Port Said, widens into a massive artery of trade and passage; it must be almost half a mile wide, shaped like an elbow. HMS *Ness* cruises slowly as we glide past the monument on the harbour walls, to our starboard. The pilot is in charge and posts a team of sharp-eyed lookouts to ensure there are no collisions as we slide noiselessly through streams of traffic. We see tugboats fussing over their charges, impatient merchantmen straining to find one of the crane-bedecked wharfs to unload their wares or secure permission for a passage to sprint south towards their final destination. The water zigzags with ferry boats and fishing boats of all shapes and sizes, while skiffs scurry about on nefarious business and, stonily, above them all, posted on the sea wall, native Egyptians, fishing poles in hand, try to catch their supper. We sailed on through a turmoil of waterborne activity to, eventually, tie up alongside the quay in one of the side docks behind the green-domed Suez Canal Authority building – it was dust, energy, flies and heat, with water and concrete walls, ships, boats and cranes swinging everywhere.

My first view of the port left me feeling that the whole place was out on some kind of unnatural limb, flung there by the people of Egypt to form a gateway from the Med to the Red Sea.

Port Said, it seemed, was a very rich city. It looked to be laid out in a maze of squares – what the yanks call 'blocks' – of buildings of all architectural types, the rudest of which were home-made corrugated iron sheds, the grandest were broad streets with fine stucco architecture and towering domes.

* * * * *

We were held on board an hour or two longer than normal, before all of our papers and passes were delivered – and with them came our first orders to stay on the main streets if we did want to disembark – I did – I had a customer to meet, so I had to go ashore. I usually had Haggis or Laddie and Chalky as company but this time I was out on my own; my partner, the Naafi manager, had set up a meeting for me with an entrepreneurial American sailor who wanted a load of cigarettes and I had plenty of them.

Cigarettes were a very acceptable currency in naval circles and this guy, apparently, would take everything I could deliver and... I was being a bit selfish; I hadn't asked the lads along because, if I had, I would then have been honour-bound to share some of my action.

My rendezvous was by a formal park, with almost English gardens decorated with lush green bushes sculpted by casual topiary and tall, brown palm trees; the park sat at the far end of a main street that sprang at a 90-degree angle to the bustling dockside road.

The quayside was full of vehicles dashing back and forth in clouds of dust, exhaust smoke and diesel fumes; some were the dull coloured trucks of the military convoys, honking their horns to demand passage; some were the flatbed lorries of private contractors, mostly open topped, but all colours and types, their loads covered in threadbare tarpaulins. There were carts drawn by pairs of horses which were enveloped in clouds of flies and rancid odour; they were accompanied by mule carts and handcarts dragged along by sweating locals.

At the water's edge, swarms of water-boys with skin like sun-blackened leather were clad only in folds of dingy fabric that formed their trunks; they splashed and toiled to fill their buckets and bags with undrinkable water that they carted off to who-knows-where. The docks themselves were no less frantic, with snaking temporary walkways atop inflated tubes that bobbed up and down on the water and snaked dangerously in the wake of the larger cruisers and destroyers. There were small boats, the size of the whaler, loaded with packs and barrels, squabbling in threes and fours to do their deals with the merchant ships posted all around.

I saw a couple of elegant Arab dhows sailing across the broad waterway, heading for their fishing grounds in the Mediterranean, the light glinting on the scimitar-curved sails as the sun rose. I saw powerful motor launches, carrying important sea captains, their propellers churning a surface shared by fleets of rowing boats occupied by three or four matelots who were on their nervous way to sample the joys of Port Said. There were naval boats, under full oar, carrying officers from a variety of navies on their way to secure their new orders – and all around, in the air or floating along the water's surface, flocks of ruthless seagulls dipped and plundered or played in the wind.

112

From the stern railing on the eastern side of the canal was the magnificent vista provided by the twin minarets of the Port Fouad Mosque. From the forward railing between the buildings was the station of the light railway. What interested me more though was the view from the starboard railing of HMS *Ness*, where I could see the street I needed. It was a wide street, lined on each side with a variety of buildings: from modern-looking apartment blocks, four or five storeys tall, to old town houses with grand timber balconies on all floors, while single-storey villas with gardens surrounded by tall stucco walls took their turn to line the pavement. Halfway along the street it widened into a diamond-shaped square that contained a tiny circular raised kerb, painted black and white and with small arrows attached to encourage the motorists to go right. Springing from the raised circle was a man-sized concrete umbrella, a sunshade, beneath which stood a policeman in full uniform, whistle in his mouth, arms waving as he directed the flow of traffic.

Here and there, amongst the buildings, solitary palms waved gently. The whole disparity of architecture and greenery combined to give the city a distinctive charm.

Closest to the docks, the pavements of my street were covered with regiments of arches in white stucco that mirrored the front of the Authority building. Amongst this splendour sat wooden Wild West-style covered boardwalks strewn with merchandise and their battalions of sellers – and formal porticos in hand-carved stone that wouldn't have looked out of place in the City of London. I noticed with some small concern, the shadow-black side streets that headed off the main street in regular and neat right-angled intervals; I breathed in deeply and fingered the knobkerrie hidden up my sleeve. Nothing left for it – time to disembark for my business meeting.

On the way to my rendezvous I began to feel the full glare of a less than friendly populace; in fact I was beginning to feel vulnerable and was wishing I'd had my mates along with me after all.

Eventually I reached the spot where we were to meet, and there was no sign of my customer. No other military men at all in fact, just the hurrying Arabs in flowing white robes and, almost in the background, a thrall of street urchins that seemed to be sucked out of the shadows by their passage before being drawn back into their hiding places by an invisible elastic force.

I stood around with my little brown Navy-issue suitcase full of contraband cigarettes, probably looking nervous, certainly rocking from one foot to the other and very definitely catching the attention of the locals. After twenty minutes he still hadn't appeared and I'd had enough so I started to walk briskly back to the ship, trying to transmit an air of certain confidence and yet feeling very tight around the anal region. The first sign of real trouble came when I slowed down by a stall to look at some sandals that I thought Freda would like. I'd just popped the press-stud on the pocket in my white belt to get the British coins that would pay for them when a very broad Arab gentleman, in flowing robes, pushed his way in front of me. He thrust his hand palm upward towards me and spat out in a thickly accented tongue probably the only English words he knew: "Money. Give me money."

I responded in true Englishman abroad fashion: "Sod off." At which point he gripped each side of his robes, opening them to expose a beltful of very sharp and wicked-looking knives. The danger implied saw me flow on a stream of released adrenalin into the Moss of old and the thought flashed through my mind, what a nice set of knives he had and how I might have me one of them. While I was thinking this, an altogether baser side of my personality noticed he had one hand gripping each side of his robe and was thus unable to defend himself while I slipped the knobkerrie from its position hidden in my sleeve into my right palm and wacked him a good-un on his left ear.

He went spark out, didn't even wail – blood everywhere. I decided against taking his knife belt. A decision which may soon turn out to be a mistake because as the fully robed and better-heeled of his Arabic brethren moved smartly away from the scene, like so many pristine white sails tacking into the wind in a jaunty boat race, his prone body was set upon by a flock of street urchins who had sprung from the shadows like so much sweat from a runner's armpit.

Pretty soon, his whole arsenal of blades had passed into the hands of new owners.

I stepped over him and continued my walk back to the ship with an air of confident poise, travelling a full twenty yards before the mist cleared from my mind as I realised that I hadn't bought Freda's sandals. I turned and watched a circle of locals bristling around the knife-carrying Arab, relieving him of everything that they could easily prise from him. Some of the nastier-looking ones were eyeing me hungrily. The silence of the moment dissolved while a growing banter of grunting voices built in volume and I decided to buy the sandals another day.

I had no idea that the day's adventures were only just starting – the crowd swelled, like a wave, but it stayed close to the fallen Arab – I didn't – I was gone – down the shaded pavements. I launched across the diamond shaped square, which had now grown into enormous proportion, feeling very exposed.

I was sweating and cold and unusually angry as I regained the covered pavement and marched purposefully towards the dock. My back felt as though it was being speared by hundreds of eyes while I moved ever closer to the outline of HMS *Ness*'s rigging that I could see in the distance; by now there were numbers of sailors mingled with the locals, so I took a deep breath and slowed to a more dignified pace.

Then, just in front of me, I saw two of the newcomers to our mess, strolling carelessly along. They had joined us at Gibraltar, were about 19 years old, came from the East End and thought they knew everything (I wonder who they reminded me of?).

As I watched them, a couple of street ragamuffins fell in with them – one on each side – giving them plenty of chat and then a very pretty girl joined them. Bait! The group stopped and I saw the locals pointing to a shadowy side street which all five of them headed for. A bad feeling visited me and my ears pricked up; I realised I still had my knobkerrie in my hand and swung it briskly in front of me – I was shaking a bit from my recent ruck and, I must admit, I was feeling slightly shocked by the thought that I might actually have done the knife man some permanent damage. Automatically, I lengthened my step.

By the time I reached the side street the two youngsters were in a lot of trouble. The girl had disappeared and there were eight or nine of these scruffy street creatures circling the young stokers, pushing them and shoving them and grabbing at their belts and pockets – one of them had been relieved of his cap and it wouldn't be long before they both lost their money. Maybe more. I glanced back down the road and a straggling group of around six or seven miscreants seemed to be sloping towards me, walking down the shady side of the street, something metal, like a freshly stolen knife, glinting in their hands.

Now I surprised myself, especially as I had a case full of cigarettes that they could have stolen. I stepped into the side street and waded in, waving me knobkerrie around and yelling like a sergeant major. I felt the knob of my kerrie catch one of them a good whack. I think it was the one that had stolen the hat, but I wasn't sure because I had my eyes tight shut! The next thing was a yell from one of my messmates as they tried to dodge the Zulu skull-cracker that I was whirling around like a Dervish and when I did open my eyes it was to see the attackers loping away like a pack of scared dogs. I puffed out me chest in a 'that's seen them off' kind of way!

Mossy, the hero! I was full of adrenalin and it took a hefty tug on my arm by one of the lads to get me to join them striding rapidly back to the head of the side street, where a skinny crowd was quickly gathering to see what was happening. I suddenly realised that I had dropped my little brown case, full of cigarettes, in the melee and it now lay on the mucky street, half a dozen paces behind us. One or two of the knife wielders had joined the crowd crossing our way out of the street and more were coming. I stopped. The lads grabbed and cajoled me to get out of there. But... I couldn't leave my contraband; I'd been too long saving my ration and I'd done too many side deals to collect them all. A stream of Cockney abuse melded with the growling of the crowd to accompany every step I took back towards my case. Dark skinny bodies darted in and out of the black shadows towards my prize. Bits of me tightened and twitched. My hands reached the case just ahead of a horde of bony fingers all intent on grabbing the same thing.

I craned my neck to see the lads, who, credit due, had followed me back and were now picking me bodily off the ground and carrying me back up the street. I held my case cradled in my arms like a baby lest the lid spring open and I lose some of my booty. The crowd ebbed and surged like a breathing beast. I grunted and chuntered and my crewmates put me down just before we reached the mass of ragged bodies reaching greasily towards us.

I shoved at the horde of delta-dwellers, pushing and snapping at them with my strangely impotent African weapon. I was unusually aggressive and wondered if the war was bringing out a nasty streak in me as the three of us drove through the throng to regain the main road – and still the crowd closed around us, steel shivered in the sun. At the very edge of the crowd I spotted the Arab who had been the previous owner of the knives before I had bent his ear with my weapon. He looked bloodied and bruised, probably a bit deaf too, but at least he wasn't 'dead' as I had begun to think and that was something of a relief. In fact, he wasn't interested in us at all; he was more interested in prising his knives from the wiry hands that now held them.

Suddenly he lost all interest in his quest, turned abruptly and he, along with the whole mob of people, simply melted away as two Egyptian policemen, pistols drawn, stepped silently towards us; they gave us a scowl, perhaps of disappointment that we had emerged unscathed; seeing the crowd disperse they holstered their weapons and continued, Dixon-like, along their beat.

The three of us were stepping tidily back onto the harbour road when I noticed the lump of Zulu lead – which, I had been assured by 'he who had sold me my knobkerrie', had been hand-attached and fused into the very body of the wood, forever. Probably in an ancient tribal ceremony performed by the village elders, with the aid of a troop of nubile young virgins, all of which carried the significance that as long as your lead was fixed to your knobkerrie so would you remain strong and fertile – it was a 'plenty of lead in your pencil' kind of thing.

Anyway, my lump of lead was no longer there.

One of the lads told me he had seen it fly off and disappear through the window of a local house when I first swung the stick – the blow I had felt being my knob-less-kerrie striking the same house's wife's freshly pegged washing, breaking her line and spreading her huge cotton unmentionables in the dirt.

They tried to tell me of the 'ginormous', rounded housewife, her hair in curlers, a nose that de Gaulle would have envied – with warts – and underneath, straggly tufts of hair sprouting from her full upper lip, who came pounding towards us on wobbly legs in half-rolled stockings, blue varicose veins throbbing all the way down them to her flabby feet, which were clad in worn-out woollen slippers. Said housewife had burst from the black hole that was her front door, with my lump of lead in one hand, a broken dish in the other and a shrill stream of colloquial Egyptian vernacular spewing from her gap-toothed mouth, in which rested a burned-down cigarette – black and tallow-looking.

My two young shipmates reckoned that it was the housewife's appearance and the action of her enormous, unrestricted, pendulous breasts, scything beneath the fabric of her voluminous garments, rather than my bold and selfless charge, that had scared the attackers off.

Such. Utter. Nonsense.

Our walk back to the ship was silent after that and, just as we reached the dock gates, and just as I had completed my transaction to sell to the two young lads five packs of fags each – I heard a real commotion stampeding along the road we had just strolled down. In the lead was Virge, closely attended by Oppo and another bespecta-cled telegraphist, called George Wigg; they were being pursued by a howling mob of angry locals.

In true English Gentleman fashion I stepped forward at once and pointed my leadless stick, sword-like in the mob's direction at the same time intoning: "Halt, you ne'er-do-wells."

CHAPTER FIFTEEN

My selfless action had stopped the mob in their tracks. Well, that and the bullets whistling past their ears from the rifles being levelled at them by the guards on the gate.

When he had – finally – got his breath back, a very shaken Virge explained that he and his two mates had tried to enter the Kasbah, when a gang of eight or nine street urchins had rushed out of a side street and before they could blink our lads were being charged at by a growing mob and had to run for their lives. They said the crowd had been stirred by a ginormous, rounded matriarch stampeding behind them – her hair in curlers, a nose that de Gaulle would have envied – with warts reminiscent of a Shakespearian witch – and straggly tufts of hair sprouting from her upper lip. With her flabby feet in woollen slippers, she was spurring them on with a soliloquy of foul and colloquial Egyptian vernacular, which spewed from her gap-toothed mouth. She was waving, what looked like, a huge pair of white unmentionables in one hand and a lump of lead in the other; her charge had urged the urchins forward.

Those mobs were growing more serious by the day, and as the port began to get more and more rowdy the army sent out police patrols of their own – a squad of five MPs were attacked by one mob and took fatal casualties. Without its plum-bum my weapon lost its appeal so, I sold the ebony stick – sans lead – to a seaman who liked to whittle and took to the colour of the wood.

The following day we set off down the Suez Canal and into one of the hottest places I have ever been. The heatwave started while we were waiting in the Bitter Lake for some huge American battlecruiser to pass by and it was while we were there that it came to pass that it was our turn for the Parrot.

* * * * *

118

Now, obviously, it's not unheard of for a naval warship to have a parrot aboard and ever since one of the more mischievous sub-lieutenants had bought a Red-tailed African Grey from a pet shop in Port Said, the *Ness* was no different. The difference was that despite assurances from the Egyptian pet shop owner – sworn on the fertility in his favourite camel's testicles – that this particular parrot was the best talker available, the bird remained tight-lipped – not even name, rank and serial number.

The officers had it in their mess for a day or two before they gave up trying – it hadn't made a sound – their steward then told them that he knew someone who was good with birds and they gave it to Virge.

I should just say that Virge – after his deflowering in Geordie-land we had changed his nickname to 'Grassy' for a week or two – but he had now gone back to Virge. He would tell his mother that it was because he still hadn't intercepted any enemy signals and therefore was a virgin in that sense. The truth of it was that whenever he was speaking to a US Navy Wren and they asked him his name he would give them his nickname, the usual reply was: "Oh, is that short for Virgil, there was a Virgil in our semester at college."

That's when he put on his best little-boy-lost look and told them it was a nickname given to him by his shipmates and it stood for Virgin! Well, he didn't need to say any more – they assumed the assumption and their female instincts took over as they helped him to change his assumed situation. Quite a lot of US Navy lasses notched Virge's virginity on their bedposts without him ever telling them a word of a lie.

What I am trying to say is that the steward had got it right in saying that Virge was good with birds – or 'chicks' as they were then. He'd just got the wrong meaning of the word – but, that's how Polly, the Red-tailed African Grey, had appeared in the Stokers' Mess – the telegraphist was desperate for our help, the thing didn't have a cage and he couldn't have it crapping all over his delicate electrical connections, so he dumped it on us.

Any road, here's how the story went – in those warm climes, as you can imagine, it wasn't unusual for us to have a number of fans going – to swish the stinking hot air about a bit and convince we ratings that it wasn't quite so unbearable.

Unfortunately for the parrot, we had one fan without a guard and the Red-tailed African Grey found this out one day when it flew into the blades and, amongst most of its other feathers and a huge quantity of down, it lost its red tail.

We could hear it squawking from the engine room, and when we made it back to the Mess, it looked like the floor was covered in a grey feather carpet. Quite remark-ably, the bird was otherwise okay and, having made its first noise it was quick to pick up many more, so, we stokers could take great credit in teaching it to speak. We never did explain how it had changed from a bird of thick and lustrous plumage – into one that looked plucked and ready for the pot – as usual, the officers blamed me and made innumerable references to me wanting the pigeon-chested thing for my cooking pot.

The thing is – Polly 'escaped' one day as we were slipping into the Red Sea – you see, we had these air scoops fitted to the portholes, to scoop in any breeze, and just as we passed the port of Suez, one of ours fell off and – with the scuttle wide open – left a clear and open orifice.

Seeing this clear hole as a chance to escape, the African 'Bald' (as it now was) went for the hole, in what it saw as its flight to freedom. What Polly hadn't sussed out was that for a bird to fly it needs wing feathers; we rushed to the porthole to save it... being lithe and swift, Bogie got there first and... was too late!

He started a running commentary, "It's hit the water – ouch – looks dazed – it has sunk... no, it's back on the surface... it's sinking – it's swimming... you lot... it's..."

When he turned round he saw he was talking to an empty room. The rest of us had sprinted for the ladder heading to the deck. Up the rungs six deep, through the door we all headed for the side and – hanging over the railing – the last we saw of it, the bird was doing a pretty spirited breaststroke heading for the coast in a sea that was as blue and calm as a postcard. And, yet... despite the evidence of our own eyes... still... I was accused of adding it to the Acting Rabbit – and – as much as I swore that my culinary creation was free of parrot, I found myself throwing the contents of that particular stew away and washing the pan out for the first time in three months.

*   *   *   *   *

Now we were in the Red Sea; what a difference to the grey and angry Atlantic. I came down with a case of prickly heat and the urge to scratch was unbearable; eventually, it got so bad that I decided to throw in the towel and visit 'Bones'. I came across him on deck, he was walking like a bow-legged cowboy and wearing a pair of Naval Issue white shorts and I noticed the angry red rash coating the insides of both thighs. He'd rubbed a load of white cream on them but the way he was walking was a very clear indication that his cure was about as much use as morals in a Turkish brothel. He was suffering just the same as me and I guessed that if he couldn't cure himself, he wasn't going to be any use to anybody else – i.e. me.

Instead the cure came from our own ranks – "Seawater," says Chalky, in his serious Hull accent, "that'll cure it."

The weather was turning and at this time the Red Sea was covered in energetic white tops stirred up by a poker-hot sandy wind that felt like it was blowing straight from the sphincter of Satan.

Rather uncharitably, because I was expecting Chalky to give us his one and only anecdote, I said: "Oh, here he goes again with his: '*I* know what it's like to be fully immersed in seawater, when I was just a lad I went out on the trawler, where my dad was Mate. We were on the North Sea and the weather started playing up. My dad had just signalled for me to go below, and I was weaving across the deck when, out of nowhere, our little boat was hit by a huge wave that washed me straight overboard... Luckily the next wave washed me straight back onboard ship and my dad never even knew I'd been in the sea'." It was Chalky's party piece and it was only ever believed by his mother – and me when I wanted something from him – today was not such a day.

So, instead of simply asking him how he expected me to immerse myself in seawater, my brain started to hold its own assumption party – I assumed that he expected me to let him hang me over the side in a bosun's chair and lower me into the water. I may have told you already, I'm not a lover of being immersed in water. I was not in a good mood.

I barked at him like a... like a... like a mardy stoker: "If you think I'm going for a dip in the sea while it's this choppy, you've the brains of a peanut!"

"Oooooo," the response came from a little knot of resting stokers, to indicate that they found my reply a tad petulant. "Of course," says Chalky, "you could do that," pause, "but..." another pause, "if it was me... I'd open the saltwater stopcock next to the shower and fill a bucket and... tip it over myself."

It's amazing how fast you can change tack if you're feeling like a twit. I followed the suggestion – a saltwater shower from a bucket – and while it didn't exactly *work* – it did ease the itching.

"Don't say thank you!" Chalky hadn't finished with me yet.

"I won't." This'll stop him, it was delivered with as much seriousness as I could muster. "Do you think I'll get a medal for it?"

The CPO broke us all up when his dry slow voice joined in with, "What do you think this is, the American Navy? – they might give you a Purple Heart for that nappy rash – King George will just slap you in irons for shedding unnecessary flakes of your scabby hide over one of his ship's decks." CPO had a wonderful turn of phrase.

At the bottom of the Red Sea we turned sharp left and aimed for the port of Aden; the terrain reminded me a lot of Gibraltar, the high peninsula and its position so close to the entry to a land-bound sea.

*   *   *   *   *

By now the urgency was draining rapidly out of our mission, the Yanks' A-bombs had brought an announcement from the Japanese government that they were about to surrender, so the initial reason for our cruise was evaporating like the bodies of Japanese civilians in Hiroshima and Nagasaki. It has always been a subject of debate in our family – should they or shouldn't they have unleashed that horror on a civilian population – was it just a case of Uncle Sam getting his tackle out, slapping it on the table and boasting, mine's bigger than your shrivelled little yellow set, boys!

On balance I think it actually saved lives, because battling an army as professional and committed – not to say cruel – as the Japanese, through the jungles of Malaysia, would have been a real nightmare. We could still be at it today!

above: Calm – my expectations of the sea were moulded by year after year on holiday at
   Cleethorpes – and Charlie assured me the waves rarely reached your knees. I notice he's
   got his trousers rolled up a bit higher mind you

top: HMS Ness *in calm seas*

above: Tanker in flames after attack

above left: Preparing to pull alongside and take off crew

above right: Survivors climbing from the sea

below: Convoy assembling

top: *Sunderland flying over convoy*

above: *Running down a submarine at sea*

top: Submarine being attacked by warships

above: Depth charge exploding

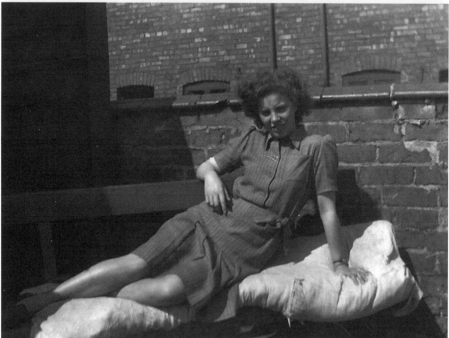

top: At sea – in my overalls

above: Freda the pin-up

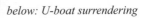

*left: Statue of Captain Walker
at Pier Head Liverpool*

below: U-boat surrendering

top: My crewmates at Londonderry – I am missing off this section – Chalky got his face on it though – row two far left and Streak three from left, with Lofty to Streak's left – Captain Steel is in the centre and on his left hand side, with his hat tilted the wrong way, my favourite Australian, the first lieutenant, Hamster is to his left

above: Sailing away, HMS Ness

CHAPTER SIXTEEN

We had to hang around Aden for a few days to wait for a flotilla of small craft to assemble into convoy formation; these were mainly landing craft heading for Malaya, and we were back in action following the convoy procedures that we knew all too well. The atmosphere in Aden was quite relaxed, thanks in the main to the large British influence, so trips into town were happier occasions.

Then something happened that enabled me to really strengthen my relationship with Tanky – here's the scenario – the *Ness* was re-provisioning and he'd just bought an assignment of lamb carcases from a local butcher – he was supervising two Arabs, who had just finished hanging them in the refrigeration room as I slid gracefully down the ladder. Shivering a bit, the two Arab-looking chaps came out and stood by the far wall muttering softly to each other.

"Nah then[9], Tank, how's it swingin'?" I rejoined cheerfully

"Hello, Raymon' – fuckin' awful." Tanky was sitting at a small table miserably shuffling his paperwork when I walked up and instantly perched myself on the edge of the table, casting my eye over the meat and wearing a 'what can I get for the Stokers' Mess' kind of attitude.

I saw that *my* refrigeration plant was full to the gunnels with the carcases of... well... of what looked to be... greyhounds!

Tanky kept his voice low: "What do you think of them, Raymon'?"

I had been tipped off by Scouse that something was not kosher when he told me that there were locals carrying the meat on board; the carcases were so skinny that the butcher's assistants had been able to carry one under each arm. It was the Liverpudlian's tip-off that had brought me down here. Now, it was obvious that Tanky was a tad on the nervous side, so I decided on a sensitive and diplomatic reply, "What are they,

---

9   'Nah then' – It's a traditional Scunthorpe greeting.

Tank – greyhounds?" Today, I would have said *anorexic* greyhounds but there was no such thing as anorexia in those days – so I didn't.

Tanky 'could be' very good at buying decent meat – he was very good at 'selling' it too. We had a long-standing arrangement where, for a few gulpers, he would let me have the best cuts – but it looked to my seasoned eye as though, this time, the flanker he was trying to pull had backfired badly and his suppliers had got the better of him. "I know," he whispered, "they're rubbish, aren't they? I can see me getting a real bollocking for buying them."

I knew what he was saying; the British Navy has this thing about feeding its sailors fresh meat to fight off scurvy. We even still got a drink of lime juice every day for the same reason. So 'the Tank' could be in real bother for provisioning with meat of an indiscriminate lineage; in fact there was more meat on the breast of that bald parrot than on one of these 'lamb' carcases.

Time for a quick negotiation: "What did he give you?"

Tanky didn't even try to hide his bribe; he uncovered some of the finest beef steaks I'd seen since Charlie sent some black-market Aberdeen Angus sirloin with Freda, when she visited me for a few days at Lowton St Mary. "Chuff me, Tank, that's beautiful."

"I know – it's the Sultan's private stock."

A little antenna was twitching somewhere at the back of my brain saying there was more, so I asked: "And?"

"What?"

"And? What else did he give you?" He pulled the covering on his secret stash a bit further back and four bottles of finest Irish malt winked up at me. He hadn't finished, "And tonight I get a date with the most beautiful girl in Aden."

I snorted, "You better just pray that she isn't beautiful in the same way that those carcases hanging in my fridge are prime lamb!" I looked hard at him, "Boy, is this gunna cost you."

"Can you get me out of it?"

"It will cost you half your bribe – except the girl, mind you, you can forget her when I've done with these chaps. So, half the bribe and one of those sides of prime beef you've been hiding from everybody in the back left-hand corner."

"Raymon' – that's too much, you are robbing me."

"Where did that pained Jewish accent come from? Stop moaning. I'll pay you for the beef in the usual way; now, do we have a deal?" And, in my mind I could also see some of his prices for our normal transactions dissolving from gulpers into the meanest of sippers.

Just at that point another Arab came out of the head, smiling and grinning and being altogether a bit too smug.

In reply to my 'super-fair' offer to him, Tanky just hissed; I held out my hand and we shook on it. Just then I had no idea what I was going to do, but it had to be down to me because right then Tanky was in a complete funk – he could see nothing coming to him but the very worst that the Royal Navy could visit on him. And that would have been pretty bad.

The boss Arab wore pristine white robes that flowed about him when he walked and the band around his head cover was decorated with what looked to be a very expensive brooch; his smile showed flashes of gold teeth and he had an air of complete superiority. He had his own spelling for this war – p.r.o.f.i.t.

He joined the other two and their smiles calmed down a bit when they saw the looks on our faces and realised that they had to come past us to get to the ladder, which was their way out.

"What did you pay?" I whispered to Tanky – he told me he'd paid what he would expect to pay for a proper lamb or mutton carcase – in cash – to the boss, while the other two unloaded the carcases, the first three of which were fine examples, then they'd swapped paperwork and money and the rest of the delivery were the 'greyhounds'. I told him to stop waffling and tell me the amount in pounds, shillings and pence. He did.

Our three Arabs were sidling around in all directions, smiling at us and saying something complimentary about the British Navy – Nelson – Battle of the Nile – Captain Cook and all that; time to act.

"Have you told him we're not happy?" I asked, in a whisper just loud enough for the three of them to hear.

"I did," was his miserable reply, "Abdul just brought out the receipt I'd given him and pointed to the words, just above my signature, that confirmed I had examined the meat and was satisfied with the quality."

What to do – we couldn't involve officers, or Tanky would catch it. "Haggis is just outside," I said to Tanky, "nip up, tell him that Herbie said there's some action coming his way and lead him to the top of the gangplank. If he's in one of his arsy moods and won't go with you, find a few of the other lads instead." He looked a bit phased but when I finished off with, "And if these three come out without me, which is doubtful, tell him not to let them off. See if you can get Chalky and Lofty too." He started to walk away, "Tank," I hissed, "don't let these three off the ship."

While Tanky climbed up the ladder leading to the deck he looked as if he was carrying the full weight of my old midwife straddled, one leg each side of his neck, on top of his shoulders. I, meanwhile, was smiling back at the three providers of – whatever the meat was – with one of Charlie's wicked gleams in my eyes.

I thought I'd better start off the negotiations on a diplomatic level: "What the devil *are* these?" I asked.

They were on to me straight away and decided on intimidation.

Boss: "Of your business it is none. We have receipt."

Minion one: "Other sailor Captain of Provisions."

Minion two: "Not you," threatening scowl, "goodbye."

Nice try, no cigar. I had moved from the table and was standing on the bottom step of the ladder; they needed to be past me to get out. Fancy Jack actually put his hand on the decorative dagger that he wore on his belt – cheeky tosser. Now he was in for it – an idea came – I was back in the days of me and the stage-door-johnnies. I gave them my biggest smile – and then they got my question again, with a twist: "These carcases look like really fine meat... I think you gave us a really fair price for them," pause to watch them glance, in a bewildered way, around at each other, "we're going to sell them on to the Sailors' Mess," biggest smile I can muster, "so it would be handy to know what they are..."

They started rabbiting on about the finest Arabian lamb but I just kept talking, "Are they hill goat? Or are they dog? Or are they some kind of scabby cat perhaps?" Now my smile dissolved and a bead of worry ran down each face, but I put my smile back and climbed up the ladder, beckoning for them to follow me onto the deck. They hadn't a clue what I was up to. At that point, neither had I, but it would come to me.

We got to the top of the gangplank and now I was alongside the one with the money. There was no sign of Chalky, but Haggis had gone along with the request and he and Lofty were lazily blocking the gangplank – while Tanky was standing close by, he wasn't going to be much use, his mind was still blanked out with worry and he was wondering what was happening – as were our Arabs.

It came to me – in a flash of inspiration! I casually wafted my hand towards Haggis and Lofty.

"These gentlemen need to see your gangplank tickets," I told them sweetly.

In response came a tripartite babble of foreign language, so I ignored it.

"You need a ticket," I smiled, "you must each have a ticket to use the Royal Navy's gangplank."

Money man frowned his deepest frown. As for Haggis, even though he hadn't a clue what was happening until it happened, he was on my wavelength and, in case one of the Arabs slipped by us, he had positioned, at the bottom of the gangplank, Chalky and Streak, the only being I knew with less meat on him than the refrigerated carcases. Beyond them, on the dockside, was a pristine truck, sign-written with the butcher's name in English and Arabic text. The back doors were open and Bogie was nonchalantly swinging his legs from his seat on the tailgate and dragging ceaselessly at an evil-looking cigarette, flicking ash deep into the vehicle.

The price of each of the three tickets, I informed them, would be one sixth of what Tanky had paid them for the – meat.

I will tell you this, if you really want to experience a torrent of abuse, try what we were doing with a dodgy Aden butcher and his staff. Your Yemeni coast-dweller is superb at stringing together filthy words that are a colourful mixture of Arabic and English. So much so that Haggis got it into his head that they were out of order; he nodded to Lofty and they picked up the nearest one by an ankle and wrist and hung him over the side of the ship with his free leg lashing about like a belly dancer's arms.

I switched position to the top of the gangplank and pulled Tanky alongside me; he was beginning to calm down. "You see," I told the stressing trio, "if you don't use the gangplank, you have to go over the side."

Haggis was grinning fit to bust; he had always wanted to throw somebody over the side – and his enthusiasm for the task was becoming infectious. The swinger's two mates caught it and their toned tans paled to a greenish grey.

It was at this point that the officer of the watch decided he had better get involved, which could have been a real nuisance – in fact, it could kybosh the whole thing.

"Stoker First Class Moss," he yelled from his position up in the bridge and then paused like Ant & Dec before they inform some reality show contestant that they have been evicted; we all held our breath. He decided to continue, "If that Arabic gentleman falls onto the quay from this height and a single drop of his blood splashes the hull you'll be hanging over that side for a week repainting it."

I smiled. He was an ally. "Can we drop him over the starboard side then, sir? Into the water?" He considered this for a while: "Yes – but chuck him out as far as you can, just in case he comes to pieces or something."

It took another few minutes and even I thought Haggis was going to chuck the first one in the sea.

At that point other sailors were wandering across to see what was happening and some were congregating on the dock wanting to come back on board ship. Bogie was keeping them at bay, redirecting them to another access with a few well-delivered Yorkshire invectives. When I saw Laddie drifting towards us I took a deep breath – here was a natural peacemaker arriving and we wanted these Arabs believing they were anything but safe. Luckily an old ally popped up when the officer of the watch ordered Laddie to join him on the bridge; he took every step up there with his neck craned to see what we were doing.

The chap being manhandled by Haggis screeched and that's when the Boss-man realised that he'd be next, and chose to shut up – and then he gave up. He came to realise that his scam hadn't come off, they knew that we knew that they had been trying to swindle the glorious British Navy and so, they handed back to Tanky half of the money he had originally given them and 'bought' their 'tickets' to use the gangplank.

Boss-man didn't give up completely though and having taken three steps down the gangplank, he turned to Tanky to ask for his bribe back, but the Captain of Provisions had disappeared down the deck ladder and was hiding in the refrigerator behind all of the skinny carcases he had just bought. He had half his money back and an excuse that while the sheep were a little thin, he had been able to negotiate a 50 per cent discount – he was desperately hoping that the Purser would see that as a good deal.

The Butcher of Aden let me know what fate awaited me if I ever set foot in his town again, but as that wouldn't be for another few months, I reckoned they would have calmed down by then!

We ate well around our mess table that night with steaks as thick as your thumb, and we had a real self-congratulatory debate centred on how everyone had instinctively known how to play his part. The officer of the watch asked no awkward questions, Haggis had deployed his mates to perfection with no time to ask what I was doing – I had no time to tell even Tanky what I was thinking, in fact I didn't know myself until I made it up while events unfolded and yet everyone did exactly what was needed.

We all put it down to the naval-training practices of putting you in a situation and giving you every chance to sort it out for yourself without the interference of a trainer.

CHAPTER SEVENTEEN

Our bellies were full, I'd been 'persuaded' to join my pals in a few celebratory glasses of Irish malt on the aft deck – so, as one who gets hammered on the merest sniff of the stuff – I was being particularly silly – when Laddie turned up I asked him to give us a song and I joined him in the choruses. I never was a particularly harmonious singer but I did think that Haggis's action, in stuffing me inside a sea locker until I promised to stop singing, was a tad less than friendly. As for his helper in that dreadful deed – the man leaning against the door to ensure I couldn't escape... Laddie... well – what can I say? Is this what it took for Haggis to really review his dislike of Laddie – and for Laddie to abandon his peacemaking habits? – one thing was for sure, that was the last time I'd offer to accompany him on one of his tunes! I guess a bunch of young Englishmen living for so long in such close quarters was bound to cause a few bad tempers... but that was no excuse, not for Laddie... it might have been if it was me... as you are about to see.

Any road, we had some fun and our Acting Rabbit was guaranteed to have the best meat on the ship – from one of the juiciest beef carcasses on board – for the duration of the voyage.

We sailed next morning from Aden, escorting the convoy of small vessels on their way to the Indian port of Cochin and, on this leg of our journey, we overtook the ship that was towing the dry dock that we had last seen in Fort William.

During this stint of our trip, any need for the landing craft in our convoy disappeared when the Japanese finally signed the document of surrender.

From India, we sailed down to Colombo, the main port in Ceylon, arriving in mid-September 1945. If you don't know that it's called Sri Lanka now, I am not telling you. I will share this with you though; I do think it's a shame they changed the name – I mean Ceylon, a lovely name, just slips off the tongue like honeyed butter. Sri Lanka on the other hand, well, to me, it sounds like you're clearing your throat – maybe my Scunthonian pronunciation doesn't do it justice.

Haggis and Chalky and me saw a bit of a sight when we went for a walk in the countryside by the docks in Colombo. Well, first of all we heard it – this kind of sour wailing, which caught our attention and diverted our eyes to a packed-earth clearing amongst some sparse trees. First we saw one of the Sumatrans; he was quite a tall lad and had his back to us, his hair was greasy black and he wore nothing on his upper torso, his skin had been almost blackened by the sun. From waist to ankles he wore a kind of scruffy wrap-around skirt thing, like the bottom half of a sarong, and no shoes. The wailing was coming from the other side of him. Chalky and I stood on the dirt path straining to see what he was looking at. Not Haggis though, off he marched towards the bloke. When he reached him, he laughed, turned to us and beckoned, "Hey, you two, come and look at this."

So we did.

The wailing was coming from a quartet of pipers, sitting cross-legged on the ground, in a semi-circle. They were dressed the same as the lad except their sarongs were more colourful. Their pipes were long thin things with a bulbous sphere a couple of inches from the mouth end. Three of them wore turbans, but the fourth was bare headed. Rising up and swaying in front of them were half a dozen cobras, about four feet long, each one with its eyes fixed firmly on one of the pipers. Another cobra lay stretched out on the ground; he was a biggy, all of ten feet in length, but he wasn't taking any part; he looked to be asleep.

"Snake charmers," said Chalky.

"Aye," said Haggis, "ask them if they know where we can get a beer."

He didn't seem impressed.

In Colombo, we picked up a new skipper, in the person of Lt. Commander Hubert Cornish Fox, as it turned out, a great bloke – proper Royal Navy, not the Wavy Navy that we'd had before – we also got a new Lieutenant – C. R. C. Morrison, again a straight braider.

Fox and Morrison weren't the only new officers we picked up while we languished for a while in Colombo, seemingly with nothing to do now the war had ended. A wet-behind-the-ears midshipman was in fact the first to board – about ten or eleven days before Captain Fox arrived; the young man immediately fell afoul of our Australian First Lieutenant.

As I may have mentioned, the First Lieutenant could be a right obnoxious so-and-so when he wanted to be. He seemed determined that the new midshipman should know his very lowly place as quickly as possible and made his life misery in those first few days. Laddie and I watched him being bawled out on one occasion. It was just after Lieutenant Morrison had come aboard and the Australian was even grouchier than usual – he must have been feeling threatened – Morrison was a gently spoken Scot and pukka RN and rumour had it he was an acquaintance of the new skipper we were soon to meet.

Anyway, I digress. On this occasion, as Laddie and I watched, the midshipman endured his bollocking and was finally excused and as he walked away from the Australian, he began to shake his head from side to side – the First Lieutenant saw him and screamed at him to halt.

I nearly jumped out of my skin and was nowhere near as tuned in as Laddie, who began speaking in a very loud voice and shaking his head in empathy with the midshipman, "Sorry, sir, won't happen again, sir, sorry to let you down, sir."

The Australian looked across at us and I hissed at Laddie to shut his trap but our peacemaker was on a roll.

And the Aussie's expression changed to bewilderment. "What the devil are you talking about?" came the charmless Antipodean's bark – back to Laddie.

"Oh no, sir, not you, sir, I was talking to Midshipman Taylor – he'd asked us to do something and when I gesticulated that we hadn't done it, he started shaking his head – I had to apologise, feels like we let the young man down and him so fresh on board." Then he cracked me one with his elbow, "Doesn't it, Stoker Moss?"

Why, oh why, oh why couldn't he have just kept quiet and let the midshipman get what was coming – now he'd put us in the firing line and me on deck in my greasy overalls and that obnoxious Aussie having told me umpteen times that he would skin me if he saw me again.

"Ahh ah," the smarmy git says, "and just what is it that you have NOT done for the midshipman?"

And that's when Laddie's roll came to a solid end; he hadn't a clue what to say next so he just looked at me. Don't look at me – I'm trying for invisible – don't look at me. Oh my God, now Aussie's looking at me too – and the midshipman – they're all looking at me – Laddie, you pillock – he'll roast me.

Oh well, dive in: "Midshipman Taylor's been put in charge of the boats, sir..." he didn't let me say any more.

"Oh has he indeed. Is. That. A. Fact?" The supercilious toenail was beginning to get me temper going. Laddie was behind his back and doing all he could with his facial expressions to tell me to keep calm. Midshipman Taylor had scampered off.

"That he has, sir, by Lieutenant Morrison, sir, and we..."

He was interrupting and he had brought his nose just that bit too close to mine, "Lieutenant Morrison?"

I blame my sarcastic response on living in each others' pockets for so long!

"Yes, sir – *Lieutenant* Morrison – sir – R. N. – sir – he served on the battleship HMS *Rodney* when it scared off the battlecruisers *Scharnhorst* and *Gneisenau* in the Atlantic – he was still on board when Rodney put two torpedoes into *Bismarck* in the Battle of the Straits of Denmark – and he joined us two days ago – sir." I knew my face was as hard as iron, what I didn't know was that my brain was running on empty.

And did I shut up, oh no: "Have you ever served on a battleship, sir? Only one of the lads reckoned best you ever did was a few months on a destroyer, before they sent you back to gunnery school."

He was very close now and looked like he was about to spit feathers; his words came out very quietly and very slowly, "Stoker Moss – you didn't tell me exactly, what it is that you failed to do for the midshipman?"

What I had in mind to say... what I should have said... along with as much grovelling as is possible for a human being... was, "We failed to get the boat ready for inspection by Midshipman Taylor." But I didn't say that. That would have been far too sensible. Instead what I said was, "We failed to collect enough money for your airfare back to that convict-ridden country of yours," and, as I stuck my nose forward towards him, riposted with, "now that we have a proper Royal Navy Lieutenant aboard."

He wasn't one to back down wasn't Morton – the voice of the Chief Stoker was drifting into my consciousness. I was remembering our little chat around his mess table – 'hard man – warrior – ruthless bastard – in a fight you'd want him with you – not against you'.

Even through the red mist I knew I was in it – I had dug myself in deeper than the main shaft at Bwinning Coal Mine – I was so deep my mind began playing tricks, the Chief's voice was becoming so clear. "Stoker Moss," clear and remarkably level and quiet, "leave this one to me, sir." Pause, strange, he sounded like he was right behind me.

He was. Right behind me that is. "Stoker Moss, will you get below and change into more suitable attire if you plan to be on deck."

"What?"

His hand said the rest as it pulled me away and propelled me towards the hatch.

Morton wasn't done. "Leave him, Chief, I haven't done with him... not by a long pull... he's about to begin regretting what he just said to me. His *superior* officer," he was almost yelling.

Then there was another voice – Edinburgh and cultured – "First Lieutenant, the new Captain is approaching, are you coming to see him piped aboard?" And at that Temporary Lieutenant Robert Kerford Morton, of the Royal Australian Naval Volunteer Reserve, turned to face the brick-wall self assurance of full Lieutenant Charles Rennie

Cowie Morrison, Royal Navy, and then walked away with a backward glance carrying a scowl that told me it wasn't over for him, not yet.

We also gained another new crewmember while we were in Colombo, when one of the ABs brought a monkey aboard; it was to be their mess pet (we stokers said it was to improve the quality of sailors who slept in there but that's by the by).

Any road up, he'd only had it a day when it got away from him and found its way into the new Captain's cabin and threw his papers everywhere – he was just about to read up about his new command and had everything in nice neat little piles. The thing didn't half make a mess and the pet's owner got a graphic illustration of Fox's harder side when he threatened to stuff the monkey into one of its owner's darker places before loading him piece by piece into the Bofors and firing him to the seagulls flying over the Gulf of Mannar. The primate disappeared from the ship very shortly afterwards – someone said they put it in a uniform but, well, I think we've done that joke about seamen already – did you pick up that we stokers didn't particularly like them?

* * * * *

Our new skipper, Lt. Cdr. Hubert Cornish Fox, brought with him orders to sail for Singapore and help disarm the surrendered Japanese Army. We set off three days later with the railings of HMS *Ness* lined with my fellow shipmates, all as smart as light bulbs in their white tropical uniforms. I was hiding below. Following the advice given to me that morning by the Chief Stoker, I had found a need to stay below and attend to something that was as far away as possible from First Lieutenant Morton.

Afterwards, one or two of the lads said they'd seen him sniffing around as if looking for me, but they were all such wind-up merchants that I didn't believe them. They also said that, in all but name, the new skipper had some kind of 'old boys' thing going with Lieutenant Morrison, and was treating him as if he was First Lieutenant rather than Morton.

As we left Colombo, we saw ships coming and going everywhere, lots of activity as various Navy units went off to negotiate local surrenders. One story that warmed our hearts was of the General of a particularly nasty Japanese division in the Malaysian port of Penang who had to negotiate the surrender of his 6,000 men under the watchful 'eyes' of HMS *Nelson*'s 16-inch guns. We sailed past the island of Penang six weeks afterwards and the Japanese influence had all but been removed – there were plenty of stories coming through Virge's radio though – of landings of marines in Port Sweetman, the gateway to Kuala Lumpur, and of Japanese soldiers surrendering without resistance, which was encouraging for us.

The monsoon season had passed and we were sailing along in light winds, perfect sailing weather with just the odd thunderstorm in the evening to make sure we knew Mother Nature was still the boss. It was hot too and very humid, not the time to be below, but I was – I was still 'avoiding' Morton.

Somewhere near Port Sweetman, just as the Straits of Malacca begin to narrow, Chalky called me up top to watch the American fleet coming the other way – I can still see it today – it was an awesome sight – the day was shiny and bright as a David Lean movie, they were steaming as if they owned the World. I spotted Morton coming and dived for cover. He stopped just in front of me and together we watched – two Battleships, two Aircraft Carriers, a number of Cruisers and a whole host of Destroyers. Coming at speed, they terrified me and I was on their side.

What a sight, bunting flying and claxons hooting; I could only assume they were on the way home. It was a mesmerising sight, even from my position peeping out from my hiding place, under the tarpaulin covering the whaler!

CHAPTER EIGHTEEN

By late October, we were in Singapore. They were very strange times, those weeks and months after the war had ended; law and order was very 'iffy' while the old order changed.

It was almost four years since the Japanese had swooped out of the jungles of Malaya to defeat the trapped British Army in a very close-run battle that many, these days, believe was won more by bluff than by military might.

We didn't know yet the full extent of the suffering levied upon the British POWs and other European nationals in the Japanese prison camps, or on the labour projects that were responsible for reducing fit men to little more than walking skeletons, if they didn't kill them altogether.

Before the war Singapore had been ruled by Europeans; it was almost another county of England, then along came the Japs and now the locals weren't sure what they wanted – in fact Singapore was under British military rule when we were there, it became a crown colony in April 1946 and gained its independence in 1963.

Even then, the locals were angling for self-rule and on top of that there were always plenty of brigands trying to take advantage of the situation and a strong threat of stray military units under small-time warlords who didn't agree with capitulation. That kind of thing had even happened amongst the super-disciplined German ranks after VE Day, when a U-boat made its way to Argentina rather than surrender – in the Far East, the situation was a lot more complicated than that.

Singapore itself is an island sitting just north of the Equator at the southern tip of the Malaysian Peninsula, from which it is separated by the Johor Straits – and east of the Indonesian island of Sumatra from which it is split by the Straits of Malacca.

We had an interesting introduction to the old colonial outpost. It wasn't in too bad a shape; the main docks were damaged and out of service and the approaches were full of sunken hulks but our new skipper was determined that he'd navigate the ship to her berth without the aid of a local pilot. It was a practice he was to follow a lot during his months in command of the *Ness*.

In Singapore, the local pilot was Japanese and there was no way that the Old Man was handing over his new command to a Nip.

After a night on the cable, he had a go at navigating us through the narrow entrance to Keppel Harbour, without the aid of tugs, but the harbour currents were wicked.

I was late taking my seat at the mess table that night; we'd had a mail delivery and it included a couple of letters from Freda – when I sat down there was quite an energetic debate going on regarding Fox's seamanship. I noticed too, how quiet Haggis was and he was fiddling. Now, Haggis was often quiet – but he never fiddled. Anyhow the debate they were holding caught my whole attention.

Chalky was sharing his opinion in defence of our new skipper. "Well, I think he's a superb seaman, he doesn't trust the local pilots right now and the way he brought us in, across that current and dodging all those wrecks was superb – needed tons of concentration."

Virge was with us and it was him disagreeing. "All I know is—"

He got interrupted; it was Chalky again. "These days the hull is patched up with so much concrete it takes us all day just to change direction. We haven't the power to handle currents as vicious as that."

Haggis just – kind of – growled and continued to shred the piece of paper that he was fiddling with – he was making a right mess.

"As I was saying," Virge just looked at Chalky but didn't pause, "I was in the whaler with the new midshipman, A. J. W. Taylor, we were sailing behind and – I saw him, with my own eyes – he rammed the concrete jetty – and then beggar me if he didn't order full astern and ram the other side, that's why we're still anchored out here."

"One of the sub-lieutenants was telling me he's got a great reputation as a sailor," was Bogie's contribution, "but what do them tits know?"

Virge was back. "The MO's orderly said he got a dose of malaria when he was in Africa and he's not always fully with it. Maybe he just took too much on."

"I'd heard he's concerned we'll be sent to Jakarta, where the rebels are blowing up everything in sight – they've got their hands on a load of ex-Jap armaments. Artillery, the lot – he's worried that *Ness* is now in such a state they think she's expendable, so they'll risk us in the front line." So sayeth Scouse the naval strategist – not. "By the way, he knocked off one of the rear stanchions. I rescued it, does anybody want it as a souvenir?"

"Are you saying... that he deliberately damaged the ship?" Slow pause. "You would think that. It's what one of you Scouse bastards would do!" Haggis's fiddling was turning to belligerence.

"Oooooh – and haven't you fallen in love with him!" I thought Scouse was being very brave mocking a Glaswegian with a sore head, but he did drop the idea of selling his knock-off stanchion.

The entertainment then switched to Bogie and Streak, with a delightful little debate that, it seemed, could turn into a scrap.

"He can't be that much of a sailor; the entrance to Keppel Harbour's wide enough."

"Not so wide – not with that tidal current running."

"Bollocks – what do you know?"

"A sight more than you, you Yorkshire pudding."

"Oooo – had a little sail boat in Bournemouth paddling pool, did you?"

"No, a skiff actually – and we sailed it on Poole Bay."

"It's a wonder tha fitted in it, you Southern wanker!"

"It's a pity your father wasn't."

I tried to slow it down. "I have heard that he's known to be very defensive in respect of his men." I thought that should get them feeling better.

Haggis came straight on to me. "Herbie – you can be a right tosser sometimes!"

I was only trying to defuse a building tension – they seemed to forget, I'm Head of Mess. If they bust each other's heads – in my Mess – it'll be my fault. Then I turned to look at Haggis and noticed how empty his eyes were.

"Well, Virge, I think you were dreaming; I never felt owt," Streak entered the debate.

"You wouldn't, you overgrown twat; you've been asleep all afternoon," was Bogie's final contribution.

"One thing for sure," Virge was heading for one of his famous finishes, having started the whole argument in the first place, "we'll have plenty of time to look around Singapore while they patch us up."

But last word went to Haggis: "Herbie, you lazy sod – are you still Head of this Mess?"

"Why?" Don't commit.

"There's no chuffing tea in this kettle."

"Okay, pal, coming up." Nothing else to say really, except: "Anybody fancy a biscuit?"

Then one of those 'moments' appeared, in the form of Laddie, who strolled nonchalantly through the door, hands in pockets, typical smile on his face: "He's having another go at the harbour."

With the exception of Laddie – and Haggis, who stayed at the table, shredding the shredded shreds of his paper into ever smaller pieces – the whoosh of air almost pirouetted the Derbyshire man like a ballet dancer, as we all sprinted towards the exit, to get a view of how well Fox would handle the ship this time. The tide was fierce – we should have had a tug forward and a tug aft – we had neither – nor did we have enough power to hold our course – but tonight, he did it – I'm sure he couldn't hear us but we all gave him a little cheer and then returned to toast his success.

Haggis had gone. I cleaned up the paper he'd been shredding and saw that it had writing on it – it had been a letter. Not a good one by the look of it.

We had our repairs made and the *Ness* was spruced up and done in just three weeks.

* * * * *

On the third day in Singapore, our new skipper accompanied by Lieutenant Morrison and dressed in full uniform, with Midshipman Taylor in tow, paid a surprise visit to the Stokers' Mess. It was just before lunch and I was getting the midday meal ready (we still called it dinnertime in them days).

"I hear you chaps are rather good at spreading the ration," it wasn't quite a question and, as he said it, Fox and Morrison, with Taylor in attendance, carrying their cutlery, sat at our table, "come on then – let's see." I served them a helping from the Acting Rabbit and a few spuds and greens to go with it and they both cleared the lot.

"Mmm. Excellent, who's the cook?"

"Moss, sir." There was almost a chorus of my messmates expressing their eagerness to answer. As for me? I found myself starting to go ever so slightly red.

"Ahh yes. Stoker Moss." Fox looked at me through a pair of cool eyes that were surrounded by lines of mischievousness. "Did you ever think of becoming an Officer's Steward?"

"Who, sir? – Me, sir? – No, sir." It came out like the rattle from a Gatling gun.

"Thought not." He looked around, "Tidy Mess, men – nice and shipshape." Pause. "By the by, Mr Morrison is the new First Lieutenant – Mr Morton sets off today to return to his native Australia." He strode to the door then stopped and turned to ask, "Who is on boat duty? only Lieutenant Morton needs a lift to the ship that's taking him to..."

"Stoker Knights, sir," I interrupted, "I'll get him to organise it." His answer was a smile that he shared with Morrison and a nod to me as he left our Mess.

And that was that, the 'orrible Aussie was gone – it would cost me a couple of gulpers to get Bogie to agree to swap duties with me, so I didn't have to drive the boat for him, but it did mean that I could go back into full circulation.

Morrison ordered the midshipman to stay behind and clean up – Taylor was an East End boy, or at least his dad was; he was very bright and very hungry, he cleaned up two plates of my cooking before we could get rid of him.

So, my old friend the First Lieutenant left us at Singapore – he had lasted just twelve days under Fox – he found himself a passage back to Australia where the clever sod eventually became a Professor of Bio-flaymin-chemistry no less – until his death at the age of 43 in 1963.

Virge always says that his final entry in the Deck Log was 'Goodbye, you Pommie bastards'. I have often wondered if his awkwardness was down to the fact that the Aussies have no idea how to play the 'Class' game and so he overcompensated with aggression.

* * * * *

Looking on Singapore from the ship, we observed a tropical town that was a mayhem of colours and activity; it was all heat and humidity and hordes of people teeming through the streets, walking amidst military vehicles, rickshaws, and lorries – not many horses (we reckoned they'd all been eaten).

The people we saw were well enough fed; the girls, who wore white tops, dark slacks and wide brimmed hats, were pretty and the young men looked strong. We had no reason to believe – yet – in the extreme deprivation that came to light soon after. Just across from where we were moored was a mesh fence that housed the Japanese POWs; we all took great delight in marching along in front of it and watching them scurry forward, bowing like automatons, trying to curry favour.

It was soon obvious that those areas of Singapore that were outside British military control were in complete chaos; the local money was valueless and the real currency was food – with cigarettes and drink and female company not far behind. My crewmates didn't find anything wrong in trading their tobacco allowance with dodgy dealers on the docks – I stayed away from all of that. I'd done a deal with the manager of a local store instead – being a non-smoker and with the Naafi manager as a partner, we had quite a hoard. It all sounds rather Del Boy-ish now, but it felt perfectly okay at the time!

My cigarette ration bought me two more safari suits, in which I imagined I cut quite a dash; they were very comfortable – Streak bought one too, his had shorts and showed off his spindly legs – he looked like a giraffe.

The harbour had all sorts of ships in and around it. Anything bigger than a cruiser couldn't make the docks for all the wrecks, so they had to stay at anchor. On our way in, HMS *Ness* had passed a French battleship (still looking for its first battle – no, stop it) and one of our carriers – it might have been HMS *Implacable* – they had been rescuing Dutch refugees and had set up a play-park, with swings and the like for the children, on their flight deck.

147

The crews from all of these ships added to the 'colour' of the harbour – especially for Virge, who was on shore patrol on the jetty when a whole bunch of them came back from a night on the town; it was 5th November and they were tossing fireworks at anything and anyone they could see.

We watched the different crews mixing up, heavy with drink and stirring themselves for a scrap – and then watched Virge melt into the crowd as he whipped off the armband and gaiters that defined him as a guard, before the mob decided that he was the one that they would use as their Guy!

It wasn't long before we saw him chatting away to three gals in US Navy uniform – we were taking bets on how long it would be before he had one of them out of hers – uniform that is!

While we were in Singapore, it was between the two monsoon seasons, the temperature was in the 80s and the humidity was wicked; it was November but the weather was great.

I had to keep the motor launch ready for a trip ashore at a minute's notice; our new skipper, Lieutenant Commander Hubert Fox, was much more into socialising than Steel had been. He appeared to be more the ambassadorial type, rather than the ferocious warrior. We did come to know him as a fabulous sailor though, and he had an edge to him when necessary – he was exactly what HMS *Ness* needed for the duties awaiting us. He was a keen sportsman too. Liked to win. He'd set up a hockey match against another crew and I heard him talking to his team – he pointed out how to use the hockey stick and what to hit with it. The ball if all was going well – members of the other team if they needed slowing down a bit!

He was one of those English country gentlemen, slightly eccentric, but a Quaker, so he wasn't an extrovert. He brought an air of 'normality' to our leisure activities – instantly entering a local sailing race, including in his crew Midshipman Taylor, who we were coming to know quite well, and the Chief Stoker. We ribbed the grizzly old so-and-so about delivering enough puff to the sails to power the craft – Captain Fox was the sail boat's skipper – I think they came in last, with broad smiles on their faces and a boat full of empty beer cans.

I ferried the Captain to quite a few dinners and lunches and parties, and saw his ability to hold copious quantities of drink – all, of course, in the name of diplomacy and 'networking'.

But life in Singapore always had a menacing undertone, worse than Port Said, where they were only motivated by robbery; the situation prompted many a stokers' table discussion about Europe's loss of its grip on the region.

* * * * *

I made a couple of unusual – for a rating – pals one day, while I was trying to pull a flanker with my laundry. I better explain – in the Navy, laundry was known as 'dhobeying' and several of the sub-lieutenants and lesser officers would bring theirs down to the engine rooms, where it was warm, to get them dry. I'd had quite a few conversations with a pair of artificers, and when they asked me to sort out some shirts that were to be laundered by a local Chinese chap, I was pleased to agree – and as a kind of reward to myself I put a few bits of my stuff in with theirs.

I had hoped that laundry-man, Wa Sher Willie, would only prepare one bill, which they would pay – unfortunately he left all of the laundry with them, instead of returning it to me as I'd asked. They had caught me red-handed, or white-shirted, if you like. They took it well and we had a real laugh about it and we started something of a friendship that would last the trip home.

One of the things the subs and I chatted about was the famous Raffles Bar; we all fancied seeing it, but the two artificers were a bit shy about going in just to look – I, of course, wasn't shy, but not being an officer, I wouldn't be let in and so a deal was done. They lent me one of their shirts and a pair of socks and we went off as a trio – something we'd do a few more times on the way home.

How the other half lived!

We were a bit overawed by the Hotel's reviving splendour and just walked in, looked steadily around and, after a few minutes, walked back out.

The officer of the watch called me over as I walked purposefully back aboard and asked me why I was wearing white socks and not the regulation blue – again I was delivered from pain by Charlie's dictum, to 'always have an answer'.

"It's the heat, sir. Ever since the Red Sea, I've had recurring bouts of miliaria – it's a spotty rash and it can blister – open to all kinds of infection – I could lose a leg – wouldn't be able to stand me watch."

Maybe I'd overdone it – he just stared at me, silent, nothing for it but to carry on. "The MO says it's caused by dead skin and bacteria that get trapped – by excess perspiration – along with the hairs on my legs – and blocks up the sweat glands – I have to try and keep cool – in my job, ehh? That's why you see me wearing the safari suit on deck. My legs are particularly bad because they're so hairy – the lighter white socks make it better."

"Are you talking about 'prickly heat', Moss? – half the crew has that."

"Aye, sir, well, if you suffer from it, sir, I can recommend a cure that the MO won't give you."

"Can you?" He was hesitating, it was time for me to keep quiet. "Only, the doc gave me a cream and it just seemed to make it worse."

"It does, sir – the gunge just adds to the blockage – he's a good doctor, sir – but he's a bit young. Inexperienced and it's his first time out here." Why I glanced conspiratorially left and right, I don't know, but that's what I did, before telling him: "Salt water, sir – from the saltwater taps in the head – fill as many buckets as you need and pour them over the infected areas."

"Does that work?"

"I can't tell a lie, sir – it's not a cure, but it doesn't half help with the itching."

He waved me on and, as I walked away, I looked back to see him scratching away at different parts of his body. I smiled to think that he now owed me a favour and stored the fact away for collection when it was needed.

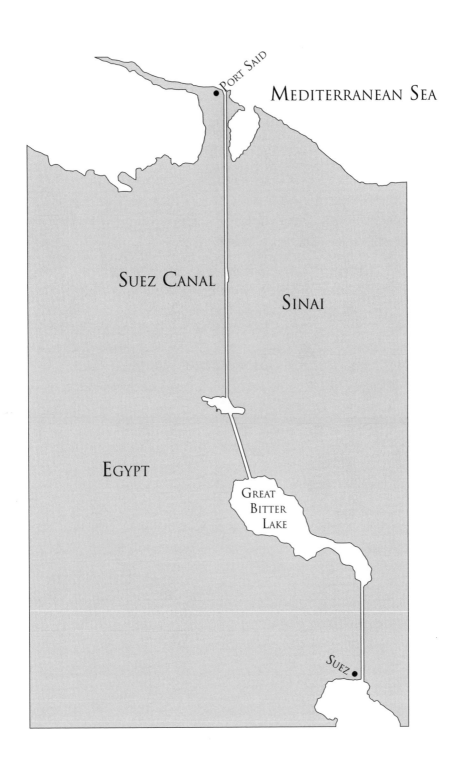

MEDITERRANEAN SEA

PORT SAID

SUEZ CANAL

SINAI

EGYPT

GREAT
BITTER
LAKE

SUEZ

STRAIT OF MALACCA

• WHE

MALAYSIA

• KUALA
LUMPUR

NIAS •

SUMATRA

TELO •

• SINGAPORE

• PADANG

• BENKOELEN

INDIAN OCEAN

• OOSTHAVEN

• JAKARTA

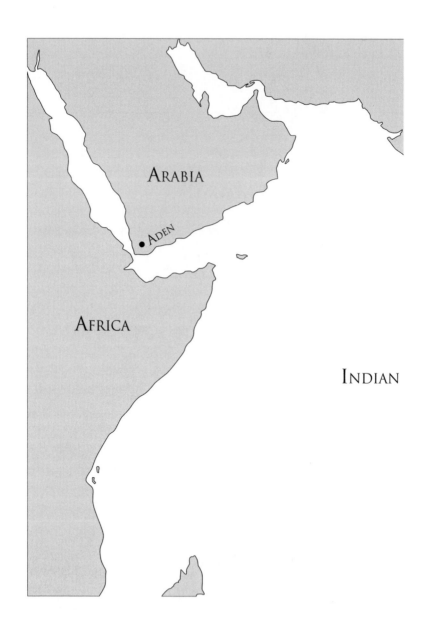

ARABIA

● ADEN

AFRICA

INDIAN

CHAPTER NINETEEN

What had begun to feel, to us, like a holiday, however, couldn't last; we were one of His Majesty's fighting ships, sitting in Singapore, full of lusty young men who were confident enough to think that perhaps we should go and pick a fight. Then our orders came – we were to visit the various Indonesian islands, off Western Sumatra, to search for Australian spotters – who had been dropped on the islands by submarine many months ago to watch and report back on manoeuvres by the Japanese armies – and now needed picking up and taking home. Once that was done, we had to visit ports on the Sumatran mainland and disarm the itinerant Japanese soldiers and destroy their weapons by dropping them into the sea.

Easy!

Or would it be?

We started by sailing north through the Malacca Straits, and I'd just been in with Virge trying to work out what he was doing all day in his Wireless Telegraph Office; I mean, whose transmissions was he listening to now we didn't have an enemy to fight?

Unfortunately, he was soon able to show me that we did have, it just wasn't as obvious as it used to be – we were slipping into the times of guerrilla war by nationalist forces and the very early days of terrorism – only we didn't call it that back then. Plus, there were still some hazards left over from the recent conflicts.

One of these hazards was bobbing happily along, just in front of us, right in the middle of the Straits of Malacca – the call came from the forward lookout – "Green four two, a mine, one cable," dignified pause, "green three six, a mine, one cable," calm space, "green three four, a mine, closing."

Virge had always struck me as a bit on the 'nervy' side, that thing about leave for instance; anyhow, now it was mines and he wasn't happy, in fact he even grabbed my arm. He hated mines. It was like a phobia for him – like someone might hate heights or spiders – really irrational. Unaware of the strength of his fears I took the gung ho approach. "Come on," says I, "let's take a look."

But he didn't move – I turned to stare at a very white face and then he was off like a supercharged jackrabbit – back towards his Mess – I thought I'd better follow. I had taken just one step when the lookout began to call again, this time just the edge of urgency in his voice, "Green two five, a mine..." then he was rudely interrupted as the starboard Oerlikon burst into action: '*pop, pop, pop*'... then I caught just a hint of panic as the gunner missed. "Green one nine, CLOSING!" – '*Pop, pop.* **Bang, whistle**' and the mine disintegrated into a mucky spout of salt water – the 'whistle' was something hard and hot flying past my left earhole and reminding me that only a stupid arsehole would stand so close to an exploding mine.

As I turned to go after Virge, Laddie popped out of the gun placement that had just been in action; he'd seen me duck and was grinning like a seaside sailor sitting in a coin machine. He seemed very happy with his work. "Marvellous shot, Raymond, dead centre, blew it in one, marvellous."

I waved and set off to find the missing telegraphist. When I finally found Virge, he was buried as deep as he could be in his hammock, with a blanket over his head and shivering like a naked Eskimo bathing al fresco.

"I hate those f-f-f-f-hucking things," he told me – in fact, he told me about five times – so I made him a cuppa and we talked about something else. There was nothing cowardly about Virge, it was just something that got to him.

PULAU WEH, SEBANG

We continued our trip along the east coast of Sumatra and around the northern tip to the island of Pulau Weh. We anchored there for a short while just off the port of Sebang and a 'pod' of the crew went swimming – directly from the ship. They seemed to be having a really good time, until I saw the Captain, Second Lieutenant and a signals officer frantically running around with hand-held loud hailers persuading the crew to get back on board as soon as they could.

They'd received a message from the establishment ashore – it told them just how dangerous the waters still were around Pulau Weh.

What did they shout to the swimmers?

One word...

Shaaaaaark!

Our next call was Emmahaven, the deep-water port on the west coast which, in those days, served Padang, the capital of West Sumatra – on the way there, running west of the Matawari Islands at latitude 96° east – HMS *Ness* crossed the Equator and we were put through a ceremony and given a certificate for crossing-the-line. Mine hangs now on the wall of my lounge – it was 22nd November 1945 and a day of high jinks, singing and dance, the skipper was tossed in the air in a blanket and the ship – for just that day – was renamed Happi*Ness*, which Laddie even managed to make up a song about. 'H-M-S... Happi-*Ness*' – has a certain rhythm, which wasn't spoiled by Bogie's version: 'Crap-peenus'!

Good job we were in a good mood or he'd have suffered some very worthy – and painful fate – most of us in the crew were very proud of our little warship.

EMMAHAVEN AND PADANG

The next day we entered port and all high spirits dissolved, but before I tell you about that I'd like to describe what I meant when I described Emmahaven as a deep-water port. The coast of Sumatra at that point sits in front of a sweeping range of volcanic mountains that run parallel with the coast; they are around 7,500 to 9,000 feet high and form a green backdrop which slopes in a gentle concave curve down to the shores.

The town of Padang had grown up on the silt bed that formed an inlet-shaped shelf of flat land that was as close as Sumatra came to a coastal plain. It had probably been deposited there millions of years ago by a huge glacier as it melted on the sides of the volcanic ridge, or something of that nature.

At the time we were there, the town of Padang was a rude collection of buildings and loose villages that sat amongst the trees and made up the capital of West Sumatra. It was fronted by a huge arc of grey sandy beach that seemed to be interrupted every few yards by loose stone breakwaters, which looked about as much use as they were ornament. And they weren't pretty.

What had once been the glacier had shrunk to five tropical rivers that drove out of the plains along with a strange collection of waterways running parallel with the beach that seemed a typical feature of Sumatra; everything was shallows and silt – Padang was a seaside town rather than a port. To the south of the town a ridge runs at right angles to the main mountain range stretching towards the sea forming the bottom of the crescent of high land around Padang; it is broken by a flat pass that leads to the real seaport, Emmahaven, which sits on the shores of the sweetly named Brandywine Bay.

The depressing thing about the place that drained away our high spirits was its run-down grandeur and the numbers of Europeans we saw. They had been wealthy people before the invasion, with their own homes and stakes in the major plantations, but had become skin and bone skeletons, drained of hope and still living behind barbed wire in makeshift camps where they were scratching around for the bleakest living.

Padang had been a Dutch enclave and the citizens of Holland were suffering more than most, but all of the Europeans, or the mixed-race Eurasians, wore a much tighter version of that mask of fear that had covered our faces during the Battle of the Atlantic.

Whilst I didn't see any, there were strong rumours of murder and bloodshed and our standing orders were not to go into the town alone and even then to stay on the main street. We were the only warship of any kind in port – along with a rather rusty tank landing ship. Virge was the first of us ashore; he had been ordered to deliver despatches to Army HQ and came in to see us when he got back; he had been issued with a little pistol and five rounds of ammunition and was waving it around and acting like the cowboy Tom Mix. We were quick to take the mickey out of him at the time, but his little trip saw him being issued with the Naval General Service Medal (SE Asia 45–46 clasp), which none of the rest of us got.

As was his way, the Captain had also gone ashore for one of his socialising-cum-scouting visits in Padang and learned from the officers of the 26th Indian Division (which was there under General Chambers) just how poor the *living* had been for the local Europeans. Within a few hours Fox sent a message back to the ship, on Port Radio, to one of Virge's colleagues telling us that on the following day, HMS *Ness* would be holding a party for 400 of the children, who were still living in the squalor of the Sumatran camps.

The next day was Saturday and there were lots of moist-eyed matelots when we saw the assortment of skinny, hollow-eyed kids of Dutch and mixed-race persuasion – they found it very hard to smile, in spite of an heroic effort by my crewmates, who were all clothed as pirates. We had dressed up the *Ness* so that she looked more like a kiddies' theme park than a warship. Unfortunately – for everybody else – I was not on motorboat duty that day – I had been seconded to music duty – me!

Ha! Typical Navy. I'm as musical as fingernails on a blackboard – anyway, what that meant was I had to organise a band to play the children aboard.

Victor Sylvester we weren't, but with yours truly on a big tin drum, Bogie on bazooka and Streak on a tin lid we started singing 'MacNamara's Band'.

Did I mention my singing voice isn't something you would pay to listen to? – you might pay a lot of money to stop it – even so we must have been good because I caught the attention of Captain Fox who approached and asked me, "Stoker Moss, what are you doing? Trying to scare the children off before we even get them aboard?"

I could only shrug and tell him that it was, "All good fun, sir," – he suggested that it would probably be okay because he was sure that they had seen worse than me – cheek – and then laughed as he told me to carry on. Before long the band had been joined by Laddie and Haggis, who were getting on better than I had known for a long while. Laddie had found a banjo from somewhere and was showing us his mastery of it, while Haggis had abandoned the gloomy mood that had beset him in Aden and took over the vocals, demoting me to percussion only – while the ship was heaving, with very brown, very young and very undernourished bodies.

Most of them ate and drank well that day, as did their parents – and they touched our hearts – all of our chocolate ration went – they were delighted because most of them hadn't had any chocolate before.

Some of them shocked us though; we'd laid out as fine a fare as we could for them and yet, when the time came for them to sit around the tables in the messes to eat, some of them simply ignored the goodies and settled only for bread, which they nibbled quite suspiciously.

The best thing was to watch them splashing happily in the temporary paddling pool we had rigged up. It brought an extra smile from my messmates as I suggested that, perhaps, we could keep it afterwards as a saltwater receptacle to cure any future bouts of prickly heat – a word with our new and very naval, Jimmy the One left me in no doubt that my hope was a forlorn one. I do think I saw him smile though!

CHAPTER TWENTY

W hile, on the whole, our guests proved children's ability to be able to find fun wherever it popped up, there were too many who looked to have been seriously damaged by their time in the Jap concentration camps.

PULAU NIAS, GUNUNG SITOLI

With the memory of the children in our minds and a grim determination in our hearts, we sailed a day later for the northerly port of Sibolga. It was located on the west coast of Sumatra, in a sheltered inlet surrounded by steep green hills. We set off again that night to patrol the string of islands to the west of Sumatra – we had with us a couple of scary-looking officers from the 26th Indian Division and a team of light-fingered interpreters, who Scouse spent a lot of time with. We made our first landing next morning at 0700 hours at the town of Gunung Sitoli on Pulau Nias Island.

It had been almost two months since the Japanese surrender, and by now we had reason to suspect that the natives may be very unfriendly to any man of a light skin colour – and unless you had their extensive tattoos woven amongst a criss-cross of deep scars – and a bone stuck through yer nose – and curly hair rather than straight – and a couple of dead bats hanging from your belt – and teeth that were stained black from chewing something strange – and... a maggot-ridden gourd on the end of their willy... barff... sorry. Sorry, but any one of them is enough to make you heave.

Okay – anyway, what I'm saying is that we had to approach with care – with Midshipman Taylor as cox on the tiller, and me controlling the throttle, we ferried an armed guard of thirty or so men, under the command of one of the Army lieutenants, to the shore.

One of our engineering chaps was sitting next to me as I headed the boat into shore – I'd noticed his hands shaking a bit as we pulled away from the *Ness*. One of the lads had told me that he had been in the service a while – he had seen action and been unlucky enough to catch a tiny piece of red-hot shell casing in the side of his head. Shrapnel, sharp as a razor. It had shaved the side of his skull and taken away a neat sliver of bone, but it hadn't touched his brain.

It had caused enough damage to require a metal plate to be fitted and his hair refused to grow back, leaving him unworried by the attentions of the ladies of the ports and open to some ruthless ribbing by his messmates, one of whom had nicknamed him Tin Head and tormented him to the point of bullying.

I had noticed that he rarely left the ship and, when on board, he stayed below most of the time. He could often be found hanging around the refrigeration plant, but I hadn't put one and one together and realised that the merciless attentions of the sun, heating up his metal plate, caused his brain to short circuit now and again. To the rest of the lads it just seemed as though he was being a wuss, with his nerves seemingly strained to breaking point – as we approached the beach his shaking got worse.

These days, the islands off Sumatra are a magnet to the bronze-skinned, bleached-haired surfing set, and on this particular day, the offshore wind was whipping the swells into the heaviest of 'kick-ass' (the yanks just don't seem able to spell arse properly) waves. In our ignorance, we were zooming down every form of Teahupoo, Maverick and Pipeline and closing rapidly on the Beach Break Foamies.

Then the tide breathed out and the bottom of the boat – fat with our crowd of tense tars – scraped softly on the tips of the coral and scared Tin Head so much that he jumped clean overboard. I looked at the coxswain and we swapped an 'if that silly sod thinks we're turning back for him he can think again' kind of look. Bogie, who was onboard because he had upset Jimmy the One and been given extra duties, couldn't resist chipping in with: "Canned grub for the sardines," which did make us hesitate, but not for long, we had our own worries. We were remembering the old stories of Captain Cook, when he was exploring the Pacific Islands, unsure whether the natives were going to welcome us, or to treat us to a hail of burning spears – and – on top of that, we weren't entirely sure if there was a squad of well-armed soldiers waiting to rake us with a hail of lead bullets carrying the wording 'Made in Japan'.

We were almost as psyched up as some wimpy soap star facing a bush tucker trial.

As we approached the beach there was only one thing for it; run the boat up onto the sand and pile out to see what was what. I was in control of the engine, the coxswain was on steering, so I had to throttle down and let the boat approach under its own momentum while I pushed and shoved my way to the front, to unfurl the rope and get ready to hit the beach running.

The coxswain chose a spot where the waves were running out of energy and eddying towards the sand. Then, just as the bottom began to drag in the shallows, I jumped out dragging the boat's rope behind me. I was dressed only in a pair of shorts, with thick-soled sandals on my feet. The water reached halfway up my thighs, it felt great – running cool against me as I ran before the motor launch up the slope of submerged sand towards the beach.

First I should tell you that the beach at Gunung Sitoli was quite shallow, probably only around twenty feet from sea line to the grass, it was grey-gold sand – not yer tropical white – in fact the beach always seemed to have about half of its depth dark/ wet sand and the other half a kind of mucky dry. The lack of any real tidal action meant that the palm trees grew right down to the beach and in some cases stood in tiny grassy islands – just a foot or two across and surrounded by the sands of the beach itself.

For a few seconds I was out on my own, the guard in the boat with guns cocked, eyes straining to catch any movement. I ploughed through the surf that was growing shallower with each stride – I was as fit as I have ever been and my chest and shoulders were bronzed and tingling in the morning sun.

Just for a second, I wondered if the iron plate in our deserter's head was going rusty as he splashed about in the briny – and asked myself if he was further out than a length of the swimming baths in Malvern; strange the thoughts that waft through your head when you are facing potential danger.

Suddenly there were three or four shipmates alongside me, helping pull the launch up onto the sand, where the boat emptied quickly, the first men taking up a defensive pattern, while those behind pushed a few yards forward and mimicked them, giving the signal for the original guards to become the assault troops and so they progressed, very rapidly up the beach to a position they felt to be safe.

I thought I'd better open my eyes again and pretended to look courageous. I had to attend to the boat and had my back to the land, when I noticed with some relief that Tin Head was back with us; his moments of panic over, he was splashing and choking as he crept on his hands and knees through the shallows and up the beach, where he flopped and sought attention that none of us gave to him.

As it turned out, the islanders were delighted to see us – there were no Japanese – but neither were there any Australians. The shore party flashed a message back to the *Ness* and we returned with the boat to embark the Captain, who, in full dress uniform, was about to undertake a serious stint of flying the flag – I had taken Tinny back to the *Ness* with me too – he really was not well.

When we reached the shore the skipper sent me back again to fetch the MO, who spent the day holding a surgery for any of the islanders who wanted medical help. Laddie, who was also famous for taking every possible opportunity to utter the phrase

– 'I'll aye a ride' – which, apparently, is Derbyshire for 'I will come with you' – had jumped at the chance of going ashore with me.

This time I was feeling much more confident; we landed at the same place and then, while Midshipman Taylor took the MO towards the village, Laddie and I messed about finding a position to tie up the motorboat.

We sailed up the beach to a river inlet and Laddie took great delight in being throttle-man for this fifty-yard trip. It looked like we'd found the perfect berth in the narrow mouth of the free-flowing river that cut the beach just north of the spot we had first landed.

The fresh water was around twelve feet wide and five feet deep. It was coloured greenish beige with white rails of speed on its surface and it easily carried the launch on a current that would hold it on its rope, tight-in towards the clean-cut bank of bright green grass on grey-brown earth. Thick collections of palm trees and other spindly vegetation grew right to the edge of the river – I steered the motorboat back and forth into the mouth of the river and anchored it against the flow to make it easier for the Captain to get aboard. Intuition told me that the kind of people he was with were free with their hospitality and, on an island like this, the hospitality could have been home-brewed and very strong. I had brought a plank with me to help the return embarkation.

I looked inland and saw the path that the river took as it fell from the island's central spine. The water, sparkling high up on the peak before winding and twisting like a Swiss road, then falling freely over vertical flat rocks, where it lost its river-like width and depth before it cut into the fertile hill that ran in a gentle arc, ever flatter down to the beach. The water's beige colouring, at that point, came from the heavy silt playing in its runs and eddies and its deep green opalescence was the result of its depth and the long strands of vegetation that waved in the current on the riverbed. Over the aeons this tiny river had sculpted the merest bay in the otherwise dead-straight eastern coast of Pulau Nias.

At the edge of this bay, where the straits between the islands and mainland Sumatra plunged to a greater depth, the *Ness* sat peaceful on her sea anchor. There was a heady scent hanging around. It was perfect. Early morning bright, air as fresh as... vanilla ice cream.

I sent Laddie off to pick up some stuff that we'd left at the original landing site. All there was for me to do was to tie the motorboat more securely by looping its line to one of the nearby bushes. There wasn't a soul in sight. It was totally quiet. Even the breeze was having a siesta.

And... the next few minutes were the most terrifying of my life!

* * * * *

Now – while you're considering the peacefulness of the scene, let me take you back to the previous night when the talk around the mess table had been of voodoo and black magic and all that sort of stuff. It was very spooky stuff and I can remember being quite vociferous about how wrong they all were – we weren't deep enough into the Pacific for all that kind of mumbo-jumbo.

I do, however, remember one of my fellow stokers pointing out that voodoo came from the West Indies and these were – or had been – the Dutch East Indies, so why couldn't there be voodoo here? It was a question that was a tad too good and I noticed the blood draining from one or two increasingly nervy faces – it was the kind of stuff to put nightmares into your subconscious.

We had even progressed to talking about the tattooed tribesmen that populated the more secret corners of Indonesia and their habits as headhunters – Bogie – the git – chose that point in our debate to drop one of the Aden sheep's heads, complete with eyeballs, on the mess table. Urrgghh!

*   *   *   *   *

Back to this morning – with the breeze waking and playing amongst the leaves and with a thick cloud meandering along high overhead, casting a slight gloom and everyone in our party gone off somewhere – I was totally alone – and yet it felt as though, from somewhere, I was being watched. I shook my head and told myself not to be stupid. The thoughts from last evening's conversation started trawling around my mind to find sense and reason, but the catch was poor as I approached my chosen mooring branch. The sun through the clouds was painting shadows that darted and shifted. It was hot, the temperature in the high 80s.

I reached out to tie my rope to the sturdiest branch and it came alive – the branch moved!

My heart stopped, the wind screeched sharply in my ears, the breakfast that I had eaten that morning headed upwards and the supper I had eaten the previous night headed downward. Luckily every part of me tightened up, or I would have been a real mess. Every hair on my head stood to attention and every pore on my skin prickled, all within a millisecond. The blood pulsed inside my head with such a pressure that I was sure it would burst from my ears. The tree started to whistle and whoop.

The whole tree was moving now – like a skinny, thin giant – a green giant – it was magic – black magic – voodoo – I was paralysed, I couldn't run, couldn't shout, couldn't breathe – pure fear.

Then a tiny part of the branch flaked off.

Argh! Oooohhhhhhhhhhhh – it's coming for me – it's going to eat m-m-err... m-m-me. What the devil? The piece was shaped... erm... like a... erm... like a frog.

A frog?

It's a bloody frog. The branch was covered in them, small green frogs – tree frogs. My head has never spun around so quickly. Had anyone seen? Where was Laddie? My messmates would strip me daily – of any dignity – if they knew I'd nearly messed myself over a two-inch-long frog – I wouldn't be ribbed, I'd be ploughed. Had I screamed? No – luckily I had been too petrified to make any noise. My whoosh of relief could be heard back on board the frigate. I saw Laddie now, standing at the landing site with his back to me. He couldn't have seen anything. Pull yourself together, Moss. Better check your kecks just in case any of that fear dribbled out. Phew, I'm okay. Time to get mad. Time to get me own back. The little bustards. I drew back one of the frog-filled branches as far as I could and let it twang. There were frogs flying everywhere, their big red 'golf-ball' eyes blinking and dizzy – whole families of them flew – mam frogs, dad frogs, brother frogs, sister frogs – that'll teach the little green slimeballs. I glanced around again. Breath becoming normal, heart settling down to around 102 beats per minute, blood pressure dropping, my eyes settling back in their sockets – my feeling of foolishness reaching record levels.

Now – you can't blame me for the fact that it was just at that stress-filled moment that one of the little green terrors decided to climb up on a small mound of sand just by my right foot. Maybe I shouldn't have kicked it from its perch with such venom, maybe that was churlish – but I did – and the moment the toe of my sandal cracked it into space some idiot standing at the edge of the beach shouted my name: "Stoker Moss!"

"WHAT?" A two-year-old in a tantrum couldn't have yelled it better – oh cripes, it was the Captain. "Errm... I mean, what is it, err, sir, how can I help you, err. Aye aye, sir, err, sorry, sir, didn't see you there, sir, err, startled me, sir. Sir." I saluted knowing he would have to return it and hoping the action would distract him.

His cultured voice was unperturbed. "Yes, fine, that was a nice kick – glad to see you're such a dab hand with the old right foot – we need a new centre for'ard. The one we've got is an ex-pro – one of the Sheffield teams – we're slaughtering them – not fair – I need to put him in goal – you can run a bit, can't you? Spot on, slip that footwear off and follow me."

It turned out that the islanders were huge soccer fans and Captain Fox had agreed to a mini-tournament, where a team from the *Ness* took on two local teams.

"Footwear off... sir?"

"That's right, Stoker – even things out – they don't wear anything on their feet, so neither will we."

"We, sir? Are you playing, sir?"

"No – I'm team manager."

"What about Laddie, sir. He's a good footballer." Laddie was just returning, loaded down with kitbags full of our contingency rations.

"He's a half back. Left half, I think. Not tall enough for centre forward." Then I caught the full – and hard – Fox stare: "Moss, don't you want to take part?"

"Well, errrm..."

"Only I would expect it of my launch pilot." He was quietly threatening to withdraw me from a very cushy job – time to change tack. "Delighted to, sir... I was just thinking of Laddie. He loves the game. Derby County fan – probably needs to see a decent game. Didn't want to deprive him of..."

"Moss."

"Sir?"

"Stow it."

"Aye aye, sir. I do understand, sir. But bare feet, sir? The thing is, sir, the islanders' feet are used to it – hardened like – mine aren't."

"Come now, Stoker, let's not whinge – I'd do it m'self but I'm in my finery."

"No, sir – aye, sir. Excuse me, sir, but are we using a regulation football[10]?"

"Is there any other kind of ball that you could play soccer with, Stoker Moss?"

I wasn't done: "Heavy leather casing, inner air bag and laces, sir."

"That's correct, Stoker – would you rather we use a beach ball? Or perhaps, frogs?" Now that was close to sarcasm!

If I remember correctly, we continued to slaughter the home team, I even scored a goal – and every one of my toenails was purple for weeks afterward. The Captain spent the afternoon entertaining the Chief of Police and then he entertained the head of the Chinese community. I've never seen anyone 'down' so much entertainment in one session, he must have had hollow legs – and hollow feet – and hollow toes – I bet they weren't throbbing with pain like my toes were.

Eventually he invited the island's High-ups to a tour of the ship – so I was needed. The three of them tumbled into the launch and we ran the rollers back to *Ness*. Once there I stayed clear; I wasn't that keen on the toffs who seemed to have managed to sit out the war with little inconvenience and, now, put themselves forward as captains of our future commercial dealings.

After I'd taken them back ashore it was time to ferry all of our lads back to HMS *Ness*. The ex-professional footballer needed a bit of persuasion. The native lasses wore

---

10   In those days a football was much heavier than it is today. It was made from an outer case, made of leather sections that were sewn together. Inside the case was a rubber bladder that was filled with air to inflate the ball – where the inner was put into the outer, there was a gap that was closed with laces – like shoe laces.

these slit skirts – rather short for the day – and one of them had been fluttering her thighs at him as he stood on his own in our goal. He was the only one in our half of the pitch. She'd also fed him with the same 'entertainment' the skipper had been drinking and now he was ready to marry her.

Sober – she made the faces on the carvings on Easter Island look like Heddy Lemarr – in his state she looked like an angel. The lads carried him back, her family wailing and bawling and offering fatted pigs and demanding he return to become one of them.

Later on, one of the toffs did row out, in a crude dugout canoe, which he had very kindly filled with pigs, chickens, eggs and fruit. I felt the Stokers' Mess should claim its fair share of this booty since our Acting Rabbit had been wholly consumed during the children's party and needed a complete revival. I still wonder why a tiny portion of such bounty couldn't have found its way into the POW camps where so many Europeans had starved to death. Had the Dutch really been such bad masters?

We sailed away that night, with a display of bangs and flashes orchestrated by Laddie on the foredeck.

*   *   *   *   *

Two days later Tin Head was complaining of loss of vision in one eye and the MO decided that he was no longer fit for duty in a climate that was hotter than a hard-working engine room. He was transferred to an outgoing vessel and within a week or two was on a flight home. In a rare period of humility around the mess table everyone discussed whether we could have been a bit kinder to him and what it must have felt like, but the stranger consequence was the effect it had on Haggis's temper.

The Scot was beginning to snap at everyone and it seemed, to me, that the eyes of the Glaswegian, who I had grown to know well, were emptying of all of their sparkle. I even heard that he had been and 'spoken to' Tin Head's tormentor, the evidence showing in his grazed knuckles and a long chat with the CPO. He wasn't put in the brig, but he was – in modern parlance – grounded, which made him disappear even deeper inside himself.

CHAPTER TWENTY-ONE

T he next island was tiny, it was just to the south of Pulau Nias and equally to the north of Padang – the smallest of a group of six. No Japanese on this island, we were looking for the Australian spotter.

PULAU TELO

Once again, I had ferried a party on ahead to ensure that the way was safe; again I was the first off the boat to make it secure. I wasn't so energetic in the waves this time – my feet ached – the cool surf did wonders, though, for my coal-black toes. For some reason, upon seeing me – the locals had headed for the hills. I can't understand why, I was like a pin-up compared to them – my mirror confirmed that daily.

The lieutenant in charge sent the Captain a signal, which told him that they had run off and that our two Malay interpreters had gone after them to try to persuade them, using their own language, that our intentions were friendly.

The Captain was proving that he had a superb skill for building relationships by blending in with the local people. For instance, he'd put on all his finery to impress the snobby head of the Chinese community and the Chief of Police on Pulau Nias and then when we had played the natives at football he'd insisted that our team wear no shoes (did I already mention that?) because our opposition wasn't wearing any. I had the deep-purple toes to prove it (did I mention that too?).

I thought I deserved a medal, in fact, if I'd been in the US Navy my purple toes would have been worth at least – a Purple Heart.

Anyhow, on this occasion he decided that instead of full dress uniform, he would go in his whites, with their short trousers, and because he didn't have any sandals, and probably because he had caught something of the spirit of the last island, he wore nothing on his feet. All was fine until he jumped out of the motorboat into the shallows and stepped right on top of a particularly sharp sea urchin. That made him hop and curse a bit.

I watched him dancing, but said not a word; neither did I smile, but for some reason he took umbrage – it could have been the fact that I was wearing my particularly thick-soled pair of rope-sandals – that I had bought for a packet of American cigarettes off a street-seller in Padang. Equally it could have been that he was reading my thoughts and picking up my lack of sympathy; it served him right, he shouldn't have been so tight; with the money he had, he should have done what I did and bought himself some thick sandals – he certainly wasn't going to have mine.

I was getting a bit hot under the collar at all this, because now I'd have to load him back in the motorboat, probably wash out his wound, wrap it up with a bandage from the first aid kit and take him back to the *Ness* so that the MO could dress it properly.

Not likely!

Lt. Commander Fox was made of much sterner stuff than that. I wondered if he'd done Public School – fagging and caning and all that, but when I raised it later one of the lads said his naval education was at the Royal Naval College in Dartmouth, where misbehaviour or simple inability to perform were rewarded with 'ticks' and 'cuts', 'whackings', 'strafes' and 'beatings'. The stuff the character of the Empire was built on. It had certainly toughened our captain.

We were on one of those typical Sumatran beaches where, rather than the dense fringe of jungle that you might imagine, there's a widely spaced crowd of palm trees, probably about fifty yards deep and standing in a mixture of sparse grasses and sand, before the jungle gets thicker.

We were standing on the wet bit, where the sand was hard from the seawater; it was a steady slope for about ten feet before the sand – an almost building site texture – flattened off and approached the trees. A trail of blood was seeping into the surf and I remembered what I'd read about sharks being able to pick up the scent of blood from miles away and so I moved clear of the tide line.

Twenty yards landward, amongst the trees, we could see the rest of our party boiling water for a brew on a fire that they had got going – the interpreters were just returning, leading a small group of senior-looking islanders. The skipper spoke to me, "Secure the boat please, Stoker, and then join me for a cuppa," and with that he marched off to join the rest – the only indication that he'd been speared was the trail of bloody footprints that he left behind. A trail he appeared not to notice at all!

But, this day's adventures hadn't finished yet; after I had run the boat up the beach and secured it with a sand anchor and a rope tied with a beautiful reef knot (thank you, HMS *Duke*) to the nearest palm tree – I joined the group. The Captain and the

Lieutenant from the 26th Indian Division were nursing their tea-cups made from the shells of half a coconut and discussing how to progress next, the Captain suggesting that perhaps the soldiers would like to remove their jackets and become a bit more casual, but the Lieutenant wasn't keen. Army compared to Navy; by-the-book versus common sense.

I noticed Captain Fox's foot was covered in sand but he'd done nothing about his wound, so I asked for a medic, but there wasn't one. One of the islanders then drew a pretty impressive knife, which put everyone on their mettle; he stuck it into the fire while telling us, via the interpreter, that the urchins could make you rather poorly if the spines weren't removed – as he spoke he reached for the Captain's foot and began to clean it up. Then he withdrew his blade from the flames and picked out three sharp-looking black spines – the skipper wasn't wincing at all, which is more than could be said for me.

I knew that if it had been me I would have been playing my best 'poor me' cards and looking forward to at least a day in bed and my only disappointment would be about HMS *Ness*'s Acting Nurse.

* * * * *

Here comes a Slight Digression. I have very few regrets about my days in the Navy, but a regret that ran high up the flagpole and was saluted by every sailor I spoke to was the Admiralty's refusal to allow women on board.

You see, when I mention that word 'nurse', the image that probably came into your mind was of a soft, warm, sweet-smelling girl, with a smile as wide as Christmas, pearly white teeth, bits beneath her uniform (siiigghh) that wobbled gently while she leaned over you to minister to your ails – she'd have a way with a thermometer that would make you sigh again and tiny, cool hands that would have your skin tingling whenever they touched you.

The Navy only had such delights in their hospitals on land – they were called Wrens and were often as delicate as the tiny bird whose name they carried – well, one or two of them were, but don't mind that, hold the angelic image for a while. On board *Ness*, we had an Acting Nurse – we had a lot of Acting things in the Navy – just like my own Acting Rabbit, the word implied something the thing was not. My Acting Rabbit was a mixture of some kind of meat, but it wasn't a rabbit.

Here's our Acting Nurse – he had a hairy chest and as much sympathy as a hungry lioness shows to a springbok – the hair on his head consisted of six long strands that he grew from behind his left ear and plastered across his bald skull to reach his right ear – nothing wrong with that, he was folically challenged, that's all. Until, that is, the gunge that he plastered 'em down with lost its strength and they sprung into your eyes, nostrils and mouth, while he was leaning over you! Yuk – yukyukyukyukyuk!

Strangely, this guy had tons of hair in his eyebrows, and he smelled!

His body stank of the weird kind of cigarettes that he smoked – initially I thought he used tobacco that had been recycled from the droppings of a camel with digestive problems – but it turned out that he had his own method of 'rolling your own'.

He got his ration in leaf tobacco and rolled it in strands of string, which he had soaked in rum. He tied the ends of the string to the wall of his cabin and twisted it about the tobacco. He could have had six-foot-long ciggies, but he cut them into two- or three-inch lengths; they were brownish in colour and lacked a very sleek form, which is why I thought they were camel droppings.

On top of all of this, his breath carried a constant whiff of stale alcohol, enough for us to worry about the strength of any anaesthetic we may need. His arms, too, were covered in black hairs and the hand on his right arm only had two digits – the little finger and the thumb. (Every conceivable joke about him biting fingernails has long since been exhausted – believe me.) His name was Morton and he spoke rather well.

Strange as it may seem, not many of us looked forward to a spell in sickbay – it was such a shame.

* * * * *

Digression ends – back to the seashore where the numbers of natives had grown and they'd taken over the tea-making duties; most of our party of about forty people were delicately sipping tea from cups shaped out of half-coconuts.

The skipper was showing just how tough a cookie he was – the native with the knife had finished and had wrapped the Captain's foot tightly in a bandage of torn linen – from his demeanour, you wouldn't have known Fox had had a spike through it. I almost got all sentimental and offered him my shoes, but, well, you know – it was his own fault and – I might have stepped on a pebble.

And...

And...

And he hadn't been bothered about my toes and that ruddy hard football – sod him.

And anyway I was prevented from doing so by, what I call, the showgirl syndrome – in a moment, everything changed, like the situation had changed in the Palace Theatre, when the showgirl with the stinky fan had her curtain call.

Here's what happened next – let me set up the scene. The beach party had been under the soldiers' command and the two officers of the 26th Indian Battalion had detailed the laying of a fire in a small clearing amongst the widely spaced Sumatran palm trees, most of which, at this point, stood in their own straggly clumps of foot-high grasses poking out of the sand. In some cases the grasses had died where the seas had encroached and the roots of the palms were getting too much attention from the seawater. When this happened the palm's fronds, at the top of their stems, which normally spread out like the ferny arms of a giant naked – green – umbrella, had died away to a bunch not much bigger than a beach ball. These rotten roots gradually lost their grip and the serrated trunks began to lean over at the most drunken of angles.

The landing party had set their fire directly under one such palm.

Now – hang on while I take a breath – just as the villager finished wrapping his bandage around the skipper's foot and just as I was routing my conscience, which had been fighting me about whether or not to lend him my sandals – just at that point, out of the trees, directly above our heads, fell a writhing pair of... snakes.

They had climbed the gentle slope of the tilted palm and built a little love nest in the remnants of the tree's palm fronds. All thoughts of an amorous nature that they may have had were dispelled by the soporific effects of the smoke and they had fallen, literally asleep, landing in the middle of the fire.

Now, you will not be surprised to hear that those Sumatran Tree Snakes weren't best pleased to be in such a hot spot – they both got out of there very quickly. Their flight was accompanied by an instantaneous flood of rich Services' cursing and a squabble of the King's finest lifting their bums clear of the spot on the sand where they had been sitting, before the snakes could charge into the dark recesses offered by the legs of their shorts! There were half-coconuts full of tea being spilt and thrown everywhere as the snakes shot off in the direction of the sea, all very fast, no time to react – so I didn't and neither did the skipper. We just sat in a dignified, kind of naval way as our companions ran off after the disappearing snakes – shooting like madmen with their short arms – errrm – I mean small arms.

The skipper couldn't resist letting his mischievous streak show and, just as the group was settling down again, and having their 'coconut cups' refilled, he... slowly... looked up to the shrunken fronds atop the tree – and, blowing on the surface of his tea to cool it – expressed his curiosity as to whether there were any more members of that particular family of snakes still up there.

The landing party decided it was time to move its fire.

Then it nearly all started to go wrong!

As the party readied itself to move off, the Army lieutenant whispered into his companion's ear and the fresh young sub-lieutenant instantly volunteered to loan his shoes to Captain Fox – I smiled a 'got away with it' kind of smile – but the skipper had spotted a snag.

"Awfully good of you, Sub. Errrm, but do you mind if I ask you what size of shoe you take?"

"Size eights – sir."

"Ahhh," smile, "'fraid I take a size ten, be a bit tight. Especially with this bandage." Then the bugger just levelled his gaze directly to me. He was after my sandals. No chance. He'd stripped me of my shoes on the other island; he wasn't going to do it again.

Just in time the village chief reminded us all of this area's previous masters when he brought out a pair of finely painted sky-blue clogs, with a yellow floral motif, for the skipper to use. He looked a right Herbert – and he knew it – but he couldn't say no and risk offence – he was blending – and he'd had enough of my attitude for one day so he requested that I: "Tend to the launch please, Stoker Moss." He also decided that he didn't need half of the party so while he strode purposefully up towards the path that led to the local's village – looking like a right Wally in his brightly painted clogs – I ferried them back to *Ness*.

CHAPTER TWENTY-TWO

I returned to the beach with (I'll aye a ride) Laddie. We were looking forward to an afternoon's sunbathing – we were close to a sandy track leading to the village – the islanders had cleared a bigger space at the beginning of the track and four light fishing boats festooned with drying nets plus a pair of outrigger canoes rested between the gaps in the trees.

Now, as it happens, they also used to do 'coding' at Lowton St Mary, where I taught fire control, which I fancied made me an expert at sign language and I used it to ask one of the natives if we could borrow an outrigger canoe. He didn't quite get the message and ran off to fetch one of his more matrimonially minded daughters – I called him back and started again.

My message got through after one of the interpreters returned to the beach, after which me and Laddie paddled away in the outrigger, leaving the interpreter to do some business with a few villagers who had wandered down to stare at us.

A few minutes later Laddie and me were, kind of, suspended on a crystal clear skin of water, beneath which was a brilliantly coloured world of corals, covered in all shades of sea urchin and anemone and fish of every type. It was beautiful; I almost began to get all philosophical. "Did you ever think about water, Laddie? It's not alive itself but without it life could not exist." The Derbyshire man was listening with hooded eyes, his face and lids toning in the Sumatran sun. "Here it is calm and cooling and clear as crystal – food for the core of a man's soul. In the Atlantic it had been angry and evil and enough to crush or freeze or simply scare the very life out of a man." I was Aristotle Moss.

Laddie snorted, so I dug him in the ribs to wake him up.

As we leaned over the side, deeply enchanted by the wonders we were seeing, we started to drift further and further out to sea, until we could hear a commotion on the beach and looked up to see the boat's owner gesticulating for us to return.

"Aw sod 'im," says I to Laddie, "it ayen't time for us to return yet."

But the native didn't stop waving and pretty soon he was joined by the interpreter; the pair of them were pointing to the menacing black fin that was slicing athletically through the water's surface just a few yards away from us; suddenly, it seemed a good time to paddle back to shore.

They told us that we had been approaching the edge of the underwater reef and if we'd gone any further we were in danger of being toppled out by sharks, such as the one we'd seen. They fed on fish and the outrigger would look to them like a particularly tasty shoal of their favourite prey – there would have been a tribe of them and when they attacked, it would be in numbers... alright! Alright, we get it – gad, I'm shivering now, just thinking about it.

Our second run-in with sharks – it wasn't to be our last!

So, here we were on an equatorial island – a beautiful place, as long as you don't go for a paddle and step on a spiky urchin, or go for a canoe ride and get bitten by a shark, or get frightened to death by a tribe of two-inch frogs, or take shade under a tree and have a pair of poisonous snakes drop in. No wonder the islanders were nervous when I first stepped ashore.

Of the Australian radio operators we heard not one word – every one of the men sent in had simply disappeared. It did cross my mind that our island hosts had, perhaps, eaten them! The reality was more likely that these brave Aussies had been found by the Japanese garrisons and killed, so we left for our own home, HMS *Ness*, and set off for Sumatra just as the sun was setting.

BENKOELEN

Our next jaunt proved the name of our class of ship – HMS *Ness* was a River-class Frigate (a class of frigates named after rivers) and on this occasion we had to sail up-river to relieve a battalion of Japanese of their weapons. We knew they were there, they knew we were coming; they were the Japanese 26th Army Division, 6,000 heavily armed and professional soldiers; they had everything, including artillery that made our firepower the equivalent of a gnat's fart in a hurricane – our ship carried 141 men.

It began a bit ominously. The Japanese commanding officer had lined up 500 of his men along the whole length of the jetty – if it was a guard of honour, my appreciation of it sat at each end of my alimentary canal; almost choking my throat and twitching mercilessly around my sphincter – if it was his way of telling us that he could turn us into so much offal if he wanted to – it worked!

Fox was his match though – and it turned out to be one of those missions where the commanding officer wins the respect of his men; despite losing that sailing race in Singapore, Captain Fox could manoeuvre a ship.

We had been fortunate so far in receiving a friendly reception from the natives when we landed, but these were Japanese; the Captain ordered the ship's guns manned, although he left the covers on and then he navigated the *Ness* up the river, to the jetty, stern first.

Now, I say river and you may be thinking Thames or Severn or Trent – this one was more waddy. The sides were a couple of feet (okay, I'm exaggerating, I'm an old tar, I'm allowed to), try again, four feet (will you take three feet six inches?) from either side of the ship – he had sailors hanging over the side to keep checking the distance. He was very animated and the stream of communication passing through the tubes from Fox to the rather spirited coxswain, Petty Officer 'Ben' Grubb, must have been close to torrential as the ship inched upriver – backwards!

His main reason for going in backwards was that it would be easier to escape if the situation turned nasty, but secondly, *Ness* was designed to hunt subs; its most prolific weaponry was the depth charges and the Oerlikons on the rear decks, so we could also cause the most devastation from that end – especially if the Japs had more of their artillery hidden on the river bed... underwater... we could drop depth charges... it's a joke!

The first ashore was a party of thirty-eight men – to form a guard for the skipper and the officers of our own 26th Indian Division. The Japanese had cleared the wharf of any locals who wanted to watch, and the Japanese CO, who spoke good English, was 'invited' aboard, while his men loaded weapons on the decks. We kept him as our guest and finally delivered him to Padang – he was an ugly little short-arse and reminded me of a wizened version of old Monkey Brand from Tobermory.

Just as I didn't spare the rats in the U-boats, neither am I going to spare these Japanese with a gush of 'didn't they do well's'. In fact they almost make me regret what I said about the Nazis, who weren't barbarians – well, the normal serving soldier wasn't... errrm... unless you were Jewish – aw sod it – I take none of it back, now where was I?

Oh yes... the Japanese runts. You see, we were moored almost directly opposite the spot on the east coast of Sumatra, where, on Baka Island, an altitudinally challenged Jap like the one on the jetty forced twenty-two Australian nurses to walk waist high into the sea, and got his men to spray them with machine gun bullets – nobody could find anything civilised about that.

What did you do in the war, Granddad?

Chalky, whose sense of right and wrong, more than his name, had sent him white with dangerously quiet rage, had a piece of paper that he read from at supper that evening: "Listen to this, it's a report from an Australian nurse:

> *A Japanese officer, smaller and more 'nattily' dressed than his men, instructed us to walk from the palm-fringed beach into the sea until we were waist deep in the waves. A couple of soldiers shoved those who were slow to respond with the tips of their bayonets. Twenty-two nurses and one civilian woman walked into the waves and we left around a dozen stretcher cases on the beach. We were fully aware of our fate and all of the nurses put on a brave face. I remember hearing Irene Drummond, our Matron, call out: 'Chin up, girls. I'm proud of you and I love you all.'*

We were deathly quiet – Chalky carried on, not quite keeping the croak out of his voice: "The woman who wrote this, Vivian Bullwinkel, was one of the survivors; she describes what happens next:

> *They started firing up and down the line with a machine gun. They just swept up and down the line and the girls fell one after the other.*

Chalky looked up. "I don't think she'd have been exaggerating. Do you?"

The silence hung for half an hour before it slowly began to evaporate, and when it did, the heat that drove it away started our blood to simmer. Laddie, in that gentle way of his, brought us down from the boil and made us think about our side's behaviour when he asked his quiet question: "How many nurses and mothers and hospital cases and babies and unarmed civilians do you think we killed in Hiroshima, when the Yanks dropped their bomb?"

"That's different!" Only Bogie was answering back – everybody else just went quiet again.

"It's fuckin' different," Haggis joined in and shot Laddie a murderous look. Then he got up – and left us; something was festering inside the big man and the friendship he had been forming with Laddie looked about to disintegrate.

"That's right… it's not so… cruel." Chalky's contribution was full of uncertainty.

"Isn't it?" Only Laddie could have got away with this argument – only Laddie was bold enough to start it – and he wasn't letting us off too easy.

"No, it's not, Laddie, the bombs had a military reason," I had joined in, "we wanted them to surrender and they did."

"Actually – they surrendered after the first bomb, they were just being awkward on the *terms* of surrender and it was to bring them into line on the details that the Americans gave as the reason for dropping the second one. Maybe the Yanks are the evil ones." Laddie certainly had got us scratching our heads a bit.

"Are you saying that we are just as bad as they are?" came the question from an unusually emotional Chalky.

"I'm not saying anything," added Laddie, "but what if the Japs argue that, in killing the nurses, they were doing the same thing – making us afraid to tackle them, showing us how ruthless they are." He paused and then continued, "Or what if they say they were robbing us of the resources to tend to our wounded or sick soldiers and thus weakening our resolve – or what if they were just stirring us up in an attempt to dissolve our fighting discipline? All military reasons." Laddie was drifting into philosophy mode.

"They're just evil little bastards – and we should wipe 'em all out," Bogie's full concentration was on his dinner plate as he spoke, "in death camps like the Nazis did with the Jews!"

The chat around the table dropped like a frozen lump of stone.

He looked up. "What? What did I say?"

The quiet table emptied.

We left Benkoelen with a pile of weapons to dump in deep waters.

From our Japanese plunder, Virge was taken with a load of nicely made fuse boxes, which he 'borrowed' to store his personal effects. Meanwhile I spotted a number of parachute flares amongst the hoard and 'collected' the silk chutes to send back to Freda so she could use them for... well, let's just say I dreamt of the kind of lingerie she'd turn them into – and, of course, be wearing for me when I returned.

My dreams that night did me the world of good!

What I'm thinking about now is getting me going too – phwoar – I don't know about you but my head's just gone into a muse of French Knickers, lacy Bustenhalters, tight Basques and Suspender Belts!

"He he, come here, Freda.

"Ouch, me back.

"Awww, I strained something

"I think I got up too quick."

"Sit down, you daft old bugger, and I'll make you a cup of tea." Freda

You're right – you're right, it was okay getting this excited when I was 21, but for a chap in his 80s it could be quite dangerous – I've broken out in a cold sweat, I need to calm down a bit.

.

Tell you what, let's have a break, you go make yourself a cuppa and we'll start again when the image in my mind settles down a bit! See you back here in a minute.

CHAPTER TWENTY-THREE

O h – you're back – just a mo, I'm not quite ready, Freda's been mopping my brow and I haven't quite finished my PG Tips. Now, there's a great British tradition that has completely changed – today it's a tea bag in me cup, with boiling water from an electric kettle. When my mum was alive we had loose-leaf tea – brewed in a tea pot, one spoon for each person and another one 'for the pot'. I mean, how can a tea bag compare with that?

Mind you, I guess if I really thought about it – a tea bag in the cup is still giving the 'one for each person' bit... It's just 'the one for the pot' that's missing. It made all the difference – you could stand your spoon up... slurp... in Betsy's brew.

Shall we continue?

Right – deep breaths – okay – our Japanese officer... I remember he spent most of his time below and every time I saw him he wore a serious mask on his face and yet his eyes were like those of an eager dog in need of a friend. He muttered in his own guttural language, it was as if he was completely at a loss about the way things had turned out.

Midshipman Taylor had a good story at the mess table the next night – the skipper was teaching the young midshipman navigation and he came down now and again to share any successes he had. He was a smart lad, for a First Lieutenant's 'doggy'.

On this occasion he described the conversation he witnessed between the classically cultured English gentleman that Fox could be when he wanted to be, and this small Japanese Major of an intense military bearing who spoke pretty good English through a very thick accent.

It went thus:

> *Japanese officer*: "There have been a few breaches of law in Benkoelen recently."
>
> *Captain Fox*: "Really?"

Japanese officer: "Yes, I don't know what you will do when the Japanese Imperial Army withdraws – it can only get worse, the Indonesians don't like you English."

Captain Fox: "Two things, Old Sunrise." Pause, "Firstly, Japan no longer has an Imperial Army, just a rabble of POWs. And secondly, the rest of the world has a pretty low opinion of the soldiers of Nippon right now – so I wouldn't concern yourself about His Majesty's subjects." And as he turned to leave, "Take *the prisoner* below, Petty Officer."

We laughed but, of course, as we sailed south through the night our merry band of stokers couldn't end the evening without the normal argument: "No, Chalky, no, it's not a debate, it's an argument, alright?"

"Sod off!"

"You what?"

"You heard."

"Charming – especially coming from you."

That's the pleasantries done with, now for the thrust of our discourse. I started this one.

"Hey, you know that Jap we've got down in the bilges?" I was simply sharing my knowledge with them and at the same time laying off any responsibility for its truth onto my friend the telegraphist. "Virge says he's their chief of counter-intelligence, a really important bloke called Major General Suzuki," nobody spoke so I filled the silence, "we've brought him along as interpreter for our next port of call; what do you think about that?"

"I think you're wrong again – he's a company Major and his name is Sato. What do *you* think about that?"

"What do you mean *again* – you said I was wrong 'again' – when was I wrong last time?" They started laughing. "I'm never wrong!"

"Except last time."

"Well, that was last time – I'm right this time..."

"If he's counter-intelligence, he probably killed all those Aussies we've been looking for." Bogie paused, "I hope we're taking the little yellow twat back to stretch his neck."

"What Aussies?" Streak.

General groan.

"Streak, you dozy hillock, what do you think we've been doing hopping between those islands?"

"Islands?"

Muttering and mumbling abounded.

"You see, Streak..." Laddie began to patiently explain.

"Forget it, Laddie, you're wasting your time, Streak's so tall his brain's surrounded by clouds."

"It's rusted up."

"How is Rusty by the way?"

"You mean Tin Head?"

"Aye, Tinny."

"He died – they're flying his body home." I got a word in.

"No," Streak again, "nobody tells me anything."

"It was in the notices."

"How do you know that?"

"Because I read notices, I keep my ears open and I care." I may have sounded slightly supercilious, but it didn't deserve the response.

"Somebody get the darts."

"Great idea, do you fancy a game."

"No, I want to sling them at Mossy."

Then the wireless knob-twiddlers (or is that wire-twiddlers) turned up and we really started.

"Well, that was a waste of time!" sayeth Virge's oppo, Oppo, I never did learn his name.

"What was?"

"Disarming them Japanese. I mean, look what they gave us."

"It's a huge pile of weapons."

"Might be – but its not *their* weapons."

"What do you mean?"

"Well, look at it – it's all stuff they've captured from us and the Dutch and the Yanks. There's three Brit 25-pounders, a miscellaneous collection of bayonets, small arms and a few busted machine guns plus a load of fuses."

"There's more than that."

"Yes, there are some Dutch carbines with 100,000 rounds of ammo. That's it!"

"Are we chucking it *all* in the drink?" I jumped in.

"Hey up – what's he up to..." Scouse was quick on the pick-up.

"I bet Moss's thinking about shooting yon Jap twat." Bogie.

"What and sticking him in his African Rabbit?" Lofty.

"Acting Rabbit, you prat." Bogie.

"Hey, Herbie – what's for supper?" Lofty. "A curry would be good."

"I'm not cooking that foreign muck – not on an English warship."

"British!"

"Whatever!"

"Phwoar – is that you!"

It came to we few from who knows who – except it was Oppo who was smiling!

A day or so later I was the Japanese General's escort as he took his constitutional stroll around the decks for some fresh air. He was the very model of an eastern Major General and his sword was one of those Samurai jobs, it was beautiful, all folded steel and watermarks on the blade, sharp as a nagging tongue and I had my eye on it. The Captain approached and spoke with him quite cordially, telling him what we expected of him when we next berthed – he was to be our interpreter with the Japanese battalion at Oosthaven.

My interest in the sword caught Captain Fox's eye and he addressed me, "Stoker First Class Moss, I hope you are not thinking of taking that sword."

"Aye aye, sir – I mean no, sir."

He took me by the elbow and led me a few yards away, "Make sure you don't, the Japanese set great honour by these things; it will confirm his status and may help us when he's talking with the next battalion of his countrymen." He explained that if we took his sword it would rob him of his dignity and he might commit Harry-Karry and our people in Padang needed to debrief him before he did that.

If we had known the whole story of the Japanese cruelty, the sword would have been mine and I'd have lent him my sharpest kitchen knife! Maybe I still would.

Instead, I just said, "Aye aye, sir."

The General caught the meaning of what Fox had said and he unleashed a bombardment of glares at me from the haughtiest expression he could muster. His scowl wasn't working though; to me he just looked like Lemon – our old horse – when it had wind.

Such hatred is a powerful and myopic thing often seen in war and carried long afterwards.

OOSTHAVEN/TELUKBETUNG

By now you have probably come to realise that the quantity and quality of our knowledge depended a bit on where we heard it – we stokers were below-stairs lads and although Virge's telegraphists weren't much better – in a social sense – they had the ear of the above-stairs lot. They practised their wireless telegraphy in a cabin that was directly beneath the bridge... so, anyway, okay, so, what I'm trying to say is we weren't always too sure of what was happening or where we were – there were days when opinions and unimpeachable and factual knowledge often differed. Today was such a day.

"Where are we?"

"We're here."

"Laugh – I thought I'd never start!"

"We're at Telong Betong."

"Where's that?"

"Here."

"Funny."

"Hey, it says in this book that Telong means headland and Betong means settlement."

"So. We're at Headland Settlement. It's in the south of Sumatra."

"How do you know?"

"A freekin' porpoise told me!"

"You been talking to that Officer's Steward again."

"Piss off."

"We are not at Telong bleeding Betong, we're at Oosthaven– a port with an old airstrip."

"Oh yeah, and how do you know?"

"A tele–ruddy–graphist told me!"

"I think you're right. Look through these binoculars; you can see an airstrip plain as day."

"You're pointing them the wrong way – that's the horizon."

"Give me strength!"

"Hey up – hey up – we're nearly there."

"Nearly where?"

The babble slowed right down and a new voice entered the fray. "I will tell you where you *nearly* are – and you had better listen well, Stoker." It was the Chief, he didn't look happy, he was talking to Lofty and he continued (just imagine that sergeant chap speaking in *It Ain't Half Hot Mum*).

"You are nearly at Telukbetung, where the Dutch had an air force base called Oosthaven, which is right in the groin of the Bay of Lampung, which in itself is off the Straits of Sunda." He took a deep breath, looked around and began once more to address us: "These straits contain the ruined island of Krakatoa."

Now he was glaring. "You are also very, very *nearly* late for your watch and therefore are very, very, very *nearly* on the toe end of my boot." His voice was rising gently in volume with every word he spoke, "And if you don't get yourself on deck immediately I will put a rocket up an orifice of yours that will see you explode with ten times the violence of that bleedin' volcano. Now get out there." Such a murderous glare.

"And you idle lot," cripes, now he was talking to us, "get your toothbrushes out and start cleaning this bleedin' filthy floor – GET TO IT!"

Then he looked at me, "Stoker Moss."

Oh oh!

"The Captain wants you..."

Oh my good night – what have I done now?

"...he needs transport ashore."

Phew!

With that we entered a port at the south end of the island where we had another 'appointment' with the Japs. Again they were well organised and trying to impress – boy, did they need to, after all of the stories we were beginning to hear – 600 unarmed Aussie POWs bayoneted on Sumatra – anyhow, the skipper didn't need my boat, he just ran us up alongside the jetty and all these bowing and scraping Japs started loading tons of stuff onto the decks.

We left them all to the mercy of the locals – and, later on, the Stokers' Mess agreed that it was logical that they would keep some arms back for self-protection – well, that's what we would have done.

We were not detailed to take any prisoners back with us though – taking them prisoner was down to someone else, it did look as though – even if they hadn't kept any guns – they'd do okay; they were well disciplined and behaved as though they had the right to be in charge.

CHAPTER TWENTY-FOUR

We left the bay of Lampung knowing that our mission was over. HMS *Ness* was returning to a warm welcome in Emmahaven and Padang, but, before we dumped the last batch of weapons into deep water, I slipped back into ways introduced to me by Charlie, when I was but a young lad, and 'borrowed' a couple for souvenirs. One was a short sword in its brown leather sheath with marks on the handle that Scouse assured me recorded the people it had run through. The second was a handgun along with a spare clip of ammunition. I felt that we, or more especially yours truly, had been pushing his luck; the natives here were a long way away from friendly and a gun may come in handy in ensuring that I survived the mistakes and rampant passions of this particular period of the peace!

Returning to Padang, we found out just how dodgy the situation really was. As *Ness* steamed over the clear blue approaches towards Emmahaven harbour during the first full week of December, we could see random fires smouldering in buildings on the dock and a huge pall of smoke billowing out of the greenery from a couple of spots on the hillside behind the town. It was a big fire. I was beside Virge at the time and the tank landing craft moored in the harbour started flashing some kind of torch at us – "What's that?"

"Shhhh!"

"Sorreeee."

"Shh, I'm concentrating. Got it. That – you iggerent stoker, was Morse code. Didn't they teach you Morse at Malvern?"

"Course they did – no – what did it say?"

He lowered his voice and studied the little pad that he'd just written on, "It says – The Gloves Are Off Now."

"Crikey – what does that mean?"

"It means," and now Virge brought his eyes from his pad and stared directly at me, "that The Gloves Are Off Now."

We heard, when we reached our berth, that the smoke was the result of two villages being set alight by the Gurkhas.

The mess table was on form that night and the conversation buzzing – we were a full complement; me, Haggis, Chalky, Bogie, Scouse, Lofty, Laddie and Midshipman Tony Taylor, now nicknamed Doggy in these relaxed moments. Virge and Oppo joined us later.

"The wogs have killed a white woman." Doggy was sweating with outraged anger.

"Never!"

"No!"

"A woman?"

"Yep, and a Brigade Major – bloke called Anderson."

"Cowardly scabs – a woman – let 'em come on here and try it."

"They were engaged to be married."

I don't know how to do seven stokers saying no – in a disbelieving manner – at the same time, so imagine it.

"The skipper knew them."

"NNNNooooo. NNNoooo."

"Yep – Brigade Major Anderson and Red Cross Nurse Anne Allingham, his fiancée, they were attacked and killed by a group of Nationalists on Monday."

"How many?"

"They don't know."

"Must have been six or seven of them, to get the better of a British Major."

"Yeah, I bet he was tough."

"Played rugger."

"Cowardly buggers."

"Bet they had Japo arms."

"One of them swords."

"Cowardly beggars."

"Why'd they do it?"

"Because they're evil little squirts. I mean, here we are liberating them from the Nips and they do this."

"They should have their necks stretched."

Virge popped his head in; he had Oppo with him – they were always a great source of info – what with his radio and that – Chalky poured him a brew. It had gone extremely quiet. Every eye was boring into him.

"It seems," he began, "that a bunch of local nationalists were upset that the British authorities seemed to be favouring the Dutch. You know the Netherlands Indies Civil Administration (NICA)."

"Yeah – yeah – yeah – yeah – yeah – yeah."

Did we 'eckers like know – well... I didn't know – never heard of 'em – NICA, what does that mean? Oh yeah, it's just there – the Dutch.

Doggy gave us more. "This whole land is a mixture of small Independence groups of a variety of social beliefs and religions – it's making governing them real tricky. There's a bloke in Java stirring it up for us and for the Dutchies."

"I don't know why Lord Mountbatten doesn't sort them out." Virge's mate spoke for the first time and nine pairs of eyes flicked onto him.

"Yeah, well, it might not be them." Virge was chucking in a wobbler.

"Might not be them?"

"...ight not be them?"

"...not be them?"

"...be them?" We weren't quite *all* talking at once.

"I picked up a signal..." he lowered his voice to a barely audible hiss, "...now... keep this to yourselves, 'cos it might be sensitive – one or two of our intelligence boffins reckon it might be the Dutch authorities did it, trying to stir up the situation to their own advantage."

"No!"

"Never did like them Hollanders."

"Arrogant bunch."

"Look at the trouble they gave us in South Africa."

"Stretch their bleedin' necks."

"Anyway." One word from Virge and silence reigns again. "We got them."

"Have we?"

"Yeah – I heard that the General posted a huge reward for information about where the bodies were buried and half a dozen local blokes came to claim it. Each one blaming the other five."

"Daft sods."

"Yeah, word is that the Gurkhas went with them to find the graves and when they did..." Virge stopped talking and just drew his forefinger across his throat, "they were given an introduction to a *khukuri*. The 26th Indian Division then set fire to their home villages just to let them know how serious we Brits can be when you piss in our vinegar."

"Yeah, good on 'em."

"Plenty good enough."

"Cowardly beggars."

"What are women doing out here anyway?"

"She was a nurse, you dunce!"

"Pity it wasn't our flaming Acting Nurse."

A single cough stopped the babble.

It was Doggy, who had been seething quietly all through, "Look, this could be sensitive stuff and... maybe I shouldn't be telling you this, but I heard it different!" He was bristling with anger.

You could almost hear the chair legs scraping against the floor as the whole 'table' drew nearer to the storyteller, except we weren't sitting on chairs – it was a row of fixed metal lockers, with cushions on top, so we couldn't move them even if we wanted to.

"I heard that the Japs knew who it was and caught them – and handed them over – you know how they're trying to make up for being evil little sods – all that directing traffic they're doing – and stuff..."

"Yeah, yeah, yeah, get on with it."

"Well, I have it from a very good source that the Japs rounded up six insurgents and brought them into Emmahaven – gave them to the Indian army unit." He took breath and looked around, "Those lads from the 26th Indian look a bit like Gurkhas but they're not."

"Well, I hope we're going to stretch their necks – cowardly beggars."

"No need," says Doggy, "the liaison officer I was talking to says he saw the natives being loaded into a lorry, along with a Sten gun. He said they didn't get very far."

"Bloody hell, this is getting murderous."

"Aye," Haggis, whose moods had been improving and was back in circulation, spoke at last, "the gloves are well and truly off – you coming into toon, Herbie?"

The murders were a very important incident in the political circles of the day.

The incident also gave we ratings another view of the hard work that Captain Fox was doing, in what we could have seen as his 'jollies' in all of the ports that we visited. The socialising gave him a better understanding of the political atmosphere in these places and enabled him to advise his men what was safe to do and what was dangerous.

Doggy told us that the skipper took this particular incident quite badly; Major Anderson had an important role in the British authorities at Padang and, in his social rounds, Captain Fox had been on a picnic with Andy and Anne – the Brigade Major and his betrothed – to us they were names and indignation, to him they were real people.

In the light of the attitudes of today, burning the villages sounds brutal, but sixty years ago, it sounded like exactly the right thing to happen. And the two lovers are still dead. Our Mess wisdom concluded that they had just happened to be unlucky – they had been targeted.

* * * * *

Having mentioned them and their fabled knives, let's talk about the Gurkhas.

I have to say that I have always been fascinated by them and – one day, while we were in Emmahaven – I shared this information with Scouse, who was proving that he had a real talent for 'acquiring' things.

When I told him I had been keen to 'acquire' a *khukuri*, his ears swivelled like an Alsatian police dog as he picked up the scent of a sale.

I had already done plenty of schmoozing of my own, but when I asked one Gurkha if I could buy his *khukuri* – and could I take a look at it please – the owner told me that to draw his *khukuri* meant that he must also draw blood. The glint in his eye gave me the hint that maybe it would be my blood that he would draw and I, kind of, went off the idea.

Before too long Scouse came back to me. He suggested that there may be a spare *khukuri* or two in a warehouse that the Gurkhas had on the docks – carrying on to suggest that perhaps we should visit it and chat up the guard and persuade him to let us in to see if there was anything in there that would be more at home aboard HMS *Ness*.

I shared with him my noble belief that the Gurkhas were superb comrades with a courage that was often unique to them; very polite and with an edge of mystery that lends a romantic glory to their regiment. Then I asked Scouse a question. "If the guard on the door is polite enough to let us into the warehouse – are you *sure* that we will be let out again?" He took my most searching look and measured my pause carefully, before I continued, "and would you like to take the first try?" And then he took it again, turned and walked away, having decided that he wouldn't – so, that was that.

While we were still in Padang we had a full inspection by the General Officer Commanding of the 26th Indian Division, Major General H. M. Chambers, OBE, DSO – he had requested the inspection so that he could personally thank the ship's company for the assistance we had rendered to his soldiers in their tasks in Indonesia.

The old class system was alive and well and we were to be treated to a pat on the head. It was the first time that I'd seen a real-life General though.

A few minutes after the inspection party departed, Haggis caught up with me, "Are we away oot, Herbie – see a bit more of the toon maybe?"

I guess he was used to the pubs and clubs of Glasgow so a heavily armed division of Nationalists weren't going to put him off – or maybe he was still spoiling for a fight, there was a lot of tension in the big man from Glasgow.

Either way, it would have been terribly rude to say no.

"Hey, Herbie," Haggis continued, "d'yee ken these four mongrels," he was waving to a small gathering of some of the more ugly examples of our shipmates – I didn't know them but I guessed Haggis did, "they want to know if yee're takin yer wee gun and if yee are – can they come wi' us."

Suddenly, I was popular outside the Stokers' Mess too – seamen can be such jessies!

Eventually I sold me gun to a merchant seaman from Australia, just before we set off back – I reckoned I could manage in Scunthorpe without it – it almost proved to be a very bad move.

CHAPTER TWENTY-FIVE

Christmas was approaching, and a day or two later the skipper had wangled some orders for us to sail to India to join the Christmas and Victory celebrations in Bombay. As we were leaving Emmahaven harbour at Padang on full railing parade, we saw a Royal Navy destroyer; it was almost stopped and waiting for us to slide past before it entered the port. Every one of its crew members was at the railings, like us, all dressed in their Tropical Whites, and as we passed in the light of early morning, all manner of signals started to be exchanged between us.

Out of nowhere, I heard my name floating across the gap between us and recognised a lad from Lowton waving at me. His name was Alan and he was a dentist's assistant; we'd spent a few nights at the pub in Lowton sharing a jug of beer.

"Hoy, Ray," he hollered, "what are you doing here?"

Now, it was a perfectly reasonable question and a less awkward so-and-so than me would have responded with a greeting – but – what did I say? "Just getting away from you." It wasn't called for really – was it? He responded with a jaunty V-sign and then the two ship's crews did the formal bit to each other.

HMS *Ness* was back out at sea and heading for some excitement that could have put us in the greatest danger we had faced since the U-boats. The weather was bad and gradually worsening and our first warning of trouble came when the Captain's cultured tones spoke over the ship's intercom telling us of approaching freak weather, which had whipped up the water spout that he was watching through his binoculars.

It was heading towards us and he told us that a spout of that nature was well capable of capsizing a River-class Frigate. He completed his announcement by saying that he was trying to manoeuvre us out of its path but underlined the danger we were in when he requested, "For those of you who believe in God, this would be a very good time to send up your prayers."

His avoidance manoeuvre almost succeeded and, eventually, the edges of the spout just brushed down the starboard of our stern, where the motorboat was stashed. I caught word that a boat was wrecked and, being young and stupid and in charge of the motorboat, I had sprinted outside to see what was what. I never got there; the spout had passed but I didn't take account of the waves it had stirred up. I had just lifted the hatch and was clearing the steps leading from the workshops when a wall of water hit me and washed me back down, filling the passage that led into our Mess. I didn't have time to sit around and splutter though, because I knew that if another wave came I'd have some very wet messmates and they wouldn't have been pleased.

I sprinted up the ladder and pulled the hatch shut.

At the top of the ladder I thanked the designer who had thought to position the hinge so that the wave, when it hit, slung the hatch further open, rather than banging it shut on my skull!

Haggis strolled steadily through the door as I climbed gingerly back down the ladder, soaked as a codfish and rubbing the back of my head, where I had banged it against the deck when I fell.

"Bumped your head, Herbie?"

"Yeah, I slipped down the ladder."

"How's your boat?" Typical Haggis, he knew what was what and got straight to the point.

"Don't know, it's still a bit rough out there."

"Come on, it'll have settled down now, let's go see."

He was a good mate, Haggis – strong, unafraid, quiet, there when you needed him – since Singapore he'd been drinking more and was often in a strange mood, but that seemed to have eased a bit lately. And while he was fully aware of the source of his ill temper, neither of us could know of the shock that waited in Bombay.

As for the motorboat, it was in a mess; it would need a lot of work before we used it again – and the spout had also stripped away a row of depth charges, but there was very little other damage. Haggis and me were on deck looking at the sorry state of the motorboat when the skipper approached – "Put a tarp over it, Stoker, and get it lashed down; we'll see what they can do with it when we get back to port."

"Aye aye, sir." I was a bit down in the dumps and rubbing my head softly. "Sir?"

"Yes, Stoker."

"What do we do now, when you want to go into port?"

"Oh, don't you worry about that, I'm sure I'll have a contact that will lend me something," he smiled, then he gave Haggis an enquiring look.

"Bumped his head, sir," came from the Glaswegian.

"Ah. Yes. Well then, as a precaution, get him down to see the MO, just in case that bang on the head has done any damage."

"Knocked some sense into him more like." Trust Haggis.

"Quite," came the answer as he went off to inspect the rest of the afterdeck. At that moment First Lieutenant Morrison proved his mettle and his difference to the last Number One – the Aussie – "Don't worry about dealing with the boat, Stoker, Midshipman Taylor will do that for you. Get him to the doc."

He was a class bloke – they both were.

Our job in – what had been – the Dutch East Indies was finished and over the next week HMS *Ness* sailed up to Bombay and the Christmas celebrations. Our captain was definitely a party animal and, this time, I was convinced he intended to let his hair down. He certainly 'stamped his foot' and showed his seniority in the status rankings during a 'sail-past' we took part in. Virge was chatting with him just outside the bridge – they were discussing which knobs to twiddle for music at an upcoming party.

The *Ness* was about to form up in a flotilla of six including two very modern destroyers – Virge thought they were Battle class – they were flashing messages to each other arguing about which one would take the lead position in the flotilla. Fox saw them bickering and stepped in with a signal of his own and all five ships fell in astern of HMS *Ness*.

That evening, our mess table discussion turned into a really silly affair. The mood, bolstered by the fact that today's mail delivery was full of Christmas cards from home – we'd all snuck off to find a quiet spot to read the messages and dab dry our eyes, away from the risk of being seen by those of our mates who'd had no mail yet and the merciless 'ribbing' that would have followed.

Eventually someone brought up the subject of the flotilla – everyone but Haggis joined in – his black mood was back and he just grunted and went up on deck – I noticed his food untouched and the card screwed up in his hand and thought perhaps I should follow him but my thought was distracted.

"So, *chew, chew, swallow*, what's that supposed to mean then?" the suppertime debate began.

"Means he's a bigwig!"

"Or... related to bigwigs."

"Or... his family are bigwigs."

"Or..." uh-oh, it's Bogie, "or... he's shagging a bigwig." Clatter: "Sorry, sorry, sorry – I said I'm soddin' sorry. WILL YOU STOP CHUCKING THAT BLEEDIN' GRUB AT ME!"

It wasn't the food he was complaining about really – it was the metal knives and forks that the food was speared on. It went quiet for a minute or two while everybody got their cutlery back – and then it started again.

"The skipper's family has got estates in Devon, *chew*."

"Yeah, I heard Devon – *swallow* – he's a Quaker, his family name's Cookworthy, they're into china clay mining and pottery making."

"I heard they're farmers – *chew, swallow* – dairy."

"I heard his family owns metal works in Cornwall."

"Somebody said he's a double-barrel – his full surname is Cornish-Fox."

"No, it's not – Cornish is his middle name – a second Christian name."

"Doggy reckons his great-granddad served under Nelson. His name was Captain Thomas Louis, he had command of a 74-gunner at the Battle of the Nile."

"Louis is a Frog name – how do you get from Louis to Fox?"

"I heard his family owns an umbrella frame factory in Derbyshire."

"Umbrella frames?"

"Yes – frames, made out of metal – so that fits with metal works – for umbrellas – they've got the patent."

"That'd be worth something."

"I heard he's been out with Maureen O'Sullivan."

"The Hollywood actress?"

"Yep."

"Did he shag her...? Oy – ow – ouch – fuck off – stop it."

My turn to speak, "Bogie, give me my fork back. The rest of you, just look at the state of this table – that's good meat – if you don't clear it up, I'm feeding the beef to the sharks and you lot can have the greyhound."

"Yes, mother."

"I mean it!"

Haggis stuck his head through the bulkhead and kind of growled, "Oy, Herbie."

"What!"

"Are we awa' doon the toon?"

"Great idea, Haggis – while these grunters clean up."

CHAPTER TWENTY-SIX

Haggis and me walked down to one of the dockside taverns, found ourselves a table outside, where, in a very quiet way, we watched some of the world's most exotic moths fly into the flames of the torches. You remember how Haggis had started to drink more seriously since we left Singapore, well, it seemed that, tonight, he was going for a personal best in whisky consumption – he'd already had a couple of doubles and, I'd matched him, well... I had had one... single... just to be soshiable, sochyable, sociable – I was still hoh-kay. On Haggis the spirit was having no effect; on me it prompted a need to release the huge curiosity that was burning inside me – about his changes in moods.

My curioshity couldn't hold its drink like what I cudahadadid and it was screaming at me to ask him – so I asked. "Haggis?"

He answered with an indeterminate noise.

"Has something been bothering you? Only, since Singapore... well, you've been..."

As usual he interrupted me, breaking in with: "I got a letter, in Singapore, from ooer lass, aboot ooer kid. Duncan." That's all he said.

I remembered the paper he'd torn into tiny pieces and I couldn't leave it at that so, on I ploughed, "Duncan?"

"Aye – Duncan."

Crikey, it was easier getting sense from a seaman.

"Your brother?" Me. No answer. Pause.

Try again: "Duncan?" Me. Silence. Pause.

"Is he okay?" Me. No answer. Pause.

"No – he's had it!" Quietly Haggis levelled his gaze at me and I saw the strangest thing – there seemed to be a film of moisture covering this hard man's eyes.

"Had it?"

"Aye. The daft sod got hi'self in one o' them Jap camps."

Time for an assumption, "Oh, I'm sorry... didn't he survive?"

"Survive, Herbie – of course he feckin' well survived, what do you think he is – a feckin' Nancy?" He gave me his gaze for a few seconds, but it was wavering. "He had malaria and beriberi, he was two years younger than me." The expletives that streamed from him were spat with a deep and dangerous anger that drained the essence from his eyes.

"No, I... sorry... well, what's up then..." except suddenly he wasn't listening to me, he was away with the ghosts and the spirits flown.

"I blame the feckin' English." That was all he said – nothing more – for fifteen minutes.

Halfway through the silence I bought him a treble and settled for a beer to try to even myself up.

"I'm English," I said, but rather timorously... just something to try and restart the conversation.

His answer was that cold empty gaze that didn't turn away.

"Oooer Duncan was thirteen and a half stone when he joined – and not an ounce of it was fat."

"I se—"

"He could run up an' doon Ben Nevis wi' a sack o' coal on his shoulders."

Me: quiet.

"They reckon he was six stone when they found him. Six feckin' stone? He was six feet tall."

"Still alive though," I tried, "they can build him up ag—" cut me off mid-flow why don't you?

"He was looked at by an English doctor, on the train. To the air strip."

Again I went for quietness.

"He had some kind of disease in his eyes. He was blind. Completely feckin' blind. F'ck... f'ck... f'ck." He smashed his huge fist down on the table with each word.

I daren't say a thing – and I was filling up.

"He was all muscle, see. He had no fat to live off. He was tough, Herbie – tough."

"I'm sor—"

"Then, ooer lass said – that the doctors told him they could make him fit again – but his eyes were done for."

Quiet.

"Damn them doctors. If they'd told him different and we'd got him home. Me Ma and ooer lass would have sorted him out, they wouldn't a let him..." long quiet bit, "he had a girl, pining for him, she'd a helped." The big man just dropped his head and one, single tear slapped hopelessly onto the tabletop. I felt I should stretch out my hand

and touch him, but, well, it was awkward like. Then he remembered I was there and breathed in.

"He stepped off the train, Herbie. Walked through all the carriages from front, where the doctor was, to back and when he could get no further – he just opened the door and stepped off. It was at full speed." The moisture had cleared away from Haggis's eyes – now, they looked as empty as a killer's conscience.

What the hell do *I* do now – I wanted to give the big feller a hug – but he'd not have that – nothing for me to say. So I just sat, and leaned a bit closer to him.

"The black dogs, Herbie, they're slavering in me heed – gnawing awa' at my mind, I need to let 'em loose, where's all the rats gone, Herbie? I'm aching to go hunting rats."

Something to say at last. "We speared 'em all, Haggis – the rats have all given up and run home tail a'tween their legs. Do you fancy a few more whiskies?"

The next day – my head was pounding like a battleship's engine, no – like a depth charge, fixed inside my skull, no – like a... well, you get the idea, it was P O U N D I N G – my temples imploding as my eyeballs jumped out of my eye sockets with each heartbeat – by gad, it hurt – never again! And my spine was just as painful as my head; you see, we had been staggering back when he started chucking bricks at the wire fencing surrounding a chicken coop that he thought was the Japanese POWs' enclosure in Singapore. A couple of friendly members of the military police came to help – so he abandoned the bricks and chucked them over too. Then he ran at the wire, trying to climb over and get to them. Luckily he fell off and knocked himself out cold. The MPs were dragging him off when I told them his story, appealed to their better nature like – they took no notice and continued to persuade him to follow them, with their stout wooden battens. But my smooth tongue – and a hefty bribe from my store of cigarettes – won the day and they left me to carry the comatose Glaswegian back – from the chicken coop to the ship.

Ah, something just moved in his hammock, wait a mo, yep it's him – he's awake – he's looking at me – he's smiling – he's out of his hammock now and humming some Scottish reel. He should be poleaxed with pain like what I am. He's off for his breakfast – he's talking to me – his black mood gone – we released it last night – he isn't suffering at all, not with a hangover, not from the batten blows... just a minute, I need to yell at him, "Oy, you noisy Scottish twat, will you SHUT it – I feel like bloody death here!"

"Herbie," he says, "there's no need for that kind of language, I'm off for eggs and bacon – want some?"

"No..." moan, "just pass me Chalky's bucket."

Now listen to him... he's ruddy well whistling.

* * * * *

199

Christmas was galloping at us now, and the skipper was about his normal duties when in port, wining and dining. I seemed to be ferrying him to some lunch or dinner almost every day; on one occasion, we had to help him settle gently into the boat on his way to dinner one evening, with his legs misbehaving due to his not having sufficient blood in his alcohol-stream after his lunchtime event. Midshipman Taylor offered me his assistance in getting the skipper into the patched-up launch; we took an arm each – around our shoulders – and kind of carried him to the boat.

We all smiled later on, when we heard he'd fallen asleep behind a sofa as the after-dinner speeches droned on and had to be revived by his driver and almost carried to the car. An obliging cruiser captain ferried him back to the *Ness*.

I'm not saying that Fox was a drunkard, because he wasn't – far from it – and most of the lads knew how valuable this kind of 'work' could be. Today it's called networking – in those days, knowing the right people and being known by them, in times of huge confusion, could get you the fuel that a dozen other ships wanted too, or the provisions, or ammunition, or medical supplies – or more important, put you on top of the list for the mail deliveries.

I don't think I'd have been as good at all of this socialising as he was though, and that showed just before Christmas when he wanted to hold another of the kiddies parties and, as I had been at the core of organising the one in Padang, he asked me to volunteer – but my heart wasn't in this one.

It was to be for the Toffs of Bombay and their children. The only deprivation that they had suffered during the war was that their servants were not able to buy them their preferred brand of tea – so I walked away from it. Virge and his pals tried to step in but they got disenchanted when the little snots wouldn't eat the food they had prepared – the guests were part of the British Raj and were not about to eat the kind of food we lowly matelots could put on – they said it wasn't good enough!

"Some of us retreated to the Mess," Virge told me later on, "we were thoroughly pissed off. One of the Royal Indian Navy officers poked his head in our Mess and said something condescending until Mulvaney – you know the guy from southern Ireland – said to him: 'And what can we do for you, you arrogant black bastard?' Needless to say, he didn't stay."

I know Lord Somewhere-or-other and the son of Lord Somewhere-else attended along with a couple of the Governor's ADCs and a bunch of the children of the servants of Government House – all healthy and chubby – not the living skeletons from Sumatra.

These were all influential people and I was the son of an... 'entrepreneur'... errrm... a 'businessman'... well, a man with a carting business... anyway, we very definitely lived in completely different worlds.

Christmas Day came – I had prepared the turkey and taken it to the cook to make sure it was cooked to perfection – all the trimmings – we couldn't trim up the Mess (the streamers might block the pumps) and no presents – we didn't get a visit off Virge either, which I though a bit odd – until he dropped in on Boxing Day. He looked as though he'd been in a boxing ring – he had two beautiful 'shiners' and there was something different about him.

Bogie spoke first. "What's up, Virge – did one of them Yanks catch you shagging his girl and give you a smacking?"

"It's your specs, isn't it?" Chalky noticed.

Virge wore spectacles – except not today. Today he was without them.

"Did yon Yank take them off ye?" Haggis didn't sound particularly interested.

"You know," said Chalky, "it always baffles me – you telegraphists all wear glasses and yet – it's your ears you use most."

"S'coz they're clever buggers," sayeth Scouse.

"They're wankers..." had to be Bogie, "that'll do your eyes in every time."

"Shut it, Knights!" Virge snapped back, he was getting hot under the collar.

Laddie calmed us down with his question, "Are you okay, Virge – what happened?"

We all sat up – attentive.

"It was yesterday. I got drunk. Missing home and all that..."

"Too much sherry in yer pud?"

"Shut it!" I glared at Bogie, who was tittering with Lofty, and then I turned back to Virge, "but – how'd you get the black eye?"

"I fell down the ladder trying to reach shore and cracked my head on the concrete. Smashed my specs to pieces."

"You should go see the doc – he'll get them replaced." Laddie was full of concern.

"I did." Pause, "And he won't." Pause, "He says I don't need them enough for Navy work."

The banter never really got going after that – I left them to it – I had things to do.

The Captain's inspection of the Mess, a few days later, didn't go well either – I had prepared our Christmas turkey and sent it off to the cook – I already said that, didn't I? Beautiful it was – any road – I'd put the giblets in a separate pan to take to the fridge to save – but I forgot and in that temperature stuff didn't save – and when the Captain stuck his head into the galley, his nose twitched, he strode over to the pan, took off the lid and the stink hit us all.

"What the devil are these, Stoker Moss?"

"Ah, sir, sorry, sir, I was saving them for gravy (always have an answer) but they've gone off a bit quicker than I thought. I'll chuck them over the side."

"See that you do." He glared and looked around the room, "We might not be at war but I will not put up with this kind of sloppiness," then he looked back at me, "sort this Mess out, Stoker Moss." And off he marched.

When we left Bombay it was to sail back to Ceylon, where we were looking forward to some shore leave – but the weather had different ideas. It was awful, wind howling out its challenge as the sea laid the full fury of its wrath on HMS *Ness*. When we cleared the shelter of the Indian coast the frigate ploughed so deep into the oncoming waves it seemed as though we would never come back up. The storm lashed the whole length of our decking, blasting it with warm salt waters. In naval terms we were 'shipping it green' and the *Ness* was creaking so much she kept us all awake.

As the middle watch was ending, a huge crashing brought us all onto our feet. One of the depth charge racks, loosened by the waterspout, had broken away and we had high explosives rolling around the deck – a cultured voice over the tannoy told us to, "Stand down, gentlemen, there's nothing we can do, the decks are too dangerous in this weather." That would have been okay if he hadn't finished with, "The charges shouldn't explode unless they catch something wrongly, and with a little luck they will be washed into the sea before that can happen."

CHAPTER TWENTY-SEVEN

A fter four days and nights under way we finally sailed into Trincomalee harbour in north-west Ceylon and we were in a pretty tatty condition, and there were wild rumours flying around about 'an incident' involving two seamen. Immediately we got a visit from the captain of the port, or Captain D, who pulled a surprise inspection and... well, let's hear what happened from the mess table.

"The old bastard's only put us on some kind of punishment duty."

"Why?"

"He says we're not in the condition expected of a Royal Navy warship."

"Now that's a surprise, we spent half that last journey underwater – it was so bloody rough."

"Bastard!"

"Typical – these jumped-up harbour commanders think they're real seamen – err – what is the punishment?"

"Don't know."

"I do."

"Okay... tell us then."

"Well, it's very convenient for Captain D – you see, what with all these half-starved POWs they're finding, Winston has banged some heads and told the men in charge to get them fed properly, cared for and treated royally."

"I bet the old cigar chewer doesn't want the bad press if they survive the camps and then die in our hands."

"Cynic."

"Do you want to hear this or what?"

"Go on."

"He's laid on a Royal Air Force air-lift system to get as many of them flown home as quickly as he can."

Virge had strolled in and was looking very – serious.

The banter continued: "Winston will want a happy story to stop all that grumbling about those bleeding A-bombs the Yanks dropped – they're evil things."

"Quite – anyway – they want a flotilla on the Bay of Bengal to be ready just in case one of the rookie flight lieutenants drops his plane in the drink."

"And?"

"I thought Foxy said we were due some leave, so why would he accept the punishment, unless they had forced him to?"

"All I know is that Captain D has sentenced us to an indeterminate air-sea rescue patrol in the Bay of Bengal."

Virge dropped the first of his typically sinister hints into the conversation with, "It's worse than that." But everyone ignored him.

"Indeterminate?"

"Yep – until he says different."

"No – can't be – surely not – surely we volunteered."

"I can only tell you what I was told."

"It is for an indeterminate period." Virge again, and this time he caught our attention, so we all went quiet. "It's a slap on the wrist for losing Elmes and Speller."

"Losing?"

"Elmes and Speller?"

"What you fucking on abaht?"

"The two ABs that got swept overboard."

"I didn't know…"

"Did we get them back?"

"What were the two stupid pillocks doing getting swept over…"

Virge had patched up his glasses and was polishing them carefully. "We did get them back," he said, "but they had both drowned."

"No."

"Yes."

"So that's why we're on this soddin' patrol instead of going home."

"Yeah, 'cos two stupid ABs got themselves drowned."

"Shut it, Bogie."

"Bet the Old Man's well pissed off."

"Actually, it's not going to be that bad," Virge was reaching his usual dénouement, turning his bad news into good. Or, at least, slightly better news, "I've heard Fox and Morrison are planning to turn it into a holiday."

"What?"

"How?"

"They've had all of the library books changed – and a rifle range set up, firing over the quarterdeck plus they've stocked up on new films – chucked out all the propaganda stuff – and the electricians are rigging a theatre for the movies – and – and they reckon we'll have absolutely minimal watches."

"Sounds great – when do we go?"

"As soon as Hubert gets the order."

"Stops his partying more like!"

By the middle of January, HMS *Ness* received orders to patrol an area of the Bay of Bengal as part of a flotilla of British warships, on air-sea rescue duty. We had a grid of sea to cover and the Captain had decreed a method of 'steaming' (well... steaming sounds so much more romantic than 'oiling' or 'dieseling', doesn't it) out to our furthest position first thing in the morning and then letting the currents and winds carry us back to the starting point during the day.

We only ever had three people on watch, the officer of the watch, the lookout and the duty sparker listening to the radio in case we got the recall.

Sounds idyllic, doesn't it? The weather was fabulous – a short burst of work for we stokers to manage and then a whole day, drifting slowly on a perfectly blue and fathom-less ocean powered only by the softest of warm, tropical breezes, under sparkling blue skies – nothing to do but top up the sun tan during the day and count millions of stars at night. And the air so fresh it tasted like ice cream.

For the first couple of hours – it was idyllic. But, remember, we were young men, we've been on this ship for months, once you've read a book, seen a film and fired a rifle, there's nothing to do except listen to the drone of the engines of an RAF plane floating across the sky thousands of feet above us – going – home.

We were desperate for a bit of excitement – Haggis tapped me on the shoulder one afternoon and asked: "Oy, Herbie, what are we going to do? Do you fancy a wee swim?"

By now you will know the answer to that question – "No, I chuffing well don't want a swim – this is the Indian Ocean – it is miles deep and I can only do one length of Malvern swimming baths – and before you say it I'm not going in with me lifebelt on – I'll look stupid." I almost sulked for a few minutes as I watched my mate rounding up a group of sailors to join him in his aquatic frolics.

Then came a touch of Moss's inspired mischief when I said to him, in front of the rapidly undressing band of swimmers: "Haggis, will you all tie one of these ropes around you...?" Haggis, in an unusually naive mood and thinking I was concerned for his safety, put one of those 'awww, in't that nice' kind of smiles on his face, like your mum uses when you give (what she thinks is) your last sweet to your sister.

The gooey look soon slipped off when I finished me sentence: "...and tie a grappling hook to your belt so we can haul in the sharks as they sink their teeth into you. I fancy a bit of shark steak!"

They all took umbrage to my spoil-sport sarcasm and I was halfway around the gangway, being chased by a dozen naked seamen all baying for my blood, when the idea struck – shark fishing – we can go shark fishing – but for real. I evaded my pursuers by ducking up the ladder to the bridge, where I requested permission from the Captain, for a spot of fishing for anyone not on watch. Which was everybody – bar three. Being the sportsman himself, he thought it a 'capital' idea.

By next morning, me and Chalky had our fishing gear sorted.

Now, if you're thinking rod and line – well, no – we didn't have a rod. Think, more like a length of inch-thick rope fixed to a convenient anchor point on the ship. This length of rope must have been about twenty fathoms long (fathoms? Look it up, I'm feeling all nautical.). The rope had to reach over the side and drift out into the ocean. About eight feet from the end of this rope we had secured a float, which consisted of an empty oil can (round and about twice the height of a bucket); it had a screw-on cap that had been hastily sealed up – at the end of the rope we secured our hook. We'd formed the hook from steel rod, in the engineers' workshops and filed it to a wicked point.

While all of this activity was going on I had persuaded Cook to give us a huge lump of cooking fat – lard – about six inches by six inches by ten inches – to use as bait. I could see the Old Man watching as we hurled all of this kit over for the first time. Like the rest of us – and the growing crowd of nosey matelots that had caught wind of what we were doing – he saw the lump of fat splat onto the surface of the water when I chucked it overboard and then gently begin to sink. Its disappearance followed a few minutes later by the 'float', which emitted a constant stream of air bubbles as it began to fill with water.

There were some harsh words as the whole group of us hauled the gear back over the side and at least twenty-five would-be engineers offered their advice – summed up most eloquently by Chalky with the words, "What dewberry chucked this container over without the seal in place?" I don't know why they all looked at me but I was let off the hook by this Irish lad who jumped in with, "Sure dat can wus sealed, I screwed it on meself."

Back to Chalky, "What did you seal it with, you dozy Mick, chewing gum?" Someone else piped up, "You could have used Navy porridge – that would have stuck it!"

Our crewmate from the Emerald Isle suddenly went very red. "Er, and what *exactly* do you mean by 'sealed'?"

The upshot of all of this was that Chalky carried the container down to the workshop and welded the sealing cap in place; he also sorted out a small problem with the hook that had nearly come loose, and he sharpened it up a bit more.

When he came back, we were in business again.

Just before I launched all of the tackle overboard, I noticed a flash of teeth marks in the bait we had used and we all got very excited and started nattering about having had a 'bite' already. In fact we spent about five minutes minutely examining the marks in the lump of fat and trying to decide what kind of shark had caused it and how big it was before a large cough from the skipper settled us back to the task in hand. About three of us wanted the glory of launching the fishing tackle this time and we did it without any further encouragement. Although one of my co-casters did give me the opportunity to use a few of the swear words that the Navy had taught me when he stamped on me toes – and them just back to their normal colour after two months being a variety of shades of purple and yellow.

* * * * *

Fishing is an odd sport – our Arthur has always been a keen fisherman – me, I get bored with it so quickly – I mean how long can you watch a metal container bobbing up and down on the water before your eyes start to get heavy.

An hour later and we'd just started discussing the suitability of the bait. Maybe the teeth marks showed that our prey had tried it and didn't like it – I tried for an alternative but, no matter how hard I leaned on him, Cook wouldn't give us the side of pork I had my eye on, he said it was for some toff's dinner that the Captain was organising. There's no concept of priorities in the Navy.

When I got back on deck they started talking about using me as bait instead – now, that was unkind – the whole exercise was my idea – to add a little excitement to their lives. They were giving me a really hard time. My mouth was going ten to the dozen, my back against the railing with a perfect arc of gradually more aggressive seamen a few feet away, facing me – when the Captain piped up.

'What a great bloke,' thought I – 'he's going to put them all on a charge for harassing me.' He didn't, he just asked a question: "Where's your float, gentlemen? It appears to have sunk again."

"Chalky, you dumbo – call yerself a welder!" I was on the attack now and yelling so loud I missed the lookout's shout down to us.

So he shouted it again. And then again. Everybody heard him before me and ran towards me, I turned to see the rope darting this way and that and then back this way again. And I joined in the demented dancing.

My hands were amongst the throng that grabbed the rope and pulled, and then the rope pulled back and we pulled again and a torrent of advice poured into our ears from every possible angle. "Play it – don't let it jerk the rope – play it – it'll break free – it'll break the mountings on the float – did you tie the hook on securely – (sheepshank) – it's a blue – it's a great white – it's a sperm shark – sperm whale, you tit – hey, could it be a killer whale, I've heard they're viscous – you mean vicious, you dolphin – play it – I would if I knew what 'play it' meant – don't let it jerk the rope – play it – I'm playing the bloomin' thing." And so it went on, like the babble of the rabble at a Cairo souk.

Eventually the rope went quiet – and we hauled and hauled – we got the float back to the surface – then inch by inch came the rope, attached to it was a Black-tipped Reef Shark, about four feet in length.

Just let's stop a moment here. We were members of His Majesty's Royal Navy. We wore a very stylish uniform – navy blue serge – with an open collar and bib. Shoes you could use as a mirror and a super smart flat-topped hat, set at a jaunty angle; black silk tie (some said to commemorate the death of Nelson) knotted in a particular way and seven creases (five if you were a short-arse) neatly ironed into the trousers. If your imagination contains this image – of a very sophisticated body of highly trained, professional naval ratings, standing to rigid attention and being inspected by the highest admiral of the fleet... well, just at this particular moment, your imagination would be dead wrong.

We looked like a scruffy bunch of young fellers, dressed in sweat-stained T-shirts and shorts of all lengths, in overalls and safari suits, with scuffed pumps on our feet and every one of us jumping and leaping about and whooping like a cowboy on an unbroken mustang.

By the time we had got the 'float' back on deck we had realised that the length of rope from float to hook could have done to be longer. And, once we had realised this, the very still shark poised on top of the ship's railing, looked much closer to three feet long than it was to four.

It hung in that position for quite a few seconds – being held on top of the railing by the weight we were putting on the rope that was tied to the hook sticking through the side of its cheek and the counterbalance of its own weight, the majority of which was hanging over the side of the ship. That's when it moved. Fell off the railing and slithered along the deck towards us.

* * * * *

It scattered our crowd of sailors like a rat at a bonfire, it even snapped its jaws at one sailor's pins as it slipped past him, taking with it half a leg of his extended shorts – it's a good job he was a little chap – if he'd been well-hung he would have been singing soprano.

The Captain was almost laughing – but, the expression on the face of the officer, who had been standing the afternoon watch for the past twenty minutes, told us that he took a less jovial view – he shared his view with the ear of the Captain and our skipper stopped laughing.

"Can I have your attention, chaps?" Captain Fox was never comfortable when all eyes were on him, even though he spoke like a real toff, "if we're going to carry on with this shark fishing, you need to lengthen the rope so that you can haul the float aboard before the fish clears the water – and then, to save anyone losing a leg, you must take a rifle and kill the shark before hauling it on deck. Is that clear?"

A hearty 'Aye aye, sir' droned out what the officer of the watch said to him next. "Ah yes and errm, Lead'n' Stoker White and Stoker First Class Moss?"

"Yes, sir." Uh oh. "Aye aye, sir."

He ignored my mistake. "Seeing as how you seem to be in charge of this exercise, you must see to it that the decks are thoroughly cleaned of any blood or mess after the fishing ends. Now, see to the one you just landed."

A delegation ran off to raid the quarter deck rifle range – returning with an armful of Dutch carbines – they seemed hell-bent on using up every one of the thousands of rounds that the Japanese army had left us, to kill this first shark!

Bullets began to ping around in every direction, before the officer of the watch took charge and made us hang the shark back over the side before we shot at it. It was a while before I let them pull it back aboard and set it on a spare piece of tarpaulin that I brought up, to keep the deck clean; most of the crowd had dispersed – surprising how a sailor will do that if there's the remotest chance he may be asked to swab the decks!

Anyway, we couldn't cook that first one; it had so many bullets in it that it was like a solid lead weight, so (again the Moss inspiration) we cut it up to use as further bait.

It wasn't long before we had our metaphorical rod in the water again and after just a few minutes we had our second shark. This one was a biggy – almost seven feet in length – we were much more careful about killing it, and by evening I had a few succulent shark steaks to practise my culinary skills on. The next day at first light, one of the lads chucked a piece of chopped-up shark over the side and the sea went mad, thrashing and boiling and bubbling. It seems the word had got around shark town and a whole shoal of them were hanging about waiting for us to chuck in more food – over the next two days we had thirteen sharks 'in the bag' after which the pastime seemed to lose its appeal to most of the crew.

For me, being the 'keeper-of-the-refrigerator' often had a few perks and being able to store the shark meat was definitely one of them. That first day I boiled a shark steak and fried it and it went down a treat – my messmates were actually complimentary and our Acting Rabbit was never short of extra meat all the way back to Portsmouth.

When I asked the Captain if he'd like a drop of Shark Fin Soup, he declined – he didn't know what he was missing – and having never prepared any, neither did I.

After about a fortnight on air-sea rescue, our patrol ended and we took up a berth in Ceylon – by now we were bored witless and it didn't take a genius to predict that there could be trouble when we hit the bars in town (not me of course – after Bombay I would never drink again).

CHAPTER TWENTY-EIGHT

C alled Sri Lanka these days, the island of Ceylon is on the toe-end of India a few degrees south of Madras and has a fabulous natural harbour just off the Bay of Bengal, which carries the fairy tale name of Trincomalee. Half the ship's company got six days' leave and then swapped with the ones who had remained on watch. Some of the officers began to drift away from the ship. We were told that HMS *Ness* was to begin its journey home six days later – 18th February 1946 – and the day before we had a small leaving party for Midshipman Taylor, who was off to take up a new position as Lieutenant on a minesweeper – the very thought of sweeping mines kept Virge away from his farewell do.

Being let off the leash on leave in Ceylon often brought out the high spirits in us. One day I was walking along with Scouser discussing the local business opportunities and the need to clear all of our accumulated stocks before we landed in England, when we passed a stand of rickshaws. Two American seamen were hanging around as if they wanted taking somewhere but the rickshaw drivers were ignoring them so – well, it would have been rude not too, wouldn't it? Scouser and me volunteered to be their taxi drivers.

"Going back to your ship, seaman?"

"Yes, sir."

"Jump in then and we'll take you there."

They did and we set off at a gentle walk, until Scouser said, "Last one to the dock gates buys the drinks." I was off like a racehorse with my Liverpudlian pal not far behind me – if it wasn't for the noise that the American sailors began to make as they held desperately onto their hats, I think we would have got away with it.

As it was they drew the attention of the rickshaws' owners, who had been on their standard two-and-a-half-hour tea break and they set off after us.

If there's one thing faster than a British stoker towing a loaded rickshaw through the streets of Trincomalee – it's a super-fit rickshaw owner who is seeing his livelihood disappear up the road in front of him – they were yelling a stream of Sri Lankan words that would make a lumberjack blush and closing on us fast.

Both Scouser and me came to the same conclusion at the same time – better to buy a drink than feel the force of the law for stealing a vehicle in a foreign clime after which we would feel the displeasure of His Majesty's Navy. Along perhaps with a kick in a delicate part, from a well-shod American seaman, who had just been treated to a death-defying ride.

We were about fifty yards from the dock gates when we dumped the rickshaws and sprinted for the gangplank to HMS *Ness*. The two American sailors took umbrage as the prongs we had been holding dug into one or another of the numerous potholes in the road and slung them ungraciously out the front of their carriages. They rolled around, cursed, rubbed the bits that hurt and picked themselves up to set off after us. I yelled back at them, "It's okay, lads, we'll forget the tip," but my dry British humour just seemed to make things worse.

After a lung-sapping sprint that Roger Bannister would have been proud of, we reached the top end of the gangplank and found ourselves under the close scrutiny of the officer of the watch. Both of us heaving and panting for breath – the two rickshaw drivers hadn't made it past the guards on the dock gates and we could see a heated debate going on amongst them. There was much yelling and pointing as more and more fellow rickshaw hauliers joined them and I saw the guardsmen drawing their guns, which brought a gradual air of calm to the ranting. The two Yanks, however, were standing on the quay writing something down in a little black book.

The officer of the watch approached us with the words: "What are you two doing running like that?"

"*Puff, gasp, inhale, puff, breathe*, just... *puff, suck, wheeze*... getting a bit of... *huge suck in*... exercise, sir," responded I.

"I doubt that very much – I think you've been up to something."

"No... *cough*... sir... *breathe in*... not really."

He didn't believe a word we said but just at that moment I spotted Virge, strolling along with his latest conquest – a blonde-haired US Wren, who was staring deeply into his eyes. Try the distraction tactic, "Isn't that one of our telegraphists, sir?" All three of us now glanced towards Virge, who was sucking silently away at the young lady's recently applied lipstick. "Should he be doing that with an American sailor of such amply proportioned bosoms?" Of course the officer of the watch couldn't see from our position just how ample her proportions were and had to jog down the gangplank to investigate further.

"Don't do it again," came drifting back from him as he picked up speed.

"Do what, sir?" I had to yell so that he could hear.

The last thing I heard was, "Whatever it was that you were going to tell me you weren't doing," and that was drifting along in the wind as he closed the distance between himself and Virge. Our mate might even have got in some trouble had it not been for our two ex-rickshaw-passengers, who thought our officer had aggressive intentions and set about slowing down his progress with a few well-delivered pushes and punches. Not one to be beaten by such puny odds, our officer of the watch hit back heartily... mainly, with his chin.

The fracas was gathering the attention of the pair's American shipmates and the odds began to look unfair, so HMS *Ness*'s watch rumbled down the gangplank like rats from a ferret-filled drainpipe and – eventually – chased our trans-Atlantic cousins off.

We were still bent over, hands on knees, praying for forgiveness from our air-starved lungs, when Laddie floated up, "Well, well, well," he said, staring at the melee, "I've never known anything like it. Should we go and try to help?" If only Scouse and I had been able to recover our breath a little quicker, we would have concurred with Laddie and gone down to try and mediate with their disagreement... still, never mind.

Virge helped to carry the comatose officer of the watch back on board, where he lay gently moaning until the ambulance turned up and... well... we would have done the decent thing and visited him in the onshore hospital if we had been sure he wouldn't apportion blame. Anyway – he had some real nurses to make him feel better – so we stayed away.

top: Water carriers in Port Said

left: Haggis (l) and Herbie
    (me) went sight-seeing
    around Bombay – I never
    felt vulnerable when I was
    out with Haggis. He was
    from the tougher side of
    Glasgow and had a chest
    like a barrel – he always
    seemed about twice the size
    he looks in this photo. Look
    at the state of his socks,
    compared to 'smarty-pants'
    on his left

above: Crossing the Equator certificate

above: In my safari suit

left: Brown as berries – Chalky and me in overalls, taking the sun on the cruise back

*above: I can't remember all the names but far left is Streak, in his safari suit with shorts, then
    me, then the lad that slept in the gun turret, then Bogie with his hand on gun turret's
    shoulder. I don't remember the name of the lad far left, but I remember he slept with his
    eyes open. The chap at the back, in specs, might be Virge, he's certainly a telegraphist.
    The one kneeling, front (r) is Lofty and the lad kneeling alongside, with all the plasters
    on his shoulder had just had some inoculations – our acting nurse couldn't hold a needle
    properly and his hand shook*

left: In uniform – after the war

below: My demob telegram to
Freda

219

above left: Captain Fox

right: Captain Fox in dress uniform

below: Sumatra's beaches

top: Post-war (1951). We'd been doing our bit to create the baby-boom as can be seen in this
seaside jaunt with some of the family, mainly on Freda's side (left to right): Me – my
firstborn, Jane - my Mam - my son Richard – Freda - nephew Barry Hardy – Freda's
brother Bill Hardy – niece Diana Price – Freda's Mam – Freda's Dad (still wearing my
old de-mob suit) – nephew David Price (front) – Bill's wife Charlotte Hardy – Freda's
sister Nancy Price – nephew Brian Hardy and my brother in law Egrin Price

above: Forty-eight years passed before I put to sea again – on a cruise around the Caribbean,
in April 2004 – Freda and me were celebrating our sixtieth wedding anniversary and the
Captain gave us a telegram from HRH Queen Elizabeth

above: With my great, great grandson, Alfie – Nov 2010

CHAPTER TWENTY-NINE

All in all we had quite a bit of trouble in Ceylon, but first, we were sent for a few days to the rest camp near Kandy and, during the checking-in process, me and Chalky were greeted by a pretty young Wren. "Nah then," she said, "how long are you boys staying with us?" She was just being polite, but what she said had stopped me in my tracks and I must have been staring at her, because she flushed slightly and Chalky gave me a dig.

"Oh, err, we're here for... errm," I turned to Chalky, who answered for me... "Six days."

The next thing I was aware of was that she was smiling at me and had opened her eyes a little as if to ask me why I was staring.

My answer was a question, "Excuse me for being so forward, but... where are you from?"

"Where am I from?" she was smiling and twisting a curl of hair on her forehead.

"Yes, where do you come from?"

"Lincolnshire."

"Lincolnshire?"

"Yes, a town called Scunthorpe."

"Well, beggar me!" says I. "I thought so," says I, "when you said 'Nah then'."

"What a coincidence," says Chalky, "that's where Raymond's from – and I hail from 'Ull."

"Beggar me," says she, staring back at me and ignoring Chalky.

Then she reaches for a second blanket and hands it over to me. "It can feel a bit cool up here at night," she says, "relatively speaking that is. By the way, which hut are you in?"

"Three," it was out before I realised... I mean, why would she want to know that?

"If you need anything else," she says, "to keep you warm like, at night like, just let me know."

Chalky then chips in with, "If you're from Scunthorpe, you might know Ray's wife, Freda, her family name is Hardy, she has loads of sisters." Then he tugged at me to go. I didn't need the extra blanket, my nights in Kandy were very warm... relatively speaking that is.

On the second day me and Chalky hired (kosher this time) a pair of bikes for a day trip to take us higher up into the mountains; we'd pedalled them painfully up the road, well, I say pedalled but most of the time we'd got off and pushed. The road was one of those multi-hairpin jobs – very steep. We had stopped halfway up for a cup of tea and a sandwich at a roadside taverna – except they didn't do tea, they called our drink coffee but really it tasted like warmed-up tannin and was the colour of second-hand engine oil.

We were kept in good service by the ornate stone springs, often with a flat marble face carrying a carving of Buddha, that appeared every other 'loop' or so; the water was so clear you couldn't see it and it had a taste so sweet it was a pleasure to drink. Above us an audience of sparse white clouds was jostling for position in an otherwise bright blue sky; one or two of those that were being elbowed to one side were giving us a black look.

When we finally reached the top, the view was astounding; below us was a rural scene of dark-skinned ladies in lamp-shade hats, working in the water-filled rice fields festooned with uncountable numbers of silver suns reflected in the water, and above them, serried hillsides of tea plantations in vibrant green. It was a perfect day, a gentle breeze coming off the sea, its draught cooled by the 6,000-foot elevation of our position – the breeze cleared our heads of the humidity waiting for us back in the camp.

Such a peaceful place.

I didn't notice that the whispering breeze had begun to muster the light clouds into an ever darkening mass but Chalky did and suggested we waste no more time before we returned, lest we get rained upon. Maybe he thought we would dissolve, or perhaps it just wasn't 'right' to get our kit wet.

At least he was thinking; the whole magical atmosphere had the effect of deactivating all of my brain cells and I started acting like a kid again. I sprinted to my bike and raced off, with Chalky catching my mood and racing on behind. The fact that the roads we were on led to Kandy and the Supreme Allied Headquarters at the Royal Botanical Gardens of Peradeniya – plus, or so Bogie told us later, the island home of Lord and Lady Mountbatten on a coffee plantation at Kundasale – meant that the road surfaces were in remarkably good repair. Bit of a One that Lady M., apparently, always being visited by some Big-Nob or other.

The first quarter mile was uphill before the roads began to meander down a series of gentle dips and inclines that grew ever more helpful to our tired legs. As the road sloped generally downward, so our spirits soared upward; after a mile the road was more down than up and we no longer had to pedal up the softening hills – our momentum carried us along.

Every now and again there was a washboard effect to the road, where the potholes had been filled with quick-drying cement; it jarred my teeth and encouraged another part of my tatty old mount to fall off. I didn't notice when one of my brake callipers bounced merrily along the road behind us, but we could cycle along with growing ease. And so we progressed, at increasing speed, perched gently on the saddle, leaning back, legs akimbo – the breeze shooting up the flapping fabric of our shorts and tickling our testosterone.

We were enjoying the power of gravity and the freedom of the ride back.

We had started, almost, above the tree line, the hillsides covered in the greenery of low scrub and bushes with just the odd specimen of tall tree flashing past us. As we descended the timbers grew thicker; Chalky reckoned they were Satinwood and Ebony, Ironwood and Mahogany, to me they were just tall trees with elegance in their height, spreading trees with straight grey trunks or covered in black bark and all peering haughtily at the dense green vines that were creeping up them, to get a better view.

Chalky reckoned he saw a sloth but he couldn't have done, we were moving too fast.

The spokes in our wheels swirled in their work, their tyres singing with excitement as they carried us, grinning like loons and catching butterflies in our teeth. The speed built up, so we had to concentrate to avoid the deeper potholes that the road menders had missed, the road bending side to side till we approached a particularly sharp rise and slowed almost to a standstill – the view at the crest of the rise, once more, was enough to take your breath.

In front of us, the road dove steeply downhill. Terraces of tea plants beginning to carpet the hillsides; the road was straight as an arrow, half a mile to a rusty iron bridge spanning an apparently bottomless gorge. No kind of handrail on either side – it was just a span of girders carpeted with loose railway sleepers; from there another 200 arrow-straight yards led to the sharpest hairpin you can imagine before the road continued to dive, in loops, down the mountainside.

We were worse than a pair of kids.

Launching ourselves forward – pedalling until our legs couldn't move any faster and yelling at the top of our voices – by the time we reached the bridge we were almost flying, teeth rattling like jack-hammers as we hurtled over the wooden sleepers.

We were side by side – grinning like pianos – looking at each other and trying to talk. Voices wobbling as we crossed the final few timbers – Chalky heard the pop as his rear tyre deflated on a loose nail and the twang of his frayed metal brake cable as it snapped under the pressure applied by his panicking fingers, his expression changed... completely.

"Ra... a... aaa-a-ay, are y-y-your bray... y... y... k... es okay?"

It took me a few yards to translate Chalky's words as he dropped away, quickly, behind me, the rubber soles on his gym shoes reaching boiling point as he manfully dragged them across the tarmac in an attempt to slow his viciously wobbling bicycle.

I caught the whiff of burning rubber and looked around as he started to swerve violently; the laugh was only half out of my mouth when I tried my brakes – they were sunning themselves in a grassy knoll alongside the road a mile and a half back.

The hairpin approached.

I wasn't slowing down

At all.

Now what?

Clouds broke for cover and the Sun shone naively on us, who it thought were just about to join the righteous.

Chalky was yelping as his feet began to burn from the heat on the soles of his shoes, but at least he was slowing drastically; my bike, on the other hand, had bolted, I'm doing close on 30 miles an hour – 31 miles an hour – 32 – 33 – 34 – 35... and hurtling towards the perfect hairpin bend; the road flattened slightly as I approached it, to my right the green of the terraced fields of tea changed to the light grey rock of the mountainside. It was steep and covered in pale green tufts of grass, which hung over the numerous ledges, and further back lush scrub and denser trees.

To my left a four-foot-high spine of grass- and bush-covered rock hid the return leg of the road beyond the hairpin. Straight in front of me the mountain stood solid and at its base, defining the whole perimeter of the road's outer edge, where it had been dug into the loose scree, was a ten-foot-tall drystone wall.

Where the foundations of the wall sat on the road a trickling stream of water darkened the cake of dried mud and bright green weeds. The whole bottom half of the wall was black in the shadow, the top half shining pure white in the Sun. A flat grassy ledge sat on top of the wall, forming a kind of long unkempt fringe. Above the greenery a number of sparse willowy trees poked out of the loose stone slopes and watched indifferently, like so many toffs in their boxes at the opera.

Immediately after the bend, the unguarded drop fell straight down into the ravine that had been carved out by the river, way, way below us. And then they softened back into the terraced ranks, after ranks, after ranks of green tea plantations, but I hadn't got that far yet and as I hammered towards the bend the rock face on my right receded and became a grassy verge and then the bank held back by the stone wall.

From the sharp, squared edges of every stone in the wall, the opaque eyes of countless hungry lizards watched me coming as they soaked in the rays of high Ceylonese sunshine. Vaguely to my rear I could hear scraping and rattling and a pained stream of curses.

Suddenly – as if they were one – the Skinks, Geckos and infant Monitors living in the wall all turned to seek safety in the deep cracks and crevices created by the granite stones – and a green Pit Viper, that had been sliding up the ramp of grass at the near end of the wall, stopped to see what was coming.

I imagine he saw a large creature with strange whirling legs that was about to impale its soft white self on all of the serrated edges of the stones and – like cheese in a grater – be shredded into bits that filled each of the tiny black pockets that the lizards had just disappeared into with torn fleshy tissue, blood and shattered bone.

The *Trimeresurus trigonocephala* swiped its forked tongue across its non-existent lips and watched me approach – I was screaming like a... steam train at full speed.

My eyes were so wide I could have done with windscreen wipers – and a full washer system to clean off all the tropical insects splattering onto their surface – I had a split second to decide what to do – I banked right – away from the turn of the hairpin bend and took to the grass verge.

Errrm – don't let that word 'verge' fool you – it was actually a kind of elevated bank that rose as it curved around towards the wall and formed the ramp of earth and flora into which the wall had been set to stop the loose rock and earth behind it from constantly falling onto the road.

The 'verge' started with a sheer face of baked soil, about six inches high, before it raised itself gently upward in a deeply rutted staging covered in a biodiversity of green and gold grasses, each as long, entwined, tough and awkward as the spaghetti of electrical wires that currently feed my home computer.

The verge became a bank and the bank went two different ways. One way climbed steeply up the hill towards the Peaks, while the other bank formed the severe ramp to the top of the wall.

All I saw was the ramp, climbing nicely up to the top of the wall – riding up that would slow me down – I aimed for it – and at the perfect moment hoisted my front wheel into the air, clear of the verge's edge.

Mis-timed it.

Hit the packed earth and buggered up the front wheel completely.

And, still sitting in the saddle, as if bike and man were one, began a cartwheel of progress – gad, it was bumpy, but eventually I'd whirled along enough to stop – I was the right way up, still a-straddle my bike, with its buckled front wheel, and now teetering precariously on the very top of the wall.

Disappointed lizards, robbed of their anticipated meal of grated stoker, were creeping to the front of their crevices, some looking upwards – at me – and some looking downwards at Chalky. He had gone for the sliding dismount in the road, and left a bloody trail of scoured skin and tissue where his bare legs, arms and other bits had acted unselfishly as his brakes.

Whilst I tried to retain some kind of balance, I watched him on the hot tarmac below me; he was picking gravel out of the deepest of the grazes on the exposed bits of skin on his elbows, knees and arse-cheeks where they had slid along the road surface. His front wheel still wistfully spinning, he looked up at me and told me how gymnastic and how *brave* he thought I was.

'Brave,' thought I to meself, 'that's a strange description.' After all it was he who had slipped off onto a stony road surface – I stayed on my bike. Then he reminded me what the bike-hirer had said about not sitting on the grass verges – on account of them being packed with venomous snakes. At that very moment the Pit Viper chose to hiss out a call to his family to 'come and get it'. I heard him and proved to Chalky just how wrong he'd been to associate me with the word brave.

I was happy, though, with the softness of my landing and I'm sure it would have been much more painful – for Chalky – if I hadn't still been in the saddle and hadn't landed wheels first, thus leaving him protected from clashing with my bony knees and sharp elbows by the best pneumatics from Fort Dunlop.

I thought his reaction a little OTT – it was only a ten-foot drop from the top of the wall and it was an accident when my left foot slipped off the pedal.

I've never heard such language – and he wanted me to look and make sure they weren't both squashed – not likely – and anyway, in such tight and tattered shorts, the swellings soon became obvious.

He stopped yelling when his lungs ran out of air, and I had about ten minutes of peace until he got some breath back into his body at which point the clouds closed in on us and the first raindrop – the size of a tennis ball – slapped the road surface just beside us.

Apart from his flat tyre and the brakes his bike was okay and I think he was being very unreasonable in not lending it to me so that I could ride it back and escape the worst of the rain; I mean with the swellings he had between his legs he could hardly walk – there was no way he could sit in a saddle!

In the days following, Chalky moaned a lot – but the tread marks soon wore off of his left cheek, lips and eyelid and the swelling was disappearing even faster. He could sit down within two days, although he was slow to join in our celebrations when the skipper gave us the news – we were going home.

CHAPTER THIRTY

The trip back to England began at a very early hour, with the Captain – who looked as bad as I felt – manoeuvring the ship (he never liked to use local pilots if he could avoid it) up alongside an oiler. That was my cue to jump around attaching hoses and recording amounts of fuel that we were taking on board – in other words to 'stoke'.

In my case, I was feeling woolly because I'd got up so much earlier than normal. In the Captain's case it was because he'd been ashore the night before for dinner with the Commodore (his immediate superior officer) and a number of fellow captains and had been well oiled himself when one of them brought him back to the ship to the tune of the choir of creatures that sang the dawn chorus.

Eventually we were ready to go and I said goodbye to Trincomalee harbour as HMS *Ness* sailed away from the east coast of Ceylon for the final time. All of we stokers not on watch donned our best tropical whites, Brylcreemed our hair, donned our caps and went to join the rest of the ship's crew in line along the railings, showing any other navy watching the right way to leave port.

Ensign flying, the whole crew at quarters, bosun's whistles whistling as we came to attention, we made our salute. We almost drew a round of applause from the bunch of officers and other ranks hitching a free ride back to Pompey.

Amongst our passengers, as we left 'Trinco' – were some of the skipper's aristocratic connections – and despite the best efforts of the petty officers we were taking on an atmosphere that more suited a cruise ship than it did a warship. Talk around our mess table that evening came to the conclusion that this was what the Navy was like in peacetime – flying the flag, most of the time cruising and partying with some short sharp shocks of action if some natives somewhere in the Empire got a bit restless.

It was February and deep midwinter in Scunthorpe, but in the seas of Arabia it was hot and the cold hard marble of fear that had developed inside us all in the Atlantic had melted away like candle wax after the gentle action of the past few months. The whole of *Ness* was relaxed; what a different ship it was to that captained by Lieutenant Commander Steel.

I had bought a small picture frame in Trincomalee and spent a few restful minutes using it to frame my 'Crossing the Equator' certificate. I used the Entertainment pages of a copy of the *Hampshire Telegraph & Post*, which I'd acquired from my pal in the Naafi, as padding behind the certificate.

Then, halfway across the Arabian Sea, en route for Aden, the mood changed as we got the call to divert, at top speed, to Bombay – it seems that the day we sailed from Trincomalee, was the day that elements of the Royal Indian Navy had decided to mutiny. That got our hearts beating. The Royal Indian Navy was as good as we were (well, almost); we had trained them, they were on home ground, they had ships as good as the *Ness* (and better) and something must have really upset them!

Anyhow, whatever it was – that was none of our concern – we merely had to sort things out in the manner decreed by the warlords in the Admiralty. We went to a full action stations wartime footing approaching the Indian port quickly but carefully, every man armed and with more lookouts than I'd ever seen before – we bristled with binoculars. Some scanned the shore for gun emplacements, some scoured the surface for minefields – others cast around for signs of enemy shipping and yet more were looking for back-up from other Royal Navy warships. It was just like the Atlantic again – except – this time, we were on our own.

The hard frozen knot was back, along with an indignant anger that the silly buggers were delaying our trip home. Everyone was on full alert, Virge's team listening for messages, the nerves of the Asdic boys taut with anticipation of a signal from an angry submarine, while the radar operative scoured the skies for warplanes of the Indian Navy.

Of the latter we saw none and Captain Fox was not about to wait for any – when we reached the mouth of the estuary it was dark. This is the estuary to the south of Bombay, it is around five miles wide and I was hoping that the skipper would sail anonymously up the centre of it, but oh no, not him, he had all of our lights on and powered along with quiet determination. HMS *Ness* was as close as he could get us to the headland dividing the estuary from Back Bay. I think he was hoping that all of the well-heeled residents of the seven-story art deco apartment buildings of Marine Drive which overlooked the bay to the front and the cricket ground to the rear, would panic and start phoning their influential friends in government. We were in clear view of the coast, passing the domed magnificence of the Taj Mahal Hotel and the arched facade of the Gateway to India. On our port side, past the yacht club, we only slowed as we approached the beginning of Bombay Quay, which must have run south to north into three or four miles of dockside, it was what made Bombay so rich.

Onboard the *Ness* the atmosphere was quiet and ominous – we had no idea how many well-trained men may have a British-engineered gun pointing at us. Fox sailed on until he could see a suitable target, an Indian Navy warship, bristling with guns and menace. With a degree of nonchalance bred into the RN officer, he simply drew up alongside our target ship and, lashing us firmly alongside, ordered our guns to bear.

We spent a night of fairly tense chit-chat mostly on what had caused them to mutiny and what we'd do to them in the morning – not even Scouse was prepared to calculate the real 'odds'. I heard later that it was racism from their British officers that had stirred them up – actually I don't think we'd ever heard of the word 'Racism' in those days and while we'd care a lot about that kind of issue these days – the attitude was quite different then. We were more focussed on 'Classism' and that was rife in both the Royal Navy and the Royal Indian Navy.

The officers got the best cabins; they were the nobility and the landowners. After them came the non-commissioned officers, which weren't of course much better in social standing than the rest of us – then the inside-brain-trades, like Virge's sparkers, and then we 'highly skilled' stokers – and then the ordinary or able seamen (the last lot may argue about their status, relative to us, but not about the status of anyone above us).

I guess, what we now call Racism was an off-shoot of Classism and was quite normal.

Anyhow, enough of this racial digression, from a spring cruise every man was on full alert as HMS *Ness* sat, deep in hostile territory, ready to act if the situation required it.

Now, the story I tell my grandchildren (to whom I would never tell a lie) is that HMS *Ness* slipped into Bombay during the night, tied up alongside the minesweeper HMIS *Kumaon* and when her crew woke up next morning and saw us beside them with our guns pointed at their superstructure, they raised their hands and gave up. And that is all as true as I sit here writing this tale.

I have been accused of ignoring some of the facts laid out by serious historians – the fact published by the Royal Artillery C troop that they had levelled their guns at the mutineers on the day before, or the fact that the Second Battalion the Black Watch had stormed the main warship in Karachi – and the fact that the RAF had flown over and shown itself as a force to be reckoned with and other British warships were arriving all the time from Trincomalee and were tied up at the Gate of India – and the fact that the politicians had just negotiated an end to the mutiny.

I ignore these facts because they are so obviously a crude attempt by the other services to steal our thunder – except of course for the Gunners of the Royal Artillery. Their eardrums were so busted and their brains so rattled and addled by all that banging and crashing when they fired their shells that they wouldn't hear thunder if it sent a bolt of lightning to strike 'em first, let alone steal it. And, as for the politicians, well, even in those days you couldn't trust what they said – and the historians make it all up as they go along – I was a Stoker and what I'm telling you is true.

In the next few weeks it turned out that the mutineers' main gripe had been about the lousy state of the food being served to the men of the Royal Indian Navy, and that I can believe!

CHAPTER THIRTY-ONE

Any road, deeds of daring done, we set off for home again the next day; the trip was a mirror of the journey out. First to Aden, where we stayed but an hour or two and I never did see anything of the butcher or his cronies, and then we sailed through the straits of Bab al Mandab and into the Red Sea.

Growing ever more like a cruise ship again, our passengers would spend the afternoon protected from the sun by an awning that had been rigged up along the length of the afterdeck. During one of these times, not long after we'd sailed into the Red Sea, Captain Fox was entertaining some of his more high-powered guests to a glass – or two – of Pimms in the afternoon – he in his whites, his guests all dressed in their finery. I was sweating buckets trying to retrieve some of the bits of wood that had been part of the motor-cruiser and seeing if it was within my joinery skills to get rid of the patched-up-heap 'look' it had worn since the waterspout.

It wasn't.

I had just finished.

As I lowered myself from the boat, an officer's runner almost collided with me. Now, let me just define the word 'runner' here – you see, he wasn't running in a physical sense, he was more like strolling, but he was 'running a message' to the bosun, or whoever was at the helm just then, to tell them to put on more speed.

He wasn't watching where he was going, 'cos he was lighting up a crafty fag and watching everywhere but directly in front.

"Nah then – old fellow, do watch where you are going," I said – except I only used one word.

"Sorry, Mossy," says he, "Jimmy the One's got me running around sorting out a firework display for the skipper's cronies." It seems a particularly loud Hooray had asked the Captain if he could see a depth charge being launched.

He then did a great impersonation of the cultured accent of the same Lord Henry, who had been on board in Bombay at Christmas: "I bet you naval chappies can make an almighty bang with one of those things – what? Thrill the ladies – what ho? Maybe even throw up the odd fish or two for tomorrow's breckers."

Toffs – some of them thought the war was laid on just for their own personal amusement!

Now, I don't have the smallest ears in the world and when they 'prick up' it is a noticeable action. The grin on my face was also a pretty clear indicator that some mischief was about to occur.

"What?" enquired the strolling runner.

"Just you hurry up," said I, "and then get back here as quick as you can; we might be in for a bit of fun, meet you there," I pointed, "beside the funnel." As he rushed, in a *bloody hell, it's hot, Red Sea shuffle* kind of way, towards the bridge, I licked my finger and stuck it into the breeze. It was a northerly wind and quite sharp too, even better.

I watched the skipper leading his party away from their shelter, towards the back railings where they could get a better view of the action. The runner returned, out of breath, but proving he had plenty of sweat inside him. I stepped as far as I could away from the smelly oik and together we watched a particularly lethargic depth charge crew go about their business.

My companion was getting nosey about what it was that was exciting me, so I told him, "We haven't had the funnel system cleaned out for a while now."

HMS *Ness* began to put on more speed although a glance at the desolate sand-whipped shores would never have confirmed that.

"Yes? And? So?" – 'Runner' was turning into a rather inquisitive bugger.

"And we haven't fired a depth charge for months?"

"No-o-o?"

"Just keep your head down and watch, you're going to get a surprise."

We waited.

The depth charge crew tossed the first canister lazily into the air and while it travelled through its arc of trajectory, splashed on the surface and slipped quietly towards its detonation depth we both held our breath.

You see, when an explosion like a depth charge goes off under the sea, its energy rebounds and reverberates against the whole structure of the ship. HMS *Ness* had taken a lot of such rebounds since she was launched and commissioned at the end of 1942, so much so that she was now known in some naval circles as 'old scrap iron' – I knew what the likely effect would be. We were likely to quiver like the skins on Buddy Rich's drum set.

They had set the charge shallow, to make (I thought) the biggest waterspout, but still it took its time slowly sinking, back and forward, towards its trigger depth.

'Boom' went the depth charge and up came the plume of white water, "Yippee" went the audience. 'What the hell' went the fishies, rattle went the *Ness*'s hull and a cloud of caked and flaked soot detached itself from the inner walls of the funnel and rose majestically into the clear blue sky. The soot was driven up into the air by the ship's reaction to the explosives and, driven backward by the forward motion of the ship and the conspiratorial breeze, landing with perfect precision, like black snow on the fancily dressed crowd leaning over the railing "Oo-ing" and "Ahh-ing" at the spray. Then the second charge exploded and an absolute avalanche of the stuff, loosened by the first explosion, took to the air like a squadron of new lads at Biggin Hill on their first scramble.

I bit my lip – chewed at the side of my mouth and tried to stop myself from titter-ing. The Captain, now dressed in his 'not-so-whites' glanced over and just at the exact time he saw us, my companion, the silly devil, started miming 'Mammy'. I had to throw myself around and slither down the railings on the ladder to the main deck, leaning over the side pretending to hurl up my dinner as the sobs of laughter shook through me. My companion, he just legged it, shrieking like an Irish banshee.

I thought I had everything under control when the dirty deck party finally passed me by, trying without any success to sweep the smutty marks from their starched shirts and pale coloured silks. The First Lieutenant's white-clad shoulders looked the mucki-est. He'd had his hat off too so his hair was caked in it and the sweat was melting the mess so that it was running in streaks down his forehead; how I wished it had been the Australian, but it wasn't, it was Morrison, and – although I knew that I shouldn't – I felt compelled to speak.

"Do you think we'll be calling in at Sudan or Jeddah to find a dry-cleaning estab-lishment, sir?" I swear my face was straight, but he just growled in a First Lieutenant's kind of way – the skipper got me though.

But not before the wife of Lord Henry sashayed elegantly past me. As I saw her face, I went cold to my bones. I heard her speaking to her companion, "It's not like the liner that took us to New York in the mid-thirties, dahling, SS something. I really don't remember the name except it was one of the queens."

You see, I knew that the only queen this lady was anywhere near in the mid-thirties was one of the male dancers that pranced about in support of her chorus troop; they wore super-tight trousers with a toilet roll shoved down the front and they weren't trying to impress the ladies.

The last time I'd seen Lady Henry she was wafting a large feather fan filled with the Eau de Cologne that I had just given her. My surprises didn't finish there though;

being shepherded behind her was a lad around 9 years of age, his nanny trying to get him to: "Hurry along please, Little Lord Henry."

As Little Lord Henry walked past he looked up at me and I noticed his eyes – they were pure blue, dark in the centre, very pale on the outside with, like, a grey line forming a circle that defined the two shades of blue. He was a miniature version of the manager of the Palace Theatre in Scunthorpe; for a few seconds I had more contrasting feelings flowing through me than is safe for any man, mainly nostalgia and acute homesickness, dangerous emotions when mixed in with a hefty dose of amusement! She wouldn't have recognised me – my one and two had switched around now – when I first met up with her I had been 12, now I was 21.

* * * * *

By the way, I'd heard – in a letter from our Arthur – that that very same manager had met a rather bizarre end when flying, with a troop of theatricalists, to entertain the troops in Italy. Apparently, he'd been complaining of constipation and for most of the flight had been sitting in the little boy's room, tight at the back of the plane. When they were spotted by a Luftwaffe pilot, who'd been out on a particularly hectic day, had got disorientated in thick cloud and was returning to his airbase without having fired a single shot and with every likelihood that his *commandant* would have him on some humiliating 'jankers' for failing to get involved in the crucial and vicious air battle that had claimed half of his squadron.

The German decided to get rid of the damning evidence – his shells – by emptying them into the side of the entertainer's plane. The Allied pilot had dived rapidly and the German one had banked to follow, firing as the Allied pilot changed direction by pulling the stick right back just as the full magazine of shells cut a beautiful arc – almost a circle – in the side of the plane. The slipstream stripped back the skin of the fuselage and – when the rest of the crew went to open the toilet door, they were almost sucked through the gaping hole, by the rush of air. The loo was still intact but there was nobody sitting on it! There was evidence in it that the experience had cured his ailment and the contents of the loo roll was flying in the air like a paying-off pennant. That story always made me shudder, shades of my first minute flight into the hands of Elsie perhaps.

But Arthur always ended on the line – "I bet that made him crap himself!"

* * * * *

"Stoker Moss," from the Captain, brought me from my reverie, "get a detail will you? – and clean up the afterdeck." He added – in his gentlemanly way: "And see to it that the funnel is given a good clean as soon as we reach Port Said." He wasn't happy, but, strangely, even in light of these extra duties and the shock I had just had – I was ecstatic, as my mind, still distracted by Lady and Little Lord Henry, filled with the question, 'I wonder what did happen to that smelly old tom?'

We were all buzzing about the incident, described at supper that night by one of our crowd, who doubled up as part of the depth charge crew.

"Have you ever seen anything as daft as that bunch of dozy twats!" I finally slapped Bogie around the back of the head for swearing in a book that may be read by children.

Then I agreed with him, "Yeah, beats me how we can chuck away all that money on depth charges, just so they can see the water spouts."

"It wasn't so they could see any frigging water spouts."

"Yes, it was – the runner told me."

"Well, he told you wrong. They sent those charges over because they fancied doing a bit of fishing and they reckoned they could blow the bloody things out of the water. Dozy Twats!" Bogie hadn't learned, even though my first crack had seen him almost swallowing his lit cigarette.

"You can say that again!" Well, I had to agree, didn't I? Especially as my own personal spot in the freezer section of the refrigeration plant now had a few buckets of fish standing in it.

CHAPTER THIRTY-TWO

Through the Suez Canal, the skipper had control of the ship all the way – he also had the navigator's job, because our original one had scooted. He even manoeuvred us into our berth in the harbour at Port Said – he was a very skilled sailor and he really did not trust the local pilots – it was early March and we stayed in Port Said a couple of days.

Other than giving my camera plenty of exercise – I had been building up a library of pictures to show everybody when I got home – I got them out the other day, they're very un-PC now, with titles printed on them like 'Fuzzy-Wuzzies' – I do remember it being windy and very dusty in Port Said.

And... actually you may want to sit down as you read this next bit... you see... while we were in Port Said... a rather unusual thing happened – I went swimming!

If you remember, on my way down the Red Sea six months ago, I fell prey to a nasty dose of prickly heat – well, this time, I managed to avoid it by taking some pre-emptive saltwater showers. And when my Raffles pals the engineering officers invited me to a swanky beach to go swimming, I fell prey to a strong case of snobbery and said yes; at the same time kidding myself that a dip in the sea would do my heat-kissed skin no harm at all.

But, I had a problem – I wasn't in possession of a pair of swimming trunks – well, why would I be? – not to worry, says my pal the engineer, sew up the fly on some of those heavy-duty underpants you've got – they'll be perfect. I should have known better. Anyway, I pulled out me needle and sewed.

This beach, they told me, had a dress code so one of them gave me a shirt, carrying an officer's insignia, and then he gave me his spare hat and told me to keep it out of sight until we were well away from the ship and led us off with a hearty, "Let's go."

I had on my own, very smart white shorts and white socks and shoes and with the officer's hat on you couldn't tell the officers from the rating, which was a good job really, because the beach they took me to was a private beach only used by officers and very wealthy Arabs – and it was very strict. It turned out that both of my companions were known by the beach's gatekeeper and we were waved through without any trouble.

I have to say that I was beginning to feel a tad embarrassed about my swimwear when my companions whipped off their shorts and ran into the water – they were both keen swimmers – they had proper swimming trunks – tailored to fit – but, by now I felt that I had to join in, I didn't want to attract attention. I knew these delta-dwelling Egyptians could be real snobs. They acted as if they were direct descendants of Cleopatra and they might have objected violently to an oik like me scamming his way onto their beach. Plus, if I'd stayed out of the water my companions would have expected me to get the drinks in and that is against my religion!

Well, it is true to say that my swimming skills hadn't improved much since Malvern, so I used my old 'walk along the bottom and wave my arms about' technique. I was concentrating hard at averting my gaze from all of the beautiful Arabian ladies lying semi-clad on the beach, just like a married man should do, and didn't notice how lustily my kecks were sucking up the Mediterranean water. They were gulping it down – and I didn't notice the effect the extra weight was having on my recently performed stitching until a small fish swam in there. After a couple of false starts I eventually got hold of the right fish and ejected it, but now I was in real trouble.

I had weighty cotton under-crackers that were heavy with water and a fly-hole that was gaping like a PO's gob. And my two friendly officers were swimming well out of my depth.

I tried to remember what I'd learned at Malvern and started kicking my legs in a kind of broke-back crawl towards them. It didn't work; all that happened was that my underpants tried to abandon ship completely and had to be pulled, with many a splutter, from their favoured position around my ankles, back up to protect my modesty.

In one moment of pure panic, I did think about abandoning them altogether – my white bits were so white and the rest of me so brown that most people would probably have thought I was wearing the latest body-hugging number from the catwalks of Paris.

But, I decided, the back seam would look too thick.

So, I tried waving to my pals and noticed that the lifeguard was levelling his binoculars at me. I was out of my depth, out of my underpants, they had dropped straight back around my ankles, and almost completely out of breath when, thankfully, my two oppos noticed me and swam lazily back.

Typical officers – I told them of my predicament and they laughed – just... laughed!

One of them told me that it was the Arab way to chop off the hands of anyone caught thieving – they wondered what they would chop off a British sailor who was trespassing on their private beach and flashing his bits at all of their demure and veiled Arab ladies. I must have looked scared because they stopped their ribbing and led me back to the beach where I was able to hide my embarrassment by walking between the pair of them until I could make it back to my shorts.

I hate swimming – ruddy well hate it!

I decided against sharing this incident with the mess table that night, even though one of them asked me what I'd been doing fraternising with the officers. I diverted their attention by asking who fancied fish and chips and raided my stores for the depth-charged mackerels (or whatever they were).

* * * * *

Then, we had a bunch of very unusual visitors come on board while we were tied up in Port Said; a cloud of locusts flew in, all whirring wings, like a pale yellow cloud, completely covering the ship from stem to stern.

It was as if *Ness* had been sprayed translucent yellow. If you went outside, a pale yellow carpet crunched under your feet, if you reached for the handle of a hatch you had to swipe a few off first – they were everywhere.

The CPO was just arranging deck-sweeping duties when, as one body, they flew off again – the iron and steel of HMS *Ness* wasn't to their taste so they went looking for something more digestible.

I had caught a couple of dozen and tried to persuade the lads that I could stick them in the meat-grinder to add a touch of colour to our Acting Rabbit, but my messmates showed no spirit of culinary adventure.

The skipper did his usual job of manoeuvring us out of harbour and had quite a few spectators in the crew – me amongst them; we knew it would be a tricky job, plus he'd had a busy time ashore and we were all looking for him to slip up. He was in his element though and performed brilliantly. We weren't so impressed with his navigating skills though when he set a course that took us right through the middle of the un-swept bit of the minefield. We only got close to one of them and the lads – eventually – sank it with a hail of small arms fire. Their accuracy of aim improved no end when Fox told them that if it took any longer he was going to sink it by ramming it!

The following day we reached Malta, where we dropped anchor. Next morning I got a visit from Virge, who had in tow a very pasty-faced young lad, who looked around 16 or 17 years old.

Virge introduced him as an old school chum of his younger brother and told me his story of woe. His family had a history of naval glories – Daddy was a Commodore – they expected as much of Virge's pal, but the young lad couldn't stand seas any rougher than a pane of glass. He'd been in the Navy six months and every time he'd gone to sea had seen nothing but the inside of a bog and the bottom of a bucket – Virge had told him that I could cure him.

"Thanks, Virge; what if it doesn't work for him?"

"It always works, Mossy." Then he put on the hurt expression I'd seen him use to seduce the Wrens.

"Don't you give me that look."

"Sorry, it's just that his dad... and his uncle... and his granddad, think he's—"

"Okay, okay, what's his name?" All the while we were talking about him, he just stood there, very quietly, very pale and going paler – we were in the harbour – maximum swell height four inches – this was going to be a challenge.

My mind was racing, so I nearly didn't hear Virge's reply, "Chuck. His name's Chuck."

"Chuck? Is he a Yank?"

"No – it's just that we thought Chuck was a better nickname than Puke, or Spew, or Hurl, or—"

"Alright, alright, alright – I get it!"

My cure worked. It is true to say that the seas from Malta to Gibraltar were almost flat calm but as each day passed Chuck got more and more colour and his youthful personality began to grow on us. We let him sling his hammock in our Mess and – he became an Acting Stoker – he particularly liked messing about in the galley and took complete control of my Acting Rabbit.

For the rest of us meanwhile, it began to feel as though Gibraltar had become the springboard for home. Our mood was light, we were allowed out to sample the drinking dens, dance halls and cinemas of Gibraltar and as it was likely to be our last shindig as a crew, we all took full advantage – me, Chalky, Haggis, Laddie, Scouse, Bogie, Streak, Lofty and Chuck. It was a good job really because as soon as we did finally land many of the lads were given draft chits and set off for their new ships with little chance of a proper goodbye.

For our party evening Virge had organised the ladies as escorts for the unattached and one of the engineering officers had a lady friend whose family had a restaurant, where we could get a very fine dinner with all the drink any of us might want and a dance floor for the energetic or romantic amongst us.

We were nearly home – and then our celebrations took a very nasty turn.

CHAPTER THIRTY-THREE

S uddenly there was to be a two-day delay at Gibraltar – I didn't know why at the time but I was told later that an able seaman, Thomas Gowdy,[11] had died in his hammock after returning from a very heavy night celebrating his shore leave. Gowdy was the lad from Ireland – Belfast – who had done the job of sealing our shark float.

He wasn't the last fatality we were to have at a time when it seemed so wrong that someone should survive the war to die on the final stretch to home – and in his bed too – remember we were all still relatively young men; Gowdy was only 22. The Captain was only 35 (he seemed ancient – to me – at the time).

* * * * *

I also met up with Les Harrison in Gibraltar; Les was one of Arthur's friends, they had gone together to sign up all those years ago – his ship (Destroyer, I think) was under repair in the harbour – we took the chance to share a (for me, rare) beer and swap experiences. Les had a thousand stories and every one of them was enough to make my blood run cold; he left me realising what an easy war I'd had and how very fortunate I had been, compared to many of the people Les told me about.

Les was a wireless operator and during a snap of action he had had a very close shave when a huge shell came through his cabin wall – luckily for Les it went out the other side without exploding.

This had happened during a week of heavy action for his ship in the Mediterranean. Les thought they were supporting the Invasion of Sicily where the RN was fighting

---

11   www.cwgc.org/search/SearchResults.aspx?surname=Gowdy&initials=T&war=0
      &yearfrom=1946&yearto=2000&force=Navy&nationality=&send.x=26&send.
      y=13

alongside the Canadian Navy and the US Navy. He said that the previous week he had witnessed an almighty explosion as an American munitions ship was hit and that seemed to signal a start to total mayhem.

It was a time of complete confusion where the Allies were squaring up to the Italian and German forces in an attempt to clear the shipping routes to the Suez Canal. Although Les was in signals there was all manner of duplicity going on with one side trying to out-fool the other and tales abounded of landings in Greece and Salerno. Of cock-ups in which British warships had shot down an RAF Dakota full of our own paratroopers, although another version of the same story had the RAF dropping the paras over the sea, instead of over land – either way it wasn't very 'friendly'! And we heard tales of Allied attacks on Allied submarines. Les even had a tale of British corpses, acting as spies, being dumped in the sea, with false identities and papers showing false strategies.

Les sent and received many of the messages – some of which seemed completely contradictory and this ordinary lad from Scunthorpe was never sure what exactly the messages meant.

He was living in a morass of weaponry with the skies full of aircraft, the seas full of warships blazing away at targets he could never see, with shells coming back from sea and shore. It was an emotionally and physically exhausting time for Les.

The day before his own adventure with the shell, Les's ship had been hit by a glider bomb from a Luftwaffe fighter-bomber – "Punched a neat little hole through the deck," he told me, "and, just as we began to sound the alert for the call to action, the bomb sliced into the Seaman's Mess.

"The Mess was full of sailors, still firmly ensconced in their hammocks or sitting around the table."

"You should have seen it, Raymond. I worked in the upper superstructure by the signals deck and was ordered below to check for survivors." He blinked a lot but there was no expression in his eyes. "It was in a for'ard mess – you should have seen it. There were only two things in there that looked remotely like a man. One was a blackened statue of a thing, a body sitting with its back to the hatch, completely seared, shoulders rounded – blackened and cracked, like charcoal, but when you saw the front – well, then he looked perfect – hair combed, smile on his face and in his hand a dice shaker.

"Sitting opposite him was the only survivor. Still as a statue. His eyelids missing, eyeballs black. The rest of the men in there looked as though they'd been through a shredder, there were bits everywhere." Les stopped for a while; I didn't know what to say, so I remained quiet.

"High explosives in a tight metal box with nowhere for the energy to go – it bowed out the walls, ceiling and deck." Pause. "Bits – just bits – except the one survivor – not another mark on him – stone deaf though and completely blind. Even the hammocks were shredded, every locker lid thrown open – blood and bits dribbling everywhere. Oh yes, and a mug of tea, sitting untouched and gently steaming on the mess table with half a ragged jawbone in it."

"The smell was awful," Les shook himself, "I couldn't breathe without gagging. I couldn't stay in there, Lord knows how they cleaned it – shovels probably – and how they knew who was who. I felt such a weakling. Next day though we had a neat row of sewn up hammocks ready to commit to the deep." For a few minutes, Les just stared.

Then he looked at me and continued; he was exorcising a nightmare, probably for the first time in three years and I was his counsellor. Not that I knew it at the time – all I did was listen. "That wasn't the worst though," he shared with me, "the very next day, during the landings, or mock landings or whatever the 'Effing Hell' they were – that was the worst. We'd been pounding the coast with broadside after broadside until we'd exhausted our supply of 4½-inch shells and it was time to go back to port to re-arm and re-provision. It was dusk, light failing fast and, just as we turned we saw a warship coming to replace us, a Canadian frigate, I think, or maybe a corvette, coming fast, bouncing about on a wind-whipped sea and then it exploded – low down on the starboard side, I was watching it come. Everything seemed to happen in slow motion. There was a plume of violence, water, flame, shrapnel and oil. And thick smoke. The ship just sagged in the water, slowed and started to sink.

"Little figures were running for the boats and slinging in life rafts and jumping over the railing – I watched them, it was surreal – the ship went down so quickly.

"We didn't know at the time, but it had run into a mine and lost a great lump of the keel. Our CO thought it was a torpedo and one of our frigates set about trying to locate the U-boat. It was dusk – prime hunting time for the U-boats.

"We approached steadily, ploughing through this thick black sticky carpet of fuel oil that had gushed out of the breach. Amongst this mess were men from the crew. I couldn't understand why the skipper wasn't being more urgent. Why he didn't lower the launch and the whaler and stuff."

He sucked in a huge bellyful of air to stop his voice cracking – I'm not even sure he knew I was there. "The sea was full of tiny twinkling lights. They were the recognition lights from life jackets, so every one of them a man – an Ally. We were at the railings slinging down any line we could, so the men in the sea could climb up. The sky was buzzing with planes – some of 'em were Hurricanes, I think, from the carrier – I think – but a lot were German – and, now we were out of ammo and we'd stopped pounding the shore positions, the enemy's gunners fancied getting their own back; we had spouts of water all about us. Good job the light was fading. – every 20mm and 40mm anti-aircraft gun on the ship, every rifle, was howling at the sky until we'd run out of shells and bullets for those guns too.

"Then everything went eerily quiet – the planes had gone back to base while there was still light enough to land – the gunners on shore had stopped squinting through the murk and gone for their evening meal – dead silence rolled in. That's when we started to hear the calls and the screams and the whistles and the choking men struggling to keep their heads above the surface.

"There were four of us, hauling a chap up the side – looked like Al Jolson he did, covered in this thick black sticky stuff – he was gasping and puking all the way up. I remember one of the lads asking if the black stuff was inflammable – 'Too bloody right,' he was told, 'it's the oil that fuels the engines.' We just kept pulling.

"The CPO walked up to us; 'No fuss, lads,' he says, 'but make this chap your last, we're about to go'."

"'Go?'"

"'Yes – they can't find the U-boat so we have to get out of here, before it gets us too.'"

"I looked down and there's the chap who would have been next, my age, waving for a rope. I caught his eye. The First Lieutenant walked up, didn't say a word to me, he just looked at us, his face calm – like a dormant volcano – 'We ready here, CPO? – Who is attending the wounded?'"

"'Aye aye, sir, we're ready, sir, the MO's among the wounded, sir,' went his reply, and to us the CPO ordered, 'Take your action stations, seamen.'

"That was it. There were dozens of them, dozens of little lights in the sea. Number One just looked down to the man we'd been about to rescue – and saluted him – and the man in the water – you know what he did...? He returned the salute, I could just make out his lieutenant's stripes amongst the cloying mess on his cuff and then our stern swung, twin props at full revolutions and we churned the black, soupy water as we powered away."

"But what about...?"

"We were in a sea of wraiths, Raymond. Dead men that weren't dead yet. It was a sea of arms and eyes and black sticky water and our props were mixing up the mess of oil and sea and blood and bones, like strawberries in a fuck... ing grinder." His voice was creaking and his eyes filmed with tears.

"What happened to them... the men in the sea?" I asked Les. His reply was a hollow intake of breath.

He just said, "I'd just got back to my cabin and the shell came through. Straight through. I heard it was a 15-inch from an enemy cruiser, but it could have been a 4-inch from a shore battery for all I knew and all I cared, what with that and the aircraft and the U-boat that's why we had to skedaddle, we were defenceless against them." Maybe he was trying to justify his part in the mess, his voice cracked when he ended with, "I started shivering like a whipped dog. It was nearly three years ago and I've not been able to get warm or stop shivering since."

I never heard him tell that story again – Les had been in a sea battle and he had seen the destruction that modern warships could visit on each other and more particularly on the crews. He had felt the breeze of a terrible, lonely death and it had left Les with a deep gash of guilt that would never heal completely.

Didn't stop him being a cunning so-and-so though, as I was about to find out.

CHAPTER THIRTY-FOUR

Now hear this – now hear this – let no one ever say that Raymond Moss doesn't have a romantic bone in his body – I do and here's the proof. While we were ashore in Gibraltar, I went in search of the perfect gift to take back to my lovely wife Freda, who was waiting for me in England.

A lot of men would probably have thought, a romantic card, some delicious local wine, perhaps something silky for her to wear.

Not me.

Neither would it be anything as corny as diamond rings, or an emerald brooch, nor luxury chocolates or a bunch of semi-tropical flowers. These are the gifts of ordinary men. I – Raymond B. Moss – proved myself to be beyond the imaginations of ordinary men. What I bought Freda – was – are you ready for this? – something that no one in the UK could buy no matter their riches – it was – *dramatic pause* – a full stalk of bananas that I would send to Freda as soon as HMS *Ness* berthed in UK waters.

No. Stop it. Stop laughing.

Remember this was 1946 – there was a shortage of food in the UK – it was a time of rationing – fruit itself was scarce – and bananas, they had been unheard of for years. It was a great gift – wasn't it, Freda?

Freda?

Well, Freda, you said they were... yes, you did... at the time.

Awe – leave me alone – it was sixty-odd years ago! In them days bananas were the best way to a young girl's heart. Les told me, he said you'd love them. I got them from one of his contacts, they cost me a fortune and he made me smuggle some whisky home for him as part of the deal.

I tell you this... don't expect me to get you bananas the next time I buy you a present. Not after the way you've been today.

Stop giggling!

* * * * *

Our next drama (this time a profitable one) came during the evening of the 24th March 1946, we had left the Mediterranean and re-entered our old friend the Atlantic – the Ocean showed us she had lost none of her charm by blowing up a storm. We were ploughing north through this weather and rolling energetically, Chuck was chewing carbonised bread as if his life depended on it, kept his colour though.

We had just cleared Portugal heading into the Bay of Biscay when one of Virge's messmates, Oppo, popped his head into our Mess, "Hey, lads, come and see this. It's Virge, should be a right laugh."

Our friend the telegraphist hadn't been gone from our Mess for long; it was his birthday and we'd been treating him to the 'odd' drink – and from the way he was walking when he left us, it looked as though some of his other mates had been treating him to quite a few 'even' drinks too.

"What's occurring?" I asked.

"The skipper's sent for him – apparently we received a distress call from a merchantman, MV *Empire Homestead*; it has broken down and it's drifting towards the Spanish coast – Virge has been on the bridge and he's just started to climb the mast."

"What – in his condition – he's plastered – and in the dark – in this swell?"

We moved as one set of 'concerned' friends to seek out a good vantage point from which we could watch Virge. We found such a spot; it was sheltered out of the wind and spray and it gave us a good view of him balanced unsteadily on the platform that held the 20-inch spotlight; he was experiencing the full blast of the weather, soaked to his soul and shivering with cold and faffing about with the electric speaker for a loud hailer.

The speaker was attached to the tip of the mast and the wire connecting it had come loose.

"Skipper wants to talk to the *Homestead* and the loudhailer is broke, he's sent Virge up there to mend it." We'd been joined by one of his other mates who was 'in the know'.

"What's he sent Virge for?" Haggis asked, "all he does all day is twiddle his knob, he knows sod all about mending stuff."

"Radio knobs," someone clarified – just in case.

"They're called tuners."

Okay, okay, we're getting technical and there's Virge up a pole, swaying one way as the ship sways the other and he's pulling away at a wire. Apparently he'd found a wire broken off and even he knew that wasn't right, so he held the raw wire leading to the speaker in the fingers on one hand, while he held the bit it should have been connected to with the fingers of his other hand. He said later that it tingled a bit, but in reality he was ~~pissed~~ – sorry, past– past the point where he could feel a thing.

A sodden Virge made a great conductor though, and Captain Fox was able to transmit his messages to the other ship through the body of our telegraphist. I always knew he was a bit of a live wire, young Virge!

We were eventually able to put a cable aboard the stricken ship and towed her into the Spanish port of Vigo, arriving at midnight. I was later to receive the grand sum of nineteen shillings as my share of the salvage money. Not bad when you think it was unexpected and represented around two weeks' wages (I think) and it was more than I had paid for the bananas – nerrr!

As for our hero, Virge, somehow he got down in one piece – took a few more glasses to celebrate his adventure – and the last thing we heard, a couple of his chums had lashed him into his hammock for the rest of the night just to keep him safe. We left Vigo the next day.

Over the next three days the Captain seemed to be getting more and more impatient. As we entered the Channel, having just passed through a bank of fog, he had HMS *Ness* as close as she could get to her top speed (around 15 knots, in beautiful weather) and had issued a prize of ten shillings (out of his own pocket) for the first man to see the White Cliffs around the Needles. We were just about home. We dropped anchor in Spithead on the evening of the 27th March 1946.

CHAPTER THIRTY-FIVE

Remember Chuck, our seventeen-if-he's-lucky Acting Stoker? Well, the next morning he sidled up to me looking as smart as ninepence. "Do I look okay, Stoker Moss? Only I have some shore leave – I'm going home."

For the next few minutes, I fussed over his Silk, straightening it for him – there was nothing gay about that, we often checked each other over for accuracy of dress – a pair of human eyes being much better than a mirror – as the PO was to prove time after time.

"Somebody picking you up?"

"Mother."

"Great – you look fine – you'll make her proud, off you go."

I felt a bit like his mam myself, as I sent him off for some shore leave with his family – lucky dog! I watched his highly polished heels whip up the ladder with the speed and surety of youth – a young sailor with a heritage of seamanship – but not the stomach – and a growing penchant for my burnt toast – he was going ashore in the motorboat. Bogie was on launch duty this day; he was in a bad mood because he was being kept so busy.

It was a calm day, grey, a fine drizzle filling the air – the kind that wets you through and you don't notice.

* * * * *

The shudder of rumour that ran through the ship gave us the first inkling that something was wrong. We didn't know what it was, but it was enough to get us out of the Mess and onto the side of the ship. Then we saw Bogie, the usual stack of cigarette smoke wafting above his head; he wasn't driving our motor launch, he was being ferried back with his coxswain. They were both wrapped in blankets and looked to be in a really scruffy state, then it was obvious they were soaked, they'd been in the water, what could have happened, where's the launch? Had the silly devil crashed it and the launch – my launch – sunk?

Number One walked stiffly to the head of the gangplank – he looked at us and his face was white and still, like stone. The Captain was ashore. Bogie was being, sort of, steered by his attendant as he stepped on deck; his legs were shivering, his face a stiff mask, lips tight and colourless, his cigarette was shaking in his mouth, his hands were clutching and releasing, his eyes were open, but they weren't focussed, he wasn't seeing anything in front of him; he was so quiet. His head just moved, mechanically, from side to side as if he was looking for something.

The First Lieutenant caught our gaze and gesticulated for us to go to him – we had no idea what had happened. Bogie looked at us, he was four steps away, but he didn't see, one leg buckled and he stumbled, grabbing the railing, the mask on his face cracked and was replaced by a look of complete bewilderment. I noticed his cigarette fall from his mouth, which gaped as a harsh sob escaped. He was shaking all up one side of his body. Chalky and Haggis went to get him and we took him down below.

I made him a cuppa but his hands were shaking so badly he was splashing tea all over his uniform; then his temper cracked and he slung the cup against the bulkhead with all the force he could muster. It shattered and the shards just missed Virge, who had come into our Mess – his face set and grim – we were all as quiet as ghosts; I raised my eyebrows at him to see if he knew anything and he nodded his head and said very quietly – "It's Chuck."

Bogie stopped shivering and just looked at the telegraphist and then, very quietly, he began to tell us what had happened. "It was like a f-f-f—" he stopped, choked out a cough and tried again, "like a fucking mill pond... like a mill pond." He cast his eyes around us all, asking a question we couldn't begin to help him with. "The lad stepped onto the side of the boat, reached for the rung of the dock ladder. He was so excited, he was saying about going home, seeing his brother and his dog, going for a game of cricket with his mates, he was worried one or two of them may have been wounded in action. The cox was fussing with a forward line, I was looking to the rear, I was smiling like... at the innocence of the lad – and then he jus... jus... jus... just... wasn't there."

Another sweep of his eyes, this time catching the gaze of each of us in turn.

"I didn't know where he'd gone."

"The cox thought he'd fallen off. I thought that was funny at first, fuckin' laughed; coxswain reacted in an instant – he was straight in the water, I ran up the ladder – he wasn't there. I saw her though – his mam – in all her finery – brolly up against the drizzle – held by a chauffeur in uniform – standing next to a shiny Rolls – a couple of gold-braiders in attendance." The breath Bogie let out was damp with despair.

"The cox surfaced and yelled at me, everybody heard him, he couldn't see the lad. I slid back down the ladder and into the water, I thought he'd gone under the boat so I swam underneath. He wasn't there. Where the fuck was he?"

The tears were prickling my nose as I watched Bogie's terrible pain, rimming in his eyes, his voice slowed right down, "Where the fuck is he?"

"I panicked... I couldn't believe it... he just disappeared... we were in the water for half an hour... it was so mucky I couldn't see a fucking thing... he was nowhere."

Nobody knew what to say – nobody said anything for five minutes or so.

Bogie broke the silence. "The ladder was okay, it wasn't broke. It wasn't slippery. I went up it easy. I saw her. Waiting for him. She hadn't seen him either. There were people all around us now – three in the water, with ropes and hooks." He stopped as his voice cracked, "He just fucking disappeared."

I couldn't take it in – he had looked so smart.

Hell, it was quiet around the mess table that evening; no one ate, I cleared away full plates. In the galley I saw the plate that Chuck had used just before he went ashore, the scruffy tyke hadn't cleared it away. He was so eager to set off and there it sat, on the edge of the sink, carrying half a slice of well-burnt toast imprinted with a perfect pattern of the last bite he took before he'd gone to the boat ride that should have seen him on the way home. I didn't move it. Nobody moved it. There was a lot of muffled coughing that night. The young man had made quite an impression on us all in his short journey from Malta.

The plate had gone next morning, I don't know who cleared it away but I suspect it was the Chief; he'd cleared it and washed it and stowed it away for the next person to use. Bogie went too. He was completely distraught and had been granted compassionate leave, sent back to his family in Leeds – I never saw him again.

Two Navy divers searched the mucky brown water for two days and found nothing. We stood and watched them. Then, a week later, the wash from a captured German cruiser that was being brought into dock caused the turbulence that washed Chuck's body out from under the pier. Gripped in his hand was a grab-handle, it had been screwed to the dock, beside the ladder – probably since Nelson's day. Rusty nails in soft timbers, it had come away when he used it to lever himself onto the ladder.

It seems that Chuck had slipped, probably bashed his head on the side of the boat and been nudged under the jetty by the action of the launch. Gone. Drowned. How could that be? How could that be? How cruel can fate be? To be touching home soil, all enemies defeated and then not to make it?

Of all of the thousands upon thousands of sad stories that came out of that time, this one really brought it all home. Even after all these years – I still find it so sad it brings a lump to my throat – makes my eyes prickle. Bloody unfair! The Navy had a custom of auctioning off dead comrades' belongings – except for the really personal stuff – and sending the money to the family – it sounds a bit macabre now, but it was just the Navy's way and perfectly acceptable at the time – I bought the bib from Chuck's uniform, I've still got it.

I still don't know if that's alright.

* * * * *

We all moved slowly over the next few days, weighed down with a heavy heart, but steadily life returned to a routine. One day, Haggis was leaving, he had a train journey to Glasgow, gone to see his Ma, he wouldn't be back.

I had a few challenges to overcome, deliveries to make – presents to post – my problem was, I had a load of contraband to get through customs. Officially, the Navy frowned on any kind of smuggling, it was a very serious offence, so, how to do it?

I had whisky for Les and a box of brandy to get ashore for the skipper. He was a very personable bloke and had asked me if I could arrange it for him – I said of course, just leave a bottle out to make it worth my while and I'll arrange it.

His contraband was the easier to smuggle ashore – I never did find out what had happened to our motor launch but Foxy had purloined a replacement, a superb motor launch, for us to use in Portsmouth harbour – it was really fast. I just opened the throttles and it purred with power – it dug its back end into the waves and lifted its snout out of the water and buzzed along. I just loaded the Captain's stuff in the launch, kept an eye on the customs boat, waited for the ferry to come in and used it as cover to reach the jetty – once ashore we were home and dry and he took it from there.

My bananas and Les's whisky needed a different technique, because I had to post them with the railway, but I knew what the customs lads were like (or so I thought) – so I wasn't worried – I took the direct route – a bribe!

Most of my shipmates had 'stuff' to get ashore, but they disagreed with me and found a different way to smuggle their goods in when, the previous evening, some of them had cast around and found an untended gate secured with just a small lock and chain. They had reasoned that the best way to get their contraband ashore was to take a pair of chain cutters and scoot through that way.

I didn't like the idea; it was furtive – sneaky – could get you into bother – so I slung my stalk of bananas over my shoulder and marched straight for the main gate – kitbag on one shoulder, bananas on the other.

"Anything to declare, Stoker First Class?"

This was bad, the duty-man knew about ranks and stuff, be calm, be calm – I had my ploy. "No, sir," says I, fully expecting him to believe me to be an honest and honourable member of His Majesty's Navy and to let me through.

He didn't, "Let's just take a quick look, then shall we?" I followed him into his office.

"Oh," says I, lifting a pack of twenty tipped ciggies from the top of me bag, "sorry, sir, I have this packet of cigarettes I forgot about. I wonder if you would take care of it for me."

He looked at me and smiled – he was thinking about it, but maybe it wasn't enough, perhaps I should offer two packs.

Then came another of those Showgirl Moments as a disturbance kicked off in the area where my shipmates were sneaking through the gate. They had been spotted and a couple of the revenue man's colleagues were trying to apprehend about sixty sailors, who were running off in all directions, across the platform, to the trains. "Get yourself out of here," he ordered, "oh, and leave the two packs of fags." With that he locked his office door behind me and shot off to join in the fun.

I saw Lieutenant Commander Hubert Cornish Fox striding across the platform in a dignified manner towards the first class compartment of the Exeter train – he probably had more contraband than the rest of us put together, but he wasn't carrying any of it – it was being wheeled on the trolley of the porter following close behind him, as well as being spread between the members of his crew that, as I watched, were skilfully avoiding the less-than-fit customs men and railway ticket collectors as they sprinted for the trains. And with that, most of the lads had gone their own merry ways and I've never seen nor heard of them since. Just like that!

* * * * *

As he said his 'farewells' to us the Captain had made a generous offer to any member of his crew who fancied a life 'on the land' – by offering a smallholding on his estate in Devon.

Fifty years later he published a book, *Letters from Sea*, all about his life in the Navy – his life finally ended shortly after he had seen in the Millennium – he was 89 years old. Typical officer – no stamina!

Meanwhile I, Stoker First Class Moss (aka international banana and whisky 'runner') was clear. I strode off merrily to the railway station to 'post' my bounty to the relevant addresses in Scunthorpe. You see, in those days the railway would deliver straight to your door; in Scunthorpe they used a quaint motorised three-wheeler thing, so my loved ones were munching on finest Spanish-sourced bananas the very next day.

Here's a little factoid – bananas were so rare in wartime because before the war the source of supply to the UK had been via Germany – so there's one vital supply they managed to cut off – they lost the Battle of the Atlantic but they won the Battle of the Banana – didn't know that, did you?

Meanwhile I wasn't quite out of the Navy yet – I remained on HMS *Ness* until the end of June before being asked to ship-sit (say that when you're drunk) on HMS *Resource* in Portsmouth, along with a petty officer, but really to be laid at the mercy of the Australian Navy, who were encouraging me to sign up for a two-year spell on one of their ships at the rank of Petty Officer.

It was tempting but, having served with an objectionable Australian First Lieutenant for much of my time on HMS *Ness*, I had been sufficiently put off the Antipodean race and by mid October I had told them Australia wasn't for me and I was on my way home. I arrived back in Scunthorpe on 4th October in full uniform and with one of the worst-fitting demob suits you can imagine, nestled in my suitcase – grey with a lighter grey wide stripe – I gave it to my father-in-law, whom it fit where it touched.

I also received the Atlantic Star for the part I played on the convoys and it surprised me how much that meant to me. They were happy days.

HMS *Ness* was 'retired' and broken up for scrap in 1956 by which time I had two daughters, Jane and Carol, and a son, Richard. Freda and I were planning to build the first of our bungalows on the top of the escarpment in my hometown of Scunthorpe – where we still live to this day – with three children, nine grandchildren and three great-granddaughters and a great great grandson, none of whom – I am delighted to say – speak German.

And that's thanks largely to the men of the Royal and the Merchant Navy.

CHAPTER THIRTY-SIX

Was it all worthwhile? Well, it was necessary and for me and many like me it was worth it, especially when I got to sea; I enjoyed the ship and I enjoyed the camaraderie. In a way I was lucky; most days the war in the Atlantic was a battle against boredom and the grinding fear of an unrelenting threat. I didn't see the same violence that Les Wright did so I was able to 'enjoy' my war. It was worth it for what followed: the freedom to raise the family – we've had a good life since 1946 – but that is a whole other story.

Maybe we'll tell it one day – hey, Richard? Richard? Richard? Where's he gone now?

THE END

Raymond Boulton Moss died, in Scunthorpe general hospital, following a long illness, on January 7th 2011

CHAPTER THIRTY-SEVEN

OUT-TAKES

During the telling of this tale, some of Raymond's stories read a little too 'imaginatively' and so quite a bit of interrogating went on – here's an example of one such 'chat' that never made the main text:

Nah then, son. [Raymond]

Nah then.

You know if I'd worked as a salesman for Montague Burtons?

Yes?

Burtons the Tailors.

Yes – I know. I know.

Well, instead of being *A Sailor's Tale*.

Y-e-s.

This could have been called... 'A Tailor's Sale'.

Is that supposed to be funny?

Please yourself. By the way – you know the term The Full Monty...?

I know, I know.

What do you know... clever clogs?

That you are going to say that it refers to a three-piece suit from Montague Burtons.

No.

Yes, you were – jacket, trousers and waistcoat.

No, I was going to tell you it's about a trio of male strippers – that used to perform in the Palace – they'd been blown up during the first war and they only had one, well, you know, 'thingy' between them.

What – do you mean one had the left ball but no dangly bit...?

That's right, and the other had the dangly bit but no balls and – the third just the right ball.

Now you're going to tell me their act was called The Full Monty.

How'd you guess – and when they dropped their kecks...

I know, I know, the ladies used to shout – hey up, it's the Full Monty.

Don't be daft – they got arrested.

What's that got to do with anything?

You know the first suit I bought you.

Y-e-s.

That was from Montague Burtons.

I remember – it cost a tenner and you got ten bob discount.

Well, the guy who sold it was no balls and all dingle – the feller in the middle.

Uuuurrgh, and you let him measure me up.

You were safe – now, do you know what the term The Full Monty refers to?

Go on then – tell me.

I don't know – I mean – why would I ask you if I knew?

We had a great time recounting this tale – I hope you had fun reading it.

APPENDIX ONE

THE CREW

The men who held these positions could change every year or two – and it is true to say that not all of the positions were active all the time – they often had more than one job to fulfil – but the following list gives a good idea of the make-up of the crew of a River-class Frigate.

[Richard Moss, Author]

SHIP'S OFFICERS

Lieutenant Commander – Captain

First Lieutenant

Lieutenants x 02

Lieutenant – Asdic

Lieutenant – Surgeon

Lieutenant – Gunnery

Lieutenant – Engineering

Sub-Lieutenant – Engineering

Pay Lieutenant – Purser

Midshipman

NON-COMMISSIONED OFFICERS

Chief Petty Officer
Petty Officer – Coxswain
Petty Officers x 02
Petty Officer Telegraphists
Shipwright 3rd Class
Chief Petty Officer – Stokers.
Petty Officers – Stokers x 06

STOKERS

Leading Stokers x 04
Stokers First Class x 08
Stoker Second Class
Stokers x 05

SEAMEN

Leading Seamen x 03
Able Bodied Seamen x 36
Ordinary Seamen x 10

ELECTRONIC SURVEILLENCE

Leading Seamen Asdic x 02
Able Bodied Seamen Asdic x 05
Ordinary Seaman Asdic

APPENDIX TWO

THE CALENDAR

There was no recourse to the logbook of HMS *Ness* – my research seemed to indicate that it has not been archived and the keeping of diaries during wartime was not permitted – the following schedule is put together using a number of sources, mainly from Captain Fox and the memories of my father and his crewmates. It will not be 100 per cent accurate, but it won't be far wrong and some dates are proven by official records.

[Richard Moss, Author]

1924

Sat	23 Aug	Raymond B. Moss	Born
Wed	08 Apr	Freda Moss (née Hardy)	Born

1942

Thu	Jul 30	HMS *Ness*	Launching at Henry Robb shipyard, Leith
	Nov	HMS *Ness*	A/Commander Trevor George Payne Crick, DSC, RN – First skipper
Tue	Nov 10	HMS *Ness*	Lt. J. O. M. Hunter, RNVR – Joining ship
Wed	Nov 11	HMS *Ness*	T/Lt. J. O. Wilson, DSC, RNZNVR – Joining as Anti-Submarine Officer
Wed	Dec 02	HMS *Ness*	T/Lt. L. B. S. Benge – Joining ship

| Mon | Dec 14 | HMS *Ness* | T/Lt. P. J. Poels, MRCS, LRCP, RNVR – Joining as Medical Officer |
| Tue | Dec 22 | HMS *Ness* | Commissioning |

1943

	Feb 15	HMS *Ness*	Left Liverpool with Convoy *UC1* for Curacao in Caribbean – 35 merchant ships + 10 escorts
Sat	Mar 06	HMS *Ness*	Arrived Curacao – after a running battle with wolf packs
Sat	Mar 20	HMS *Ness*	Departed Curacao with *CU1* – 8 merchant ships (fuel oil) + 11 escorts
Thu	Apr 01	HMS *Ness*	Arrived Liverpool
Fri	Apr 16	HMS *Ness*	Escort for *WS29* – Clyde to Freetown – 24 merchants + 14 escorts
	Apr 16	Convoy *KMF13*	Leaves Clyde for Freetown – 11 merchants + 10 escorts – 1 troop ship
Tue	Apr 20	HMS *Ness*	Left Convoy *WS29*
	Apr 20	HMS *Ness*	Joins Escort for *KMF13*
Fri	Apr 23	HMS *Ness*	Arrives at Algiers with Convoy *KMF13*

1943

Sat	Apr 24	HMS *Ness*	Leaves Algiers as Escort for Convoy *MKF13* – 16 merchant ships + 12 escorts
Wed	Apr 28	Convoy *WS29*	Arrives at Freetown
Sun	May 02	HMS *Ness*	Arrives Clyde with *MKF13*
Fri	May 07	HMS *Ness*	T/Lt. T. G. Coles, RNVR – Joining HMS *Ness*
Wed	May 19	HMS *Ness*	Joined Escort to Convoy *WS30* from Clyde – 20 merchant ships + 19 escorts
Wed	May 19	Convoy *KMF15*	Left Clyde with 14 merchant ships + 13 escorts – carrying 23,000 troops

Sun	May 23	HMS *Ness* & HMS *Active*	While escorting Convoy *WS30* the ships spotted and sunk Italian submarine *Leonardo Da Vinci* Crick won Bar to DSC: For great skill and daring in action with enemy submarines
Sun	May 23	Nazi Navy	Withdrawing U-boats from Atlantic
Tue	May 25	HMS *Ness*	Left Convoy *WS30* to join escort for Convoy *KMF15*
Fri	May 28	HMS *Ness*	Arrived Algiers with *KMF15*
Fri	May 28	HMS *Ness*	Departed Algiers as Escort for Convoy *MKF15* – 26 merchant ships + 11 escorts
Sat	Jun 05	HMS *Ness*	Arrived at Clyde with Convoy *MKF15*
Wed	Jun 16	R. B. Moss	Joining Navy – Basic Training at Malvern
Wed	Jun 16	R. B. Moss	Photo taken at Malvern
Sun	Jun 25	HMS *Ness*	Joins Escort for *KMS18A* – which left Clyde on 20th June with 8 tank landing ships + 6 escorts
Tue	Jun 29	HMS *Ness*	Arrived Gibraltar
Mon	Jul 19	*KMF20/WS32*	Combined convoy left Clyde for Gibraltar/Freetown with 13 merchants + 12 escorts – 5,000 troops
Wed	Jul 21	R. B. Moss	Ended Basic Training
Thu	Jul 22	R. B. Moss	To Portsmouth HMS *Victory* Training
Sun	Jul 25	HMS *Ness*	Joins Escort for *WS32* Freetown leg
Tue	Jul 28	R. B. Moss	Training at HMS *Victory* ends
Tue	Jul 28	HMS *Ness*	Arrives at Freetown with *WS32*
Wed	Jul 29	R. B. Moss	Begins Fire Training at HMS *Raven*, Southampton
Tue	Aug 17	HMS *Ness*	Leaves Clyde as Escort to Convoy *WS33* – 7 merchant ships + 12 escorts – carrying 3,000 troops
Mon	Aug 23	R. B. Moss	19th Birthday
Tue	Aug 24	HMS *Ness*	Arrives at Gibraltar with Convoy *WS33*
Fri	Sep 03	Italian Gov.	Surrendering to Allies
Wed	Sep 08	Italian Navy	Surrendering to Allies
Mon	Sep 27	HMS *Ness*	A/Lt. Cdr R. H. Marchington, MBE, RNVR – Taking over as skipper
Tue	Oct 12	R. B. Moss	Training at HMS *Raven* ends
Wed	Oct 13	R. B. Moss	Starting as Fire Trainer at HMS *Gosling*, Lowton St Mary

Fri	Nov 05	HMS *Ness*	Leaves Freetown as Escort for Convoy *SR7* – 2 merchants + 4 escorts
Fri	Nov 12	HMS *Ness*	Arrives Gibraltar with Convoy *SR7*
Sat	Nov 20	R. B. Moss	Dated picture taken at Lowton St Mary
Thur	Dec 02	HMS *Ness*	T/Lt. L. H. Clarke, RNVR – Joining ship

1944

	Jan	HMS *Ness*	Based at Gibraltar – Escorting convoys to Freetown
Sun	Jan 02	HMS *Ness*	Escort OS62/*KMS37* depart – 20 merchants + 2 escort
Fri	Jan 07	HMS *Ness*	Left Convoy OS62/*KMS37*
Tue	Jan 11	OS62/*KMS37*	Arrived Freetown
Wed	Jan 12	HMS *Ness*	Escort on *SL146* leaving Freetown – 35 merchant ships + 6 escorts
Sat	Jan 15	HMS *Ness*	T/Lt. A. C. Locke, RNVR – Joining as Supply Officer
Su	Jan 23	Convoy *SL146*	Rendezvous with *MKS37* heading for Liverpool
Mon	Jan 24	HMS *Ness*	Left Convoy *SL146/KMS37* – To return to Gibraltar
Sat	Feb 05	HMS *Ness*	Depart UK as Escort for Convoy *OS66/KMS40* – 27 merchant ships + 6 escorts
Tue	Feb 15	HMS *Ness*	Arrive Freetown with Convoy *OS66/KMS40*
Mon	Feb 21	HMS *Ness*	Depart Freetown – Escort to Convoy *SL150* – 26 merchant ships + 6 escorts
Wed	Mar 01	HMS *Ness*	T/Lt. (E) W. J. Hales, RNVR – Joining ship
Fri	Mar 03	HMS *Ness*	Left convoy at its rendezvous with *MKS41*
Wed	Mar 14	HMS *Ness*	Departed UK with Convoy *OS70/KMS44* – 24 merchant ships + 6 escorts
Thu	Mar 23	HMS *Ness*	Left convoy
Sat	Mar 25	Convoy *OS70*	Arrived Freetown
Mon	Apr 01	HMS *Ness*	Depart Freetown Escort to *SL154* – 29 merchant ships + 4 escorts
Sun	Apr 02	R. B. Moss	Travelling to Scunthorpe
Mon	Apr 03	R. B. Moss	& Freda Hardy Married in Scunthorpe

Mon	Apr 03	HMS *Halladale*	Lt. Cdr J. E. Wolfenden, DSC, RNR – Taking command
Tue	Apr 11	HMS *Ness*	Left convoy after its rendezvous with *MKS45* – returned to Gibraltar
Wed	Apr 12	HMS *Ness*	T/Sub-Lt. E. G. Winterflood, RNVR – Joining ship
Sun	Apr 23	HMS *Ness*	Escort to Convoy *OS74/KMS78*
Wed	May 03	HMS *Ness*	Arrive Freetown with Convoy *OS74/KMS45*
Thu	May 11	HMS *Halladale* (*K417*)	Commissioning
Thu	May 11	HMS *Ness*	Departed Freetown with Convoy *SL158* – 26 merchant ships + 3 escorts
Sun	May 21	HMS *Ness*	Left convoy when it combined with *MKS49*
Sun	Jun 04	HMS *Ness*	Departed Gibraltar with Convoy *KMS52/OS78* – 14 merchant ships + 3 escorts
Tue	Jun 06	D-Day	HMS *Ness* based at Gibraltar – Escorting convoys
Tue	Jun 06	R. B. Moss	Fire Trainer at Lowton St Mary
	Jun 13	HMS *Ness*	Arrived Freetown with *KMS52/OS78*
Sat	Jun 17	HMS *Ness*	At Freetown
Thu	Jun 20	Convoy *SL162*	Convoy departing Freetown – 25 merchant ships + 2 escorts
	Jun 22	HMS *Ness*	Joins Convoy *SL162* as Ocean Escort
	Jun 30	HMS *Ness*	Convoy *SL162* rendezvous with Convoy *MKS53* from Gibraltar
Wed	Jul 12	Convoy *SL162*	Arriving Liverpool with *MKS53*
Sat	Jul 11	HMS *Ness*	Escort for Convoy *OS82/KMS56* – 16 merchants + 3 escorts
Fri	Jul 21	HMS *Ness*	Arriving Freetown with Convoy *OS82/KMS56*
Sun	Jul 30	HMS *Ness*	Departs Freetown with Convoy *SL166* – 21 merchant ships + 3 escorts
Wed	Aug 09	HMS *Ness*	Convoy *SL166* – Rendezvous with *MKS57* – *Ness* leaves for Gibraltar
Tue	Aug 15 (est)	HMS *Ness*	Stoker 1st Class Alan Gordon – Arriving Gibraltar in HMS *Ramilles*
Mon	Aug 21	HMS *Loch Katrine*	Commissioning
Tue	Aug 29	HMS *Ness*	Alan Gordon – Joining HMS *Ness* at Gibraltar
Thu	Aug 31	HMS *Ness*	A/Lt. Commander R. S. Steel, RNVR – Taking command of HMS *Ness* in Gibraltar
Mon	Sep 04	HMS *Ness*	Convoy *OS87/KMS61* docks at Gibraltar

Wed	Sep 13	HMS *Ness*	Convoy *OS87/KMS61* docks at Freetown
Mon	Sep 18	HMS *Ness*	Convoy *SL171* sails from Freetown
Fri	Sep 29	HMS *Ness*	Convoy *SL171* arrives Gibraltar
Sun	Oct 08	HMS *Ness*	Convoy *SL171* arrives at Liverpool
Tue	Oct 10	HMS *Ness*	T/Lt. R. W. C. Henley, RNVR – Joining *Ness* as Gunnery Officer
Mon	Oct 30	R. B. Moss	Leaves HMS *Gosling* at Lowton St. Mary
Sat	Nov 25	HMS *Ness*	Leaves Freetown with Convoy *SL178* – 19 merchant ships + 4 escorts – final Freetown voyage
Wed	Dec 06	HMS *Ness*	Convoy *SL178* rendezvous with *MKS69* – *Ness* leaves convoy
Fri	Dec 22	R. B. Moss	In Portsmouth for Petty Officer training
Sat	Dec 23	HMS *Ness*	Arrives Portsmouth and pays off 80 per cent of crew
Fri	Dec 29	HMS *Ness*	T/Lt. R. K. Morton, RANVR – Joining *Ness* as First Lieutenant
Fri	Dec 29	HMS *Loch Katrine*	Commissioned – begins sea trials – journeys to Tobermory as escort for carrier and training
Sun	Dec 31	HMS *Ness*	Takes on new crew – Sea trials in Channel

1945

Fri	Jan 05	HMS *Ness*	Completes sea trials in Channel – gone badly
Sat	Jan 06	HMS *Ness*	Sails from Portsmouth to Southend
Wed	Jan 10	HMS *Ness*	Escort for *TBC34* – from Southend to Milford Haven – 3 merchants + 2 escorts
Sat	Jan 13	HMS *Ness*	Arrived Milford Haven with TBC34
Sun	Jan 14	HMS *Ness*	T/Sub-Lt. B. W. Gillet, RNVR – Joining ship – Sailing to Tobermory for training
Mon	Jan 15	HMS *Ness*	Arrives Tobermory – Adm. Stevenson
Mon	Jan 15	R. B. Moss	Joining HMS *Ness* at Tobermory
Sat	Jan 25	HMS *Loch Katrine*	Passage to Londonderry to join Escort Group *EG20*[2]

Mon	Jan 28	HMS *Loch Katrine*	Sets sail to Gibraltar with *EG20* as Escort to *KMF39* – 19 merchant ships + 11 escorts – 24,000 troops
Sun	Feb 04	HMS *Loch Katrine*	Arrives Gibraltar with *KMF39*
Wed	Feb 07	HMS *Ness*	Arrived Londonderry to re-provision
Thu	Feb 08	HMS *Ness*	Sails to Gibraltar to begin escort duty
Fri	Feb 09	HMS *Loch Katrine*	Cdr. J. V. Waterhouse, DSO, RN – made Commander of HMS *Loch Katrine*
Wed	Feb 14	HMS *Ness* & HMS *Loch Katrine*	Departs Gibraltar escorting *MKF39* – 19 merchant ships + 7 escorts (troops & mail)
Tue	Feb 20	HMS *Ness* & HMS *Loch Katrine*	Arrives Londonderry transferred to *EG24*. *Loch Katrine* is senior ship
Sat	Mar 10	HMS *Ness*	Escorting Troop Convoy *KMF41* from Clyde to Gibraltar – Convoy joined by HMS *Chaser*
Sat	Mar 17	HMS *Ness*	Arrived Gibraltar with Convoy *KMF41* – 18 merchants + 11 escorts
Sun	Mar 25	HMS *Ness*	Departed Gibraltar with Convoy *MKF41* – 11 merchant ships
Wed	Mar 28	HMS *Ness*	T/Lt. A. I. Clutterbuck, RNVR – Joining HMS *Ness*
Thu	Mar 29	*MKF41*	Arrives in Liverpool
Fri	Mar 30	HMS *Ness*	Arrives in Londonderry after escorting *MKF41*, which docked at Liverpool
Sat	Mar 31	*KMF42*	Convoy *KMF42* leaves the Clyde – Convoy of 13 merchant ships + 5 escorts
Sat	Mar 31	HMS *Ness*	Crew on shore leave in Londonderry
Sun	Apr 01	HMS *Ness*	Sets off with *EG24* and four other ships to pick up *KMF42* – 13 merchant ships + 5 escorts
Sat	Apr 07	HMS *Ness*	Arrives Gibraltar with Convoy *KMF 42*
Thu	Apr 12	HMS *Ness*	Leaves Gibraltar with Convoy *MKF 42* – Convoy of 14 merchant ships
Tue	Apr 17	HMS *Ness*	Arrives Liverpool with *MKF 42*
Tue	Apr 17	*KMF43*	Departs Clyde
Wed	Apr 18	HMS *Ness*	Sails from Liverpool to pick up *KMF43* – Convoy of 13 merchant ships
Mon	Apr 23	*E.G.24*	Arrives Gibraltar with Convoy *KMF43*

Sun	Apr 29	*E.G.24*	Leaving Gib. on last escort to Liverpool – *MKF43* – 17 merchant ships and 5 escorts
Mon	Apr 30	Adolph Hitler	Committing suicide
Wed	May 02	Adolph Hitler	Death announced on UK radio
Wed	May 02	Admiral Dönitz	Appointed Fuhrer
Fri	May 04	Admiral Dönitz	Ordering U-boats to surrender
Sat	May 5	*MKF43*	HMS *Ness* in *EG24* arrives Londonderry – Convoy went to Liverpool
Mon	May 07	Germany	Surrendering
Mon	May 07	HMS *Ness*	Patrol Blue Surrender Route starts
Mon	May 17	HMS *Ness*	Patrol Blue Surrender Route ends
Sun	May 20	HMS *Ness*	Leaving Londonderry for new armaments
Fri	May 25	HMS *Ness*	In South Shields having Bofors gun fitted
Wed	May 30	HMS *Ness*	Depart for Immingham
Fri	Jun 01	HMS *Ness*	Arrive Immingham – for radar re-fit
Sun	Jun 10	HMS *Ness*	Depart Immingham
Tue	Jun 19	HMS *Ness*	Arrive Londonderry
Wed	Jun 20	R. B. Moss	Home to Scunthorpe on leave
Wed	Jun 20	HMS *Ness*	T/Sg. Lt. G. N. Arthurs, MB, BS, RNVR joins as Medical Officer HMS *Ness*
Sun	Jun 24	HMS *Ness*	Crew photograph in Londonderry
Sun	Jun 24	R. B. Moss	Returns too late for photograph
Mon	Jun 25	HMS *Ness*	Departs for Far East
Tue	Jun 26	HMS *Ness*	Pick up cable around propeller and return to Fort William
Mon	Jul 02	HMS *Ness*	Enters dry dock in Fort William
Tue	Jul 03	Freda Moss	Travels to Fort William
Wed	Jul 11	HMS *Ness*	Leaves Fort William
Sat	Jul 14	HMS *Ness*	Arrives Londonderry
Tue	Jul 24	HMS *Ness*	Departing for Far East
Mon	Aug 06	Japan	USA drops A-bomb
Thu	Aug 09	HMS *Ness*	Leaving Gibraltar for Far East
Thu	Aug 09	Japan	USA drops 2nd A-bomb
Wed	Aug 15	Japan	Announcing it will surrender
Thu	Aug 16	HMS *Ness*	Arriving Port Said
Fri	Aug 17	Indonesia	Declaring Independence
Wed	Aug 29	HMS *Ness*	Arriving Aden

Sat	Sep 01	HMS *Ness*	Departing Aden to escort small craft to India
Sun	Sep 02	Japanese Gov.	Surrendering
Sun	Sep 16	HMS *Ness*	Arriving Colombo, Ceylon
Sun	Oct 07	HMS *Ness*	T/Mid. A. J. W. Taylor, RNVR – Joining HMS *Ness* as Midshipman
Mon	Oct 15	HMS *Ness*	Lt. C. R. C. Morrison, RN – Joining HMS *Ness* (new 1st Lt.)
Thu	Oct 18	HMS *Ness*	Lt. Cdr. H. C. Fox, RN – Taking command of HMS *Ness*
Sat	Oct 27	HMS *Ness*	Arriving Singapore
Tue	Oct 30	HMS *Ness*	T/Lt. Robert Kerford Morton, RANVR – Leaving HMS *Ness*
Thu	Nov 22	HMS *Ness*	Crossing Equator on way to Sumatra
Fri	Nov 23	HMS *Ness*	Arriving Padang, Sumatra
Sat	Nov 24	HMS *Ness*	Holding children's party in Padang
Mon	Nov 26	HMS *Ness*	Arriving Sibolga
Tue	Nov 27	HMS *Ness*	Arriving Pulau Nias
Wed	Nov 28	HMS *Ness*	Arriving Pulau Telo
Thu	Nov 29	HMS *Ness*	Arriving back at Sibolga
Sat	Dec 01	HMS *Ness*	Arriving back at Padang
Sat	Dec 01	HMS *Ness*	Inspected by General Chambers
Mon	Dec 03	HMS *Ness*	Departing for Benkoelen
Mon	Dec 03	Padang	Murders of British Major's party
Tue	Dec 04	HMS *Ness*	Arriving Benkoelen
Fri	Dec 07	HMS *Ness*	At Telukbetung
Sun	Dec 09	HMS *Ness*	Back at Padang
Sun	Dec 09	Gen. Chambers	Wrote letter of thanks
Mon	Dec 10	HMS *Ness*	Departing for Bombay
Tue	Dec 25	HMS *Ness*	Children's party in Bombay

1946

Tue	Jan 01	HMS *Ness*	Setting off for Trincomalee
Sun	Jan 13	HMS *Ness*	Crewmen died –
			ELMES, Edwin T., Able Seaman, C/JX 546910,
			SPELLER, Ashton F., Able Seaman, P/JX 523705
Mon	Jan 14	HMS *Ness*	Arriving Trincomalee
	Jan	HMS *Ness*	T/Sg. Lt. C. O. Kennedy, MB, ChB, RNVR –
			Joins as Medical Officer
Sat	Jan 19	HMS *Ness*	T/S. Lt. D. F. Webb, RNVR – Joins ship
Mon	Jan 21	HMS *Ness*	Takes station patrolling
Wed	Feb 06	HMS *Ness*	Returning to Trincomalee
Thu	Feb 14	HMS *Ness*	T/Mid. A. J. W. Taylor, RNVR –
			Promoted to Sub-Lieutenant
Sun	Feb 17	HMS *Ness*	T/Sub-Lt. A. J. W. Taylor, RNVR –
			Leaving HMS *Ness*
Mon	Feb 18	HMS *Ness*	Departing for return journey
Mon	Feb 18	Indian Navy	Beginning mutiny
Fri	Feb 22	HMS *Ness*	Arriving Bombay
Sat	Feb 23	Indian Navy	Mutiny Ends
Sat	Mar 02	HMS *Ness*	Arriving Aden
	Mar	HMS *Ness*	T/Lt. G. A. Lang, RNVR joined ship.
Fri	Mar 08	HMS *Ness*	Arriving Port Said
Thu	Mar 14	HMS *Ness*	Arriving Malta
Tue	Mar 19	HMS *Ness*	Arrives Gibraltar
Thu	Mar 21	HMS *Ness*	Crewman died –
			GOWDY, Thomas, Able Seaman, D/JX 649845
Sun	Mar 24	HMS *Ness*	Towing tanker into Vigo
Wed	Mar 27	HMS *Ness*	Arriving Portsmouth
Tue	Apr 02	HMS *Ness*	T/S. Lt. (E) W. B. Cornock, RNVR – joins ship
Sun	Jun 30	R. B. Moss	Left HMS *Ness*
Mon	Jul 01	R. B. Moss	On HMS *Halladale* at Portsmouth
Tue	Oct 01	R. B. Moss	Demobbed
Fri	Oct 04	R. B. Moss	Returned to Scunthorpe

POST-WAR

HMS *Ness*	1956 Sept	Sold to J. Cashmore Ltd and scrapped at Newport
HMS *Loch*	1949	Sold to New Zealand, renamed HMNZS *Rotoli Katrine*
	1967	Sold for scrap
HMS *Halladale*	1949 Apr	Sold to Townsend Bros – became Dover-Calais car ferry
	1962 Jan	Sold to W. Rostedt, Finland – renamed *Norden*
	1962 Jun	Rebuilt and renamed *Turist Expressen*
	1962	Re-registered to Uuno Heinonen
	1962 Nov	Sold to Ferryboats of Porloma, renamed *Ferrymar II*
	1987	Broken up in Aruba

APPENDIX THREE

HMS *Ness*'s First Convoy

Convoy *UC1* – Liverpool to Caribbean
15th February to 6th March 1943

On 12th December 1942 Winston Churchill and Franklin D. Roosevelt discussed the need to increase the amount of oil entering the UK by 100,000 tons per month – the mechanism was to be a new series of tanker convoys to sail every twenty days directly between the West Indies and Great Britain. Convoy *UC1* was the first of these convoys – the main core of which was destined to take the return voyage from Liverpool to the Dutch West Indies.

These fuel convoys came about because Britain's stocks of petroleum were being critically depleted by increasingly aggressive military operations in north-western Europe and the western Mediterranean, actions such as El Alamein.

Convoy *UC1* is the first major duty undertaken by HMS *Ness*, following the ship's sea trials and came just twenty-five days after she was commissioned.

This was a Fast or 'Greyhound' Convoy (capable of 9 or 10 knots) in which thirty-five merchant ships set sail from Liverpool – the primary destination was the fuel processing plants on the island of Curacao, near Aruba, just north of Venezuela. The speed of the convoy was an important factor because U-boats were capable of up to 16 knots on the surface, when powered by their diesel engines, but underwater they were powered by electric motors and their speed dropped to around 8 knots.

As was normal with convoys, ships started the voyage that were heading for other destinations, some into the Mediterranean and some further east via the Suez Canal, others to South Africa and South America.

Escort

The escort comprised warships from both the Royal Navy and the US Navy, giving an indication that the fuel was for both Allied armies.

Royal Navy – Escort Group 42 under Commander L. F. Durnford-Slater, RN – consisting of the Sloops: HMS *Weston* (senior ship), HMS *Folkestone*, HMS *Gorleston* and HMS *Totland*, plus the River-class Frigates HMS *Exe* and HMS *Ness*

United States Navy – 14th Destroyer Division – Benson-class Destroyers: USS *Charles F. Hughes*, USS *Hilary P. Jones*, USS *Lansdale* and USS *Madison*, which carried the division's leader, Commander W. H. Duvall.

Schedule

15 February	Convoy departs Liverpool on journey of 4,000 miles
16 February	Sails south with protection from both Escorts and air-cover
17 February	Sails south with protection from both Escorts and air-cover
18 February	Sails south with protection from both Escorts and air-cover
19 February	Sails south with protection from both Escorts and air-cover – three ships have turned back
20 February	Convoy splits with 10 ships going to Gibraltar – Escorts refuelled – air-cover no longer available
21 February	Convoy of 22 ships plus Escorts approaches Azores. U-boat pack the 'Rochen' group, consisting of eight subs, had failed to find its targeted trans-Atlantic convoy and was directed to refuel from a tanker positioned south of the Azores. The 'Robbe' group, with eight U-boats, was patrolling to the north of the Azores and had been ordered to transfer its patrol to Gibraltar.
22 February	**0425** – The Admiralty informed the Convoy Escort's commander that their wireless telegraphy (W/T) tracking systems had picked up radio transmission from a U-boat near to the convoy.

1309 – U-522 sighted the convoy and reported back to U-boat command. U-522 under Kapitänleutnant Herbert Schneider, KC shadowed convoy. U-boat command began forming a pack from two existing groups – Rochen plus three boats from Robbe – and ordered the U-boats to attack.

1435 – The escort was told that there was a German U-boat sixty miles to the south.

1930 – U-522 lost contact with the convoy. Telegraphists on the convoy's HF/DF heard radio transmissions between the U-boats. Meanwhile, MV *Athel Princess* had broken a compressor and had lost contact, straggling eight miles behind the convoy.

23 February **0645** – U-522 sighted the straggling tanker *Athel Princess.*

0741 – MV *Athel Princess* was hit by two torpedoes. USS *Hilary P. Jones* and USS *Lansdale* were ordered to go after the sub. USS *Hilary P. Jones* rescued 50 crew from *Athel Princess*, which then sank. HF/DF contact continued, indicating U-boats radioing each other ahead of the convoy.

1200 – U-522 and U-87 from Rochen group, found the main convoy shortly after noon. U-202, U-504, and U-558 also made contact.

1345 – Admiralty indicated there 'probably' were two U-boats in contact with the convoy.

1418 – The masthead lookout on HMS *Weston* sighted a U-boat ahead. USS *Charles F. Hughes* was sent to hunt for it, but without success.

1436 – U-522 radioed U-boat Command that it was attacking the convoy.

1450 – HMS *Totland* obtained a sonar (underwater) contact at a range of 2,000 yards – she attacked U-522 and sank it with the loss of all its crew. Admiralty radioed new intelligence increasing its estimate to three U-boats.

1900 – Admiralty radioed to say that six other U-boats were closing from the north-west. In an effort to throw the pack off, the convoy altered course 50° to port. At the same time destroyers *Charles F. Hughes* and *Hilary P. Jones* conducted sweeps along the flanks, astern and ahead.

2040 – As the convoy began to alter course, *Charles F. Hughes* obtained a radar (surface) contact at a range of 8,000 yards and steamed to attack.

2058 – As the convoy was changing direction, A/Commander Trevor George Payne Crick, Captain of HMS *Ness*, radioed that he was attacking a U-boat that he believed had passed through the main body of the convoy – it proved inconclusive.

2117 – HMS *Totland* obtained a radar contact with a U-boat and the position was attacked.

2122 – U-382 torpedoed the tanker *Empire Norseman*, which began to limp and slow. A second torpedo exploded without hitting anything.

2130 – Several minutes later, U-202 began her run for an attack firing a total of four torpedoes from her bow tubes, the first of which struck *Murena*, which was damaged, but able to continue. A second torpedo from U-202 struck the tanker *British Fortitude* again without stopping it.

2217 – The slowing tanker *Empire Norseman* was now targeted by U-202 and hit on the starboard side with two torpedoes, but one failed to detonate. The tanker was stopped by this attack and the crew disembarked onto Carley rafts.

2220 – Now the stricken tanker *Empire Norseman* was hit on the port bow by a torpedo from U-382. HMS *Totland* went to aid *Empire Norseman* and rescued crew members.

2221 – U-202 fired a stern torpedo, which hit *Esso Baton Rouge* and the 'abandon ship' sounded. The 68-man crew disembarked into three lifeboats – one was killed and three seriously burned. HMS *Totland* began hunting the U-boat and, obtaining a radar contact at a range of 3,800 yards, fired ten rounds of star shells, forcing the U-boat to dive. A sonar contact showed two torpedoes fired at HMS *Totland* but they were too deep and passed straight underneath. HMS *Totland* responded with an attack using its Hedgehog mortar, which failed when the weapon malfunctioned. HMS *Totland* prepared for a second attack and obtained, but later lost, a second radar contact. USS *Charles F. Hughes* began to hunt for the U-boat that had fired at HMS *Totland*. HMS *Totland* then resumed rescuing the master, 41 crew members and eleven gunners of *Empire Norseman*.

2330 – George Roskell, of Walmer Bridge in Preston, was one of the 11 DEMS gunners on *Empire Norseman*, he remained on board defusing armaments, such as depth charges, to prevent further injuries to survivors in the sea. When he abandoned ship, he swam to a Carley float, which was eventually spotted in one of HMS *Totland's* spotlights. Within 90 minutes all survivors had been picked up by HMS *Totland* and were subsequently transferred to Dutch ship SS *Maaskerk*. Along with the rest of the survivors and the survivors from SS *Esso Baton Rouge*, George arrived in Trinidad aboard SS *Maaskerk*, on 6th March.

Lieutenant Commander L. E. Woodhouse, Captain of HMS *Totland*, reported leaving the sinking *Esso Baton Rouge* with 'only 30 feet of her bow above the water'.

2345 – The drifting hulk of SS *Empire Norseman* was finally sunk with a torpedo from U-558, which hit the engine room.

The report by Commander L. F. Durnford-Slater, RN described the attack being carried out by 'at least' four U-boats. Two of them were thought to have been driven off by the escorts while the third penetrated the convoy's defensive screen and torpedoed the ships just as the convoy was completing its course alteration. The fourth U-boat was thought to have later finished off *Empire Norseman*.

This report indicates some of the uncertainty and confusion that reigned at such times, as does a description by George Roskell of an event that began as he was dashing aft, along the flying bridge, surrounded by acrid smoke, yelling shipmates and clamouring alarms, on his way to remove the fuses from the depth charges. George ran smack into the Chief Engineer and the rim on his tin hat badly gashed the Chief Engineer's forehead. Later on, when they were both in a lifeboat, the Chief Engineer had a wad of cotton wool placed over the badly bleeding wound; he had been handed a cigarette and as he lit it he accidentally set the cotton wool alight. This caused him more distress than the original collision, but much amusement amongst the other crew members in the lifeboat.

24 February   **0400** – SS *Esso Baton Rouge* finally sank.

0700 – The U-boats still had contact and continued to shadow the convoy.

1330 – USS *Madison* obtained a contact off the starboard bow and attacked without effect. The convoy executed an emergency turn to port.

1345 – The Admiralty estimated that Convoy *UC1* was being shadowed 'by up to 8 U/Bs'. The hunt for the U-boat was continued by the destroyer USS *Madison.*

1400 – The convoy returned to its base course.

In the afternoon, the escorts obtained several HF/DF bearings, which were run down – no result. U-boat Command ordered 'in the twilight, search energetically for contact. All boats must get involved. The convoy must be smashed up'.

1730 – The convoy altered course 45° to port in a further attempt to throw off the U-boat pack.

To maximize the effectiveness of their radar, the escorts switched tactics and made their defensive circle much larger. Sweeping for U-boats in front of the convoy to counter the classic wolf pack tactic of lying in wait in front, while individual U-boats harassed from the rear.

2200 – USS *Hilary P. Jones* obtained a radar fix 7.5 miles astern of the convoy.

The U-boat was closed upon; it submerged and was attacked with depth charges. USS *Hilary P. Jones* sighted, chased, forced to dive and attacked two more U-boats. USS *Charles F. Hughes* was sent to search off the port beam where HF/DF indicated a U-boat.

2309 – HMS *Totland* obtained a radar contact and a few minutes later sighted a periscope, but was unable to attack due to failure of its sonar.

2320 – HMS *Weston* obtained a sonar contact and attacked four times with depth charges before the echo faded.

2336 – HMS *Totland* made another radar contact, forced the vessel to dive, and attacked twice with depth charges.

25 February   **0113** – HMS *Weston* heard three torpedoes on sonar. While searching for the U-boat the sloop obtained a radar contact 5,600 yards away and USS *Lansdale* was sent to search the area without result.

Radio messages from the U-boats indicated that U-382, U-218, U-43 and U-558 had been 'detected by destroyers and attacked with depth charges', while a number of other subs had been 'driven off' by escorts. It appears that U-382 had been damaged and was forced to withdraw and U-87 had to cease operations because of a shortage of lubricating oil. While there were no contacts during the day, the convoy's escorts intercepted 46 radio transmissions from U-boats in the vicinity.

1656 – U-boat Command urged the pack to renew the attack.

1730 – USS *Madison* conducted a sweep ahead of *UC1*.

2035 – An underwater explosion was heard by *Weston*, which five minutes later gained 'a doubtful' sonar contact that disappeared after being attacked.

2130 – USS *Lansdale*, to the starboard, obtained a radar contact at a range of 4,000 yards. The U-boat dived and was attacked with depth charges.

2143 – A second radar contact was obtained, probably with U-202 at a range of 3.5 miles; the target was damaged by USS *Lansdale* under the command of LCDR Valery Havard Junior, with fire from its 5-inch guns. When sonar contact was also made, the warship dropped depth charges before returning to its station.

2235 – The Admiralty reported that there were 'at least 8 U-boats in your immediate vicinity'.

26 February **0910** – The Admiralty radioed that 'continued heavy W/T traffic indicates U/Boats still in contact'.

Four of the U-boats – U-43, U-202, U-521 and U-558 – were forced to give up, due to damage and shortage of fuel. Three U-boats – U-66, U-504 and U-382 – continued to stalk the convoy.

27 February USS *Lansdale* sighted a U-boat on the surface recharging its batteries and *Madison* sent to assist without success.

1944 – An HF/DF bearing was obtained on a radio transmission.

After this there were no further contacts.

2324 – U-boat Command ended operations because of 'poor prospects of success'.

01 March **1540** – American shore-based aircraft from the West Indies began to escort Convoy *UC1*.

04 March Injured from SS *Esso Baton Rouge* were put ashore at Antigua.

06 March   Convoy arrived at Curacao. SS *Maaskerk*, with survivors aboard, arrived in Trinidad.

08 March   The *British Fortitude* arrived at Cuba, was later repaired at Galveston and returned to service in May 1943.

01 April   Return Convoy *UC1* arrives Liverpool with nine merchant ships carrying petrol, fuel oil, lubricating oil and paraffin – no losses.

In the battle for *UC1* the Allies lost three ships and had two damaged, while the Germans lost U-522 and others took damage. These losses were acceptable to the Allies, whose objective was the safe and timely passage of shipping.

Fate and Destinations of the Merchant Ships in Convoy *UC1*

Four ships had mechanical trouble and returned to Liverpool (or failed to sail), or to an alternative port, they were:

Turned Back
- MV *Clavella* – MV *Fort Wedderburne* – MV *Sembilangan* (Dutch)

Walvis Bay – Namibia
- SS *Cape Hawke* – Straggler put in at Namibia

A further eleven ships left the convoy for Gibraltar.

The Mediterranean Group:

It is likely that on or around 20th February, these seven ships split from Convoy *UC1* and headed for Gibraltar to join up with other convoys to take them to their final destination.

DESTINATION – PERSIAN GULF

- MV *Bardistan*
- MV *Clan Murdoch*

DESTINATION – BOMBAY/CALCUTTA

- MV *City of Durban*
- MV *Martand* (Br)
- SS *Malakand* (Br)

DESTINATION – SUEZ/ALEXANDRIA

- MV *Cornish City*
- MV *Custodian*
- MV *Kaimata* (Br)

THE SOUTH AFRICAN GROUP:

It is also likely that on or around 20th February, these three ships split from Convoy *UC1* and headed for Gibraltar to join up with another convoy that would take them to Freetown in Sierra Leone, where they would join a convoy to take them to their final destination.

MV *Blommersdijk* (Dutch) – MV *Clan Mcneil* (Brit) – MV *Delius* (Brit)

The rest of the twenty ships with all of the escorts set off across the Atlantic and quickly lost their air-cover.

DESTINATION – CURACAO

- SS *Athel Regent* (Br) – SS *Cymbula* (Br) – SS *Eclipse* (Br) – SS *Empire Marvell* (Br) – SS *Gulfpoint* (US) – SS *Saintonge* (Br) – SS *San Adolfo* (Br) – SS *San Ambrosio* (Br) – SS *Tide Water* (US) – SS *Tijuca* (Norway) – SS *Vinga* (Norway) – SS *Kaia Knudsen* (Norway)

Destination – Aruba
- SS *Mobilgas* (US)

Destination – Trinidad
- *Maaskerk* (Du)

Destination – South America
- *Empire Castle* (Br) – Buenos Aires

Three were sunk – the first being the MV *Athel Princess*, commanded by Captain E. C. B. Martin which, due to mechanical problems, had become isolated – it was torpedoed by U-522 – in its distress it launched a flurry of white rockets, which went unappreciated by the Commander of the convoy as they were a clear indication of the convoy's position.

Sunk
- MV *Athel Princess* (Br), under Captain E. C. B. Martin, was sunk by U-522.
- SS *Empire Norseman* (Br), under her master, William Sharp Smith, was sunk by U-382, U-202 and U-558.
- SS *Esso Baton Rouge* (US), under Master James S. Poche – this was the second torpedo attack on SS *Baton Rouge* – the previous April it had been damaged and grounded by U-123 – but was subsequently raised and repaired.

Damaged – Diverted to Cuba
- SS *British Fortitude* – damaged by U202; SS *Murena* (Du) – damaged by U-202, arrived Gitmo, 8th March.

FATE OF THE NAZI U-BOATS IN THE ATTACKING WOLF PACK

Prior to the attack there were two wolf packs active in the area:

- Rochen, made up of U-43 – U-66 – U-87 – U-108 – U-202 – U-218 – U-258 – U-264 – U-504 – U521 – U-558.
- Robbe, made up of U-103 – U-107 – U-382 – U410 – U-437 – U-445 – U-511 – U569.

U-boat U-522 also played a leading part – some reports describe U-522 as being previously part of the Rochen pack, but equally, U-522's commander, Kapitänleutnant Schneider, KC may have been patrolling alone – he had sailed from Lorient on 31st December and had already torpedoed three ships when he sighted the convoy.

Once Schneider's reported sighting of Convoy UC1 was received the submarines were hurriedly put together as a wolf pack by U-boat Command, using elements from the two separate groups – they seemed to struggle to work within the usual wolf pack method of placing a line of U-boats ahead of the convoy as a trap, with two or three individual U-boats aft of the convoy driving it into the jaws of the trap. This was probably due, most of all, to the speed of the convoy. The combined wolf pack only really worked effectively as a group on one day, 23rd February, when U-202 and U-382 sank two and damaged two tankers. Even then it looks more like the actions of a group of individuals rather than the teamwork of a pack.

The group of U-boats fared very badly during the rest of the war – nine of them being sunk by August that year, their ineffectiveness in the attack and subsequent destruction, may bring the Nazi propaganda surrounding the wolf-pack Aces into serious question and cast doubt on the competence of the individual commanders or U-boat Command.

The following is a list of the U-boats in action against Convoy UC1:

U-43   Commanded by Oberleutnant Hans-Joachim Schwantke (promoted to Kapitänleutnant posthumously) – this U-boat was sunk just over four months later on 30th July 1943, south-west of the Azores, in position 34.57N, 35.11W, by a homing torpedo from an Avenger aircraft of the US escort carrier HMS *Santee* with all hands lost (55).

U-66   Commanded in the action by Kapitänleutnant Friedrich Markworth, who in the previous November had attained an Iron Cross 1st Class and went on to attain a Knight's Cross in July 1943. The U-boat was sunk on 6th May 1944 while under the command of Kapitänleutnant Gerhard Seehausen, by depth charges, ramming and gunfire from Avenger and Wildcat aircraft of the US escort carrier USS *Block Island* and by the destroyer escort USS *Buckley*. It was west of the Cape Verde Islands, in position 17.17N, 32.29W, that 24 of the crew were killed including Seehausen and 36 survived.

U-87   Commanded by Joachim Berger (again promoted to Kapitänleutnant posthumously), the U-boat was sunk just five days after the action, on 4th March 1943, west of Leixoes, in position 41.36N, 13.31W, by depth charges from the Canadian corvette HMCS *Shediac* and the Canadian destroyer HMCS *St. Croix*, all hands were lost (49 dead).

U-108   Commanded in the action by Korvettenkapitän Ralf-Reimar Wolfram, the U-boat was sunk on 11th April 1944 at Stettin by bombs; raised; taken out of service at Stettin 17th July 1944; scuttled there 24th April 1945.

U-202   Commanded in the action by Günter Poser, who had been promoted to the rank of Kapitänleutnant at the beginning of February. The U-boat was sunk four months later at 0030hrs on 2nd June 1943 south-east of Cape Farewell, Greenland, in position 56.12N, 39.52W, by depth charges and gunfire from the famous Captain 'Johnnie' Walker, DSO & Bar, RN, in the British sloop HMS *Starling*. It is not known whether Poser was amongst the 18 dead or the 30 survivors.

U-218   Commanded in the action by Kapitänleutnant Richard Becker, who was skipper until August 1944. The U-boat eventually surrendered at Bergen, Norway, on 8th May 1945 and was transferred to Loch Ryan in Scotland later that month for her final fate when she was sunk in Operation Deadlight, on 4th December 1945 off Northern Ireland.

U-258   Commanded in the action by Kapitänleutnant Wilhelm von Mässenhausen, this U-boat was sunk the following month, on 20th May 1943 in the North Atlantic, in position 55.18N, 27.49W, by depth charges from a British Liberator aircraft (Sqdn 120/P). All hands were lost (49 dead).

U-264 Commanded in the action by Kapitänleutnant Hartwig Looks, this U-boat was another victim of Johnnie Walker, being sunk almost a year later at 1707hrs on 19th February 1944 in the North Atlantic, in position 48.31N, 22.05W, by depth charges from the British sloops HMS *Woodpecker* and HMS *Starling*. This time there were no casualties as all of the crew were taken prisoner.

U-382 Commanded in the action by Kapitänleutnant Herbert Juli, who died aged 78 in 1994 – he was replaced by Oberleutnant Leopold Koch when the U-boat returned to its base. This U-boat was sunk in January 1945 at entrance four at Wilhelmshaven, Germany, by British bombs. Raised on 20th March 1945 and scuttled on 8th May 1945.

U-504 Commanded in the action by Kapitänleutnant (later Korvettenkapitän) Wilhelm Luis, this U-boat was sunk five months later at 1543hrs on 30th July 1943 in the North Atlantic north-west of Cape Ortegal, Spain, in position 45.33N, 10.56W, by depth charges from the British sloops HMS *Kite*, HMS *Woodpecker*, HMS *Wren* and HMS *Wild Goose*. There were no survivors, all hands lost (53 dead).

U-521 Commanded in the action by Kapitänleutnant Klaus Bargsten, who had attained his Iron Cross 1st Class in 1940 and went on to attain a Knight's Cross in April 1943. The U-boat was sunk on 2nd June 1943 in the North Atlantic south-east of Baltimore, in position 37.43N, 73.16W, by depth charges from the US patrol craft USS *PC-565*. Kapitänleutnant Bargsten was the only survivor, the other 51 crew members were killed in the action – he died aged 89 years in 2000.

U-522 Commanded in the action by Kapitänleutnant Herbert Schneider, KC, this U-boat was sunk during the action by depth charges from HMS *Totland*, all aboard were killed.

U-558 Commanded in the action by Kapitänleutnant Günther Krech, who was seen as a 'Top Ace' and had attained his Iron Cross 1st Class in 1940 and went on to attain a Knight's Cross in 1942. The U-boat was sunk on 20th July 1943 in the Bay of Biscay north-west of Cape Ortegal, Spain, in position 45.10N, 09.42W, by depth charges from a British Halifax and a US Liberator aircraft (Sqdn 58/E, 19th A/S USAAF/F). Most of the crew (45) were killed, but Kapitänleutnant Krech and four others, including the gun crew, were captured alive.

U-569   Commanded in the action by Oberleutnant Hans Johannsen, who received his Iron Cross 1st Class when his boat returned to base in March. The U-boat was then scuttled two months later, on 22nd May 1943, in the North Atlantic, in position 50.40N, 35.21W, after being badly damaged by depth charges from two Avenger aircraft of the US escort carrier USS *Bogue*, 21 dead and 25 survivors.